D1432110

INTERSCIENCE MONOGRAPHS IN PHYSICS AND ASTRONOMY
Edited by R. E. MARSHAK
University of Rochester

Volume I: E. R. Cohen, K. M. Crowe, J. W. M. DuMond
THE FUNDAMENTAL CONSTANTS OF PHYSICS

Volume II: G. J. Dienes and G. H. Vineyard
RADIATION EFFECTS IN SOLIDS

Additional volumes in preparation

RADIATION EFFECTS IN SOLIDS

G. J. DIENES
Department of Physics, Brookhaven National Laboratory, Upton, New York

G. H. VINEYARD
Department of Physics, Brookhaven National Laboratory, Upton, New York

INTERSCIENCE PUBLISHERS, INC., NEW YORK
Interscience Publishers Ltd., London 1957

Library of Congress Catalog Card Number 57-13251

INTERSCIENCE PUBLISHERS, INC., 250 Fifth Avenue, New York 1, N. Y.
For Great Britain and Northern Ireland:
INTERSCIENCE PUBLISHERS LTD., 88/90 Chancery Lane, London W. C. 2

PRINTED IN THE UNITED STATES OF AMERICA
BY MACK PRINTING COMPANY, EASTON, PA.

Preface

The study of radiation effects in solids is now proceeding more intensively than ever before, and the subject can be expected to develop greatly in the next few years. Nevertheless the field has already reached a certain level of maturity, and a very large set of experimental results are at hand, coordinated at least qualitatively by a body of theoretical ideas. It thus seems appropriate to bring out a small volume surveying the subject in its present state. It is not the authors' intension to extoll the accomplishments of the theory unduly. Indeed, we have emphasized its shortcomings as well as its achievements, and hope that a critical awareness of limitations of present theoretical pictures will lead most quickly to their improvement. Similarly, in the experimental realm, while summarizing the basic information that has been gathered, we have tried to point out many gaps and to reveal numerous cases where inadequate control of purity, temperature, radiation conditions, and other variables make results difficult to interpret and of uncertain generality.

The book is concerned mostly with the physics of radiation effects, not with the chemistry of such effects, and not at all with biological effects. This means that displaced atoms have been given more prominence than ionization, and that organic substances have been given far less space than other types of solids. It should be also noted that we are primarily concerned with energetic radiation, of x-ray energies and higher, and thus effects of optical, infrared and ultraviolet irradiation are omitted. Although these phenomena (luminescence, photochemistry, etc.) are unquestionably radiation effects, their study goes much farther back, they have been reviewed in many places, and the theoretical ideas involved are sufficiently different from those relevant to high-energy radiation to allow a practical separation.

The book deals mainly with fundamentals, and this means that preference is given to simple systems and to irradiations carried out under controlled and analyzable conditions. At the same time a survey is given of the more striking physical effects arising from irradiations, many of these being observed in complicated situations where theoretical understanding is difficult.

It is hoped that the treatment given will be of use to graduate students, to scientists in fields other than radiation effects, and to specialists in radiation effects who desire a broad and integrated review of the fundamentals of their field.

The writers are indebted to their colleagues in the Solid State Group at Brookhaven National Laboratory for many helpful discussions, to R. W. Powell and R. A. Meyer for aid with the section on annealing of the Brookhaven Reactor, and to Mrs. Alice Whittemore for dedicated assistance in the preparation of the manuscript.

G. J. Dienes
G. H. Vineyard

June 6, 1957

Contents

CHAPTER 1

Introduction

While some aspects of the interaction of various nuclear radiations with solids have been studied for many years, the very active interest in radiation effects in solids at the present time is largely the result of wartime research on nuclear reactor development. E. P. Wigner recognized in the latter part of 1942 that energetic neutrons and fission fragments, born in the fission process, would have the ability to displace atoms from their equilibrium positions. He reasoned that heavy bombardment of a solid by such energetic massive particles might lead to serious technological effects. This observation prompted an immediate program of theoretical and experimental study on the nature and magnitude of the effects to be expected. Publication of basic studies commenced in 1946, but much technological and basic information remained classified until the United Nations International Conference on the Peaceful Uses of Atomic Energy in 1955.

As may be expected, much of the early work was concerned with applied problems of interest to reactor technology. During the last decade the emphasis has changed slowly as it became clear that the study of radiation effects can lead to new and valuable insight into the properties of imperfections in solids. The relation of physical and chemical properties to the defect structure of solids has become an increasingly important part of solid-state research. Irradiation with energetic particles is a new and powerful tool in this field since a large number of defects thus can be introduced into a crystal in a reasonably well controlled manner.

During the last few years the subject has achieved a certain degree of maturity. There is a theory for the production of simple point defects, namely interstitial atoms and vacant lattice sites, by energetic particle bombardment. A number of basic experiments have been done which support the simple theory in some ways but depart from it in other respects. It has been recognized that more cooperative effects, involving a few or perhaps a large number of atoms, may be of importance, and an outline of a theory of these cooperative effects is at hand. Thus, many diverse experimental observations can be and have been correlated, although the finality of the prevailing picture is difficult to judge. It is possible that present ideas will be considerably altered as more exact theoretical work becomes available and more carefully controlled experiments are performed.

Present interpretation of the changes in the properties of solids brought about by high-energy radiation centers around the production of several types of defects in the solid by the radiation. These defects are: (*a*) vacancies, (*b*) interstitial atoms, and (*c*) impurity atoms. Each of these simple defects is described briefly below.

(*a*) *Vacancies.* Vacant lattice sites may be created by collisions of energetic particles with the atoms in a solid lattice. The energy transferred in these collisions is usually sufficient for the recoiling atom to create further vacant lattice sites by subsequent collisions. Thus, for each primary collision, a cascade of collisions resulting in vacancies is initiated.

(*b*) *Interstitial atoms.* The atoms that are displaced from their equilibrium positions in the lattice will stop in an interstitial, or non-equilibrium, position, provided they do not recombine immediately with a nearby vacancy.

(*c*) *Impurity atoms.* Impurity atoms are formed under neutron bombardment by transmutation. A special case of this is the introduction of fission products by the fission process. The effect of fission fragments is usually more pronounced than that of neutron-induced transmutation, although both mechanisms are often insignificant compared to other radiation effects.

These defects were described briefly because the whole book deals essentially with the production and nature of such defects and their relation to the physical and chemical properties of solids. In addition to simple collisions there are other important processes leading to observable radiation effects. They are (*d*) replacement collisions, (*e*) thermal and displacement spikes, and (*f*) ionization effects. These processes may be described briefly as follows:

(*d*) *Replacement collisions.* If a collision between a moving interstitial atom and a stationary atom results in ejection of the stationary atom and leaves the interstitial with insufficient kinetic energy for it to escape from the vacancy it has created, then this atom will fall into the vacancy, dissipating its kinetic energy through lattice vibrations as heat. Calculations show that for a reasonable choice of energy parameters the number of replacement collisions may exceed the number of displacement collisions. The result is the interchange of moving atoms with lattice atoms, which can lead to observable effects in polyatomic materials.

(*e*) *Thermal and displacement spikes.* A fast particle moving through a lattice, or an atom that has been hit just hard enough to vibrate with large amplitude without being displaced, will rapidly transfer energy to its neighbors, which become abnormally excited. Thus a region of material around the track of a fission fragment or knocked-on atom will be heated to a high temperature. The region of excitation expands rapidly, and at the same time there is a drastic decrease of temperature. The result is called a thermal spike, i.e., rapid heating and quenching of a small volume of the material. Calculations indicate that the duration of a high temperature of approximately 1000° K in a region involving some thousands of atoms might be 10^{-10} to 10^{-11} seconds. When the energy of the fast moving atom falls below a transition value (which depends on the atomic number) the mean free path between displacement collisions becomes of the order of the atomic spacing. Then each collision results in a displaced atom, and the end of the trail is believed to be a region containing of the order of one- to ten-thousand atoms in which local melting and turbulent flow have occurred during a very short time interval. This is called a displacement spike, and is probably important only in heavy metals.

(*f*) *Ionization effects.* The passage of charged particles or gamma-rays through a solid may cause extensive ionization and electronic excitation, which in turn lead to bond rupture, free radicals coloration, luminescence, etc., in many types of solids. These effects are most important in the various insulators and dielectrics, ionic crystals, glasses, organic high polymers, etc.

The writers believe that the scientific future of the field of radiation effects is a promising one. Such studies will provide a very valuable supplement to other methods of altering the properties of solids and the processes occurring in them. The interaction of radiation with matter is a fruitful field in itself in which much remains to be done. But perhaps more important is the fact that a new tool is at hand with which to probe the intricacies of the structure-sensitive properties of solids.

The writers' interest has been to a large extent in the fundamentals, and this is reflected in the plan of the book. By far the largest portion of the book is concerned with the theory of displacement production and the basic experiments which were designed to test the theory. This material is covered in Chapters 2 and 3. In Chapter 4 point defects and clusters of defects are discussed together with the physical property changes expected from the presence of such entities. The mobility of the crystalline defects is taken up in Chapter 5, together with the healing or annealing of radiation effects due to the recombination of defects or to their disappearance from the solid by diffusion. In Chapter 6 some special topics are treated, most of which are rather complex and cannot be interpreted in a simple way, but which are important in many phases and solid-state research. While the emphasis is on fundamentals the practical importance of various radiation effects is pointed out throughout the volume. For engineering details, however, the reader will have to consult the original literature or the appropriate review articles in various books and journals. A general bibliography is given at the end of this chapter, and each chapter, we believe, is fully supplied with references.

General Bibliography

Books

Proceedings of the International Conference on the Peaceful Uses of Atomic Energy, United Nations, 1956, Volume 7 (particularly pp. 421–496 and 615–682).

Nuclear Fuels, edited by D. H. Gurinsky and G. J. Dienes, D. Van Nostrand Co., Inc., New York, 1956 (particularly Chapters VII–IX).

Metallurgy and Fuels, edited by H. M. Finniston and J. P. Howe, Pergamon Press, New York, 1956 (particularly Chapter 8).

F. Seitz and J. S. Koehler, "Displacement of Atoms During Irradiation," in *Solid State Physics* (editors F. Seitz and D. Turnbull), Academic Press, Inc., New York, 1956, Vol. 2, pp. 307–442.

Report of the Conference on Defects in Crystalline Solids, The Physical Society, London, 1955 (particularly pp. 81–108, 222–261).

Effects of Radiation on Dielectric Materials, Washington, 1954, Office of Naval Research Symposium Report-ACR2.

Proceedings of the First and Second Conferences on Carbon, University of Buffalo, Buffalo, New York, 1956, pp. 125–149.

Action des Rayonnements de Grande Energie sur les Solides (editor Y. Cauchois), Gauthier-Villars, Paris, 1956.

General and Review Articles (not including those given at the International Conference on the Peaceful Uses of Atomic Energy)

1. E. P. Wigner, "Theoretical Physics in the Metallurgical Laboratory of Chicago," *J. Appl. Phys.*, **17,** 857 (1946).
2. Milton Burton, "Radiation Chemistry," *J. Phys. & Colloid Chem.*, **51,** 611 (1947).
3. J. C. Slater, "The Effects of Radiation on Materials," *J. Appl. Phys.*, **22,** 237 (1951).
4. K. Lark-Horovitz, "Nucleon Bombarded Semiconductors," *Reading Conference on Semiconducting Materials*, Butterworth's Scientific Publications, London, England, 1951, pp. 47–78.
5. F. Seitz, "Radiation Effects in Solids," *Phys. Today*, **5,** 6 (1952).
6. G. J. Dienes, "Radiation Effects in Solids," *Ann. Rev. Nuclear Sci.*, **2,** 187 (1953).
7. G. J. Dienes, "Effects of Nuclear Radiations on the Mechanical Properties of Solids," *J. Appl. Phys.*, **24,** 666 (1953).
8. S. Siegel, "Radiation Damage as a Metallurgical Research Technique," Chapter in *Modern Research Technique in Physical Metallurgy*, ASM, 1953, pp. 312–324.
9. G. R. Sutton and D. O. Leeser, "How Radiation Affects Structural Materials," *Iron Age*, **174,** 97 (1954).
10. J. W. Glen, "A Survey of Radiation Effects in Metals," *Phil. Mag. Suppl.*, **4,** 381 (1955).
11. G. H. Kinchin and R. S. Pease, "The Displacement of Atoms in Solids by Radiation," *Rept. Prog. in Phys.*, **18,** 1 (1955).
12. K. Lintner and E. Schmid, "Bedeutung von Korpuskularbestrahlung für die Eigenschaften von Fest Körpern," *Ergeb. exakt. Naturw.*, **28,** 302 (1955).
13. H. Brooks, "Nuclear Radiation Effects in Solids," *Ann. Rev. Nuclear Sci.*, **6,** (1956).
14. G. H. Vineyard, "Theory and Mechanism of Radiation Effects," IMD Special Report Series No. 3, *Nuclear Metallurgy*, AIME, New York, 1956, Vol. III, pp. 1–13.
15. D. F. Thomas, "Irradiation Effects on Physical Metallurgical Processes," IMD Special Report Series No. 3, *Nuclear Metallurgy*, AIME, New York, 1956, Vol. III, pp. 13–31.
16. D. S. Billington, "Irradiation Effects in Reactor Materials," IMD Special Report Series No. 3, *Nuclear Metallurgy*, AIME, New York, 1956, Vol. III, pp. 31–54.
17. C. D. Bopp and O. Sisman, "Radiation Stability of Plastics and Elastomers," *Nucleonics*, **13,** No. 7, 28–33 (1955).
18. C. D. Bopp and O. Sisman, "How Radiation Changes Polymer Mechanical Properties," *Nucleonics*, **13,** No. 7, 51–55 (1955).
19. J. A. Brinkman, "Production of Atomic Displacements by High Energy Particles," *Am. J. Phys.*, **24,** 246 (1956).
20. G. J. Dienes, "Displaced Atoms in Solids—Comparison Between Theory and Experiment," in *Symposium on Radiation Effects in Materials*, ASTM, 1957.

CHAPTER 2

The Interaction of Radiation with Matter

2.1 Introduction

The interaction of energetic radiation with matter is a complex phenomenon, and it is useful to resolve it into primary and secondary stages, which will be discussed in that order. This analysis is based on the sequence of events following the arrival of a particle or quantum of energy, and implies nothing about the relative importance of the two stages in producing observable property changes.

The primary or direct effects consist in the displacement of electrons (ionization), the displacement of atoms from lattice sites, excitation of both atoms and electrons without displacement, and the transmutation of nuclei. Irradiation with energetic charged particles always produces primary ionization, and, depending on conditions, usually produces primary atomic displacements. Irradiation with neutrons produces ionization only as a secondary process, the primary result being atomic displacement, while irradiation with gamma-rays produces only ionization as the important primary effect, atomic displacements sometimes resulting secondarily. Nuclear transmutations can in principle be produced by any of these forms of radiation, but occur to an appreciable extent (at energies up to 10 Mev) only when certain materials of high cross section are irradiated with neutrons. In this category may be included neutron capture, (n, α) reactions in lithium and boron, and fission. Other special nuclear effects may be observed under bombardments at extremely high energies ($>$ 100 Mev), but these will not be considered here (1). Excitation of nuclear and electronic motion without permanent displacement also occurs very generally but is chiefly important as a secondary process, and it will be treated explicitly in the latter connection.

The secondary effects of the interaction of radiation with matter consist of further excitation and disruption of the structure by electrons and atoms which have been knocked on. The total number of atoms displaced in such cascades must be estimated, and this involves treating further interaction between moving charged particles and undisturbed material. The basic laws governing the secondary stages are in all cases the same as those governing the primary stage of charged particle bombardment; hence the stopping of charged particles in matter is taken up first.

2.2 Moving Charged Particles

An atom moving through matter at high energies is slowed down by numerous collisions, some of which impart appreciable energy to target atoms but most of which impart energy to individual electrons of the target. Such a moving atom would be expected to be heavily ionized when it is moving at high speeds and to acquire electrons as it slows down (2). Roughly speaking, those electrons whose orbital velocities are greater than the velocity with which the atom is moving will remain attached; those electrons which have an orbital velocity lower than that of the atom will be stripped away. This means that protons or deuterons moving with energies in the megavolt range will be completely ionized, while knock-on atoms will be only rarely ionized, except for the lightest elements. Fission fragments at birth, because of their extraordinarily high energy, carry about 20 units of net positive charge, which becomes progressively neutralized as the fragment slows down.

The collisions which the moving atom undergoes can be divided into two classes, elastic and inelastic. In an elastic collision the moving atom interacts with an atom of the target material, imparting some energy to the target atom and losing a like amount of energy (thus, the collision is elastic in the sense that the total kinetic energy of incident and struck atoms is conserved, not that the incident atom is scattered without loss of energy). In an inelastic collision, there is loss of energy because of electronic excitation. In all collisions of importance here the interaction force is the Coulomb force between nuclear and electronic charges. In elastic collisions it is sufficient to consider that the electrons partially screen the nuclear charges but play no other role; thus in these collisions the electron cloud responds adiabatically to the approach of the two nuclei and partakes of no excitation. Further discussion of this process will be given later. The inelastic collisions, on the other hand, require that electrons interact directly with the incident particle, being left in excited states after its passage.

In general, inelastic collisions are much the more frequent while the atom has high energy, and elastic collisions become more important after the atom has slowed down. The transition from inelastic to elastic behavior is not abrupt but can be fairly well fixed by the following argument: If the moving atom has a velocity much less than that of an electron in the target, that electron will usually behave adiabatically in the collision, i.e., be left without excitation. If the moving atom has a velocity equal to or greater than that of the electron, electronic excitation becomes probable. Following arguments of this type a limiting energy for ionization, E_i, can be found, such that when the moving atom has energy E less than E_i, it will not lose energy to an appreciable extent by ionization, and such that when $E \gg E_i$ the ionization losses will exceed those due to elastic collisions by a large factor. Seitz (3) suggests that, in insulators

$$E_i = {}^1/_8(M_1/m)I \qquad (2\text{-}1)$$

where M_1 is the mass of the moving atom, m is the mass of an electron, and I is the lowest electronic excitation energy, given by the low-energy limit of the main optical absorption band. In metals there is no lowest electronic excitation energy, but inelastic collisions become infrequent for atom velocities low compared to the velocity of electrons at the Fermi level. Thus, for metals one may take (4)

$$E_i = {}^1/_{16}(M_1/m)\epsilon_F \qquad (2\text{-}2)$$

where ϵ_F is the Fermi energy, given approximately by

$$\epsilon_F \cong (3\pi^2)^{2/3} a_0^2 N_e^{2/3} E_R$$

where a_0 is the Bohr radius of hydrogen ($a_0 = \hbar^2/me^2 = 5.29 \times 10^{-9}$ cm), E_R is the Rydberg energy (13.60 ev), and N_e is the number of conduction electrons per unit volume.

Most common insulators have an electronic excitation energy, I, of about 5 ev, and the Fermi energies of most metals lie between 2 and 12 ev. Consequently equations 2-1 and 2-2 reduce to a typical value of E_i, in both metals and insulators, of about ${}^1/_2 M_1/m$ (ev). Individual variations away from this typical value are by not more than a factor lying between ${}^1/_2$ and 2, which is also about the precision with which the concept of a limiting energy for ionization can be defined. This leads to the useful rule of thumb that ionization is unimportant whenever the energy of a moving atom, in kev, is less than its atomic weight, regardless of the material in which it is moving. Thus, for protons this limiting energy is about 1 kev, for deuterons 2 kev, for knock-on copper atoms 65 kev, etc.

From this rule it may be seen that the energy of fast charged particles is mostly dissipated in electronic excitation when the particles are brought to rest in matter. The specific rate of energy loss by ionization is also of interest in radiation damage studies. Theories of this are neither simple nor complete, but, for energies above E_i and below the relativistic region, the following expression for the energy loss per centimeter of path by ionization will suffice (5):

$$-(dE/dx)_e = (4\pi e^4 Z_1'^2/mv^2)\, N_0\, Z_2' \ln (2mv^2/J) \qquad (2\text{-}3)$$

Here E is the energy of the moving atom, v is its velocity, $Z_1'e$ is its charge, x is the distance which it has traversed, N_0 is the density of atoms in the medium, m is the electronic mass, J is the mean excitation potential of the electrons in the stopping material, and Z_2' is their effective atomic number. J and Z_2' can only be found approximately from theory. Z_2' is the number of electrons likely to be excited, namely the number for which the excitation energy is less than $(m/M_1)E$, and J can be well approximated as 10 Z_2 (ev).

The total range of the charged particle can be found by integrating expressions such as equation 2-3 and making allowance for the failure of the formula at low energies. The results are not simple, and range-energy curves for several common materials can be found in Bethe and Ashkin (5). For rough calculations, it is useful to know that, approximately, the range R of a charged particle of initial energy E is given by

$$R = CE^{\gamma} \qquad (2\text{-}4)$$

where C and γ can be empirically determined. For high, nonrelativistic energies, $\gamma \cong 2$, and γ lies between 1 and 2 in most other cases.

It has been pointed out already that the most important primary process in irradiation is the displacement of atoms. Moving charged particles produce displacements primarily by elastic collisions, interacting essentially one at a time with the stationary atoms. According to the analysis of Bohr (2) and others, it is adequate to assume that, in such collisions, the moving and stationary atoms interact with a screened Coulomb potential energy, of the form

$$V(r) = (Z_1 Z_2 e^2/r)e^{-r/a} \tag{2-5}$$

Here r is the separation of the two atoms, and a is the screening constant. At close approach equation 2.5 describes the Coulomb repulsion of the two nuclei, of charge Z_1e and Z_2e, respectively. At separations of the order of a the repulsion is lessened by the partial screening of the nuclei by the two electron clouds, and at somewhat larger separations, the screening is essentially complete. The screening radius is given by the approximate relation

$$a \cong a_0/(Z_1^{2/3} + Z_2^{2/3})^{1/2} \tag{2-6}$$

where a_0 is the Bohr radius of hydrogen.

In the energy range of present interest, it turns out that the collisions can be calculated from classical mechanics with good accuracy in most cases; a discussion will be given here in classical terms as far as possible to help the reader visualize the processes. A moving atom colliding with a stationary atom will be deflected from its course by an amount which depends on its energy and on its distance of approach, the deflection being greater for smaller energies and for closer approaches. Also the momentum, and hence the energy, transferred to the stationary atom increases as the angle of deflection increases. The probability for any given amount of energy transfer can be conveniently measured by the area of a ring-shaped region in which the path of the incident particle must lie in order for this energy transfer to occur. This area will be spoken of as the differential cross section for energy transfer. Whenever the nuclei of the two atoms approach to a distance much less than the screening radius a, the nuclear Coulomb repulsion produces most of the deflection and the collision can be calculated by ignoring the screening altogether. This problem is easily solved and leads to the familiar Rutherford scattering laws. More distant collisions are partly screened, and no simple expressions can be found for the cross sections. Simplicity sets in again for very distant collisions, which occur more nearly as if the colliding bodies were hard elastic spheres. The assumption of hard-sphere behavior has been much used in displacement calculations, although it is not really very accurate in the range in which it is applied. Everhart, Stone, and Carbone (6) have made numerical calculations of screened Coulomb scattering which cover the intermediate range between the Rutherford and hard-sphere limits.

The scattering is governed by a parameter, b, given by

$$b = 2Z_1Z_2e^2/\mu v^2 \tag{2-7}$$

where μ is the reduced mass, $\mu = M_1M_2/(M_1 + M_2)$ and v is the velocity of the incident particle. b, the distance to which the two nuclei would approach in a head-on collision in the absence of screening, is called by Bohr the "collision diameter," and should be thought of as measuring the reciprocal of the energy of the incident atom. The condition for Rutherford scattering for all but unimportantly small angles of deflection is that the collision diameter be much smaller than the screening radius, $b/a \ll 1$. For collisions to be approximately of the hard-sphere type, it is necessary that b/a be much greater than 1. An idea of whether the Rutherford or hard-sphere approximation is appropriate can be had by comparing the energy of the moving atom to a critical energy E_A so defined that $b/a = 1$ at $E = E_A$. The elastic collisions are of Rutherford type when $E \gg E_A$, and approximately of hard-sphere type when $E \ll E_A$. From equations 2-6 and 2-7 one finds

$$E_A = E_R[2(M_1 + M_2)/M_2]Z_1Z_2\sqrt{Z_1^{2/3} + Z_2^{2/3}} \tag{2-8}$$

For protons or deuterons incident on any substance, typical bombardment energies will be well above E_A. Maximum energy knock-ons in light elements will have energies above E_A; in heavy elements they will have energies below E_A.

In radiation damage considerations, the most important characteristic of a collision is the energy transferred to the struck atom. This may range from zero in glancing collisions to a maximum, T_m, which is transferred in a head-on collision. From energy and momentum conservation it is easily seen that

$$T_m = [4M_1M_2/(M_1 + M_2)^2]\,E \tag{2-9}$$

In Rutherford collisions, small energy transfers are more probable than large, the differential cross section for energy transfer T to $T + dT$ being

$$d\sigma = C(dT/T^2) \tag{2-10}$$

where the coefficient C is given by

$$C = 4\pi a_0^2(M_1/M_2)\, Z_1^2\, Z_2^2\, (E_R^2/E) \tag{2-11}$$

Equation 2-10 is valid for T ranging from T_m down to some small but finite lower limit at which electronic screening can no longer be neglected. In cases of present interest this lower limit lies well below that energy at which atomic displacements can be produced. If it is assumed that an atom is always displaced when it receives energy greater than a certain threshold E_d, and is never displaced at lower energies, the total cross section for production of a displacement can be found from equation 2-10 to be

$$\sigma_d = \int_{T=E_d}^{T=T_m} d\sigma = C(1/E_d - 1/T_m) \tag{2-12}$$

With the help of equations 2.9 and 2.11 this can be placed in the alternative form

$$\sigma_d = 16\pi\, a_0^2 Z_1^2 Z_2^2 \frac{M_1^2}{(M_1 + M_2)^2} \frac{E_R^2}{T_m^2} (T_m/E_d - 1) \tag{2-13}$$

The average energy transferred in those Rutherford collisions which displace atoms, $\bar{T}$, is an important quantity and is now easily calculated as

$$\bar{T} = \int_{T=E_d}^{T=T_m} T\, d\sigma \Big/ \int_{T=E_d}^{T=T_m} d\sigma = \left(\frac{E_d T_m}{T_m - E_d}\right) \ln\left(\frac{T_m}{E_d}\right) \tag{2-14}$$

In typical cases $\bar{T}$ is much less than T_m, which emphasizes the strong preference for low-energy transfers in Rutherford collisions.

In hard-sphere collisions, on the other hand, all energy transfers from zero to T_m are equally probable, and the differential cross section for energy transfer T to $T + dT$ can be shown to be

$$d\sigma = C'\, dT \tag{2-15}$$

where $C' = \pi a_1^2/T_m$ and a_1 is the diameter of the effective hard sphere, approximately the screening radius as given by equation 2-6.

For screened Coulomb collisions at energies in a rather broad range in the neighborhood of E_A the differential cross section is neither of the Rutherford nor of the hard-sphere type, and can be represented by the formula (7)

$$d\sigma \propto T^{-n}\, dT \tag{2-16}$$

where the exponent n ranges between 1 and 2. The approach to hard-sphere behavior is not very evident from this expression, and perhaps the only justification for the extensive use which has been made of the hard-sphere model is that the displacement cascade is not very sensitively dependent on the form of the energy transfer cross section.

The case of electron bombardment requires special treatment since, because of its small mass, the electron must travel at relativistic velocities in order to produce displacements. The maximum energy which can be transferred in a collision by an electron of mass m and kinetic energy E is

$$T_m = \frac{2(E + 2mc^2)}{M_2c^2} E \tag{2-17}$$

Here c is the velocity of light, and it has been assumed that $m \ll M_2$ and $E \ll M_2c^2$. This reduces to the nonrelativistic equation 2-9 when $E \ll mc^2$. The scattering involved in collisions that produce displacements is primarily due to the Coulomb interaction between the electron and the target nucleus, but the nonrelativistic Rutherford scattering law is inadequate. Relativistic Coulomb scattering has been treated by Mott (8,9) and McKinley and Feshbach (10). Even with use of numerous approximations the formulas are somewhat involved, and the reader is referred to the above sources and to the review by Seitz and Koehler (11) for details. The principal results of the relativistic calculations are the following:

(*a*) The threshold electron energy for transferring energy greater than E_d (i.e., for displacing an atom) must be found from equation 2-17 rather than from equation 2-9. The distinction is important for substances of atomic weight greater than about 10, assuming $E_d =$ 25 ev.

(*b*) The total cross section for producing displacements rises steeply from zero at the threshold energy and then becomes constant as the bombardment energy increases. For T_m between E_d and about $2E_d$ equation 2-13 can be applied, taking $Z_1 = 1$, $M_1 = m$, and using the relativistic form (equation 2-17) for T_m. The constant cross section approached for $T_m \gg E_d$ is not given by equation 2-13, which declines in this region, but can be shown to have the value

$$\frac{8\pi a_0^2 Z_2^2 E_R^2}{M_2c^2 E_d} \tag{2-18}$$

By contrast, in the heavy-particle case one is usually dealing with the region where, according to equation 2-13, the cross section rapidly declines as the bombardment energy increases.

(*c*) As in atomic particle bombardment the primary knock-ons are distributed approximately according to the inverse square of the energy. Thus the mean energy transferred to atoms which are displaced is approximately the same as in equation 2-14.

(*d*) The penetration and energy loss of electrons in matter is more complicated than with heavy particles because of relativistic effects and radiative losses. In general, the penetration of Mev electrons is about two orders of magnitude greater than that of protons of the same energy, and the attenuation of energy with penetration is subject to considerably greater fluctuation. These questions are discussed at length by Bethe and Ashkin (5) and Evans (12).

2.3 Neutron Irradiation

Since the neutron carries no charge it produces radiation damage only by direct interaction with nuclei. A fast neutron imparts momentum to a nucleus with which it collides, and the nucleus recoils, taking its electron cloud with it. The only atomic electrons having an appreciable chance of being left behind are those with orbital velocities lower than the recoil velocity of the nucleus. In accordance with the earlier discussion of the charge carried by a moving atom one sees that this fate threatens only the outermost electrons, if any. Elastic collisions are the most probable interactions, and the energy imparted to the atom ranges from zero to a maximum T_m given by equation 2-9, where now M_1 and E are the neutron mass and energy, respectively. The distribution of recoil energies is related to the distribution of angular deflections of the neutron. The simplest approximation, and the one which has been commonly made, is that the neutrons are scattered isotropically. In this case it can be shown that all recoil energies between 0 and T_m are equally probable, just as with hard-sphere collisions. The differential cross section for transfer of energy T to $T + dT$ can be written

$$d\sigma = (\sigma_T/T_m)\, dT \tag{2-19}$$

where σ_T is the total neutron cross section (considered now to be entirely due to elastic collisions). The mean energy transferred per collision is then

$$\bar{T} = {}^1/_2 T_m$$

σ_T ranges between 1 and 10 barns (1 barn = 10^{-24} c
of fission energies, and is, with many exceptions, roughly
tional to the two-thirds power of the atomic mass. Neutrons fr
fission have a broad range of energies from zero to 15 Mev, with an average energy of 2 Mev (13). In reactor irradiations (14), the neutrons striking the sample may be distributed according to the raw fission spectrum or may be considerably degraded in energy, depending upon how much moderator lies between the specimen and nearby fuel elements. Calculations of irradiation effects have usually been made under the assumption that all neutrons possess a single effective energy, lying somewhere between 1 and 2 Mev. This procedure may be defended on the grounds that the error introduced is less than that of other stages of the calculations, but one should be clearly aware of the crudity of the assumption, and it is to be hoped that eventually work will be done with calibrated fluxes and energy distributions. A start in this direction has been made by Primak (15).

Assuming a mean neutron energy of 2 Mev, equations 2-9 and 2-20 predict a mean energy of primary knock-ons of

$$\bar{T} = (4/A)\,(1 + 1/A)^{-2} \cong 4/A \text{ (Mev)} \tag{2-21}$$

where A is the atomic mass of the target material. Thus, knock-on hydrogen atoms will receive a mean energy of 1 Mev, carbon 280 kev, copper 61 kev, and uranium 17 kev. All of these energies are strikingly larger than the mean energies of primary knock-ons in charged-particle bombardments.

The foregoing discussions employed the assumption that fast-neutron scattering is isotropic. This actually is not a very good approximation. Measurements (16,17,18) and theory (19) show that Mev neutrons are scattered quite preferentially in the forward direction; this means that the average energy transferred is less than that calculated under the assumption of isotropy. There is also the possibility that some of the scattering events are inelastic, which again means that less energy will be transferred than with isotropic elastic scattering. Measurements of Jurney (20) of inelastic and transport cross sections for fission neutrons allow a correction for anisotropy to be computed. The further correction for inelastic processes can be estimated and proves to be less important. The factor, f, by which the right-hand side of equation 2-21 must be multiplied to get the mean energy transferred is given in Table 2.1. This is the average correction factor for the fission energy spectrum.

Table 2.1. Correction factor, f, to allow for anisotropy in fission neutron collisions, to be inserted in right-hand side of equation 2.21.

Element	f
Be	0.56
C	0.84
Al	0.58
Cr	0.57
Fe	0.57
Ni	0.64
Cu	0.60

The anisotropy effect thus reduces the mean energy transferred by a factor between $^1/_2$ and $^2/_3$ in most elements. The correction would be more important at higher neutron energies, less important at lower energies.

The production of nuclear reactions by neutrons is sometimes of importance and can give rise to distinctive radiation effects. The (n, α) reactions in Li^6 and B^{10} have large cross sections for thermal neutrons (1,000 and 4,000 barns, respectively), and the two energetic charged particles emerging from the reaction can produce important radiation effects, with highly localized damage (21,22). The same observation, to an even greater degree, applies to fissionable materials, principally thorium, uranium, and plutonium. All elements possess appreciable neutron cross sections leading to capture with γ-ray emission, and in some cases to transmutation. Simple capture is not ordinarily of importance in radiation damage. Transmutation may be of importance, although in most pile irradiations far more atoms are displaced than are transmuted.

An example in which transmutation occurs with unusually high frequency is that of gold. Here the thermal-neutron cross section for transmutation (to mercury) is 96 barns, whereas the scattering cross section for fast neutrons is about 6 barns. In a typical pile irradiation, where the ratio of thermal flux to fast flux is about 5, and assuming (see section 2.4) about 140 atoms displaced per primary knock-on, there will be about 1 atom transmuted for every 2 atoms displaced. With most common elements, transmutation occurs with frequency lower than this by one to many orders of magnitude. It must be remembered, however, that the cross sections for processes leading to transmutation are largest for thermal neutrons, whereas the production of displacements by collision requires fast neutrons, and so the relative importance of transmutation may be very much greater in irradiations with thermalized beams. Occasionally unusual experiments can be performed by neutron-induced transmutations. An example is the work of Cleland and Crawford on indium antimonide (23).

2.4 Theory of Displacement Production

In the preceding sections it has been shown how atoms can be knocked from their lattice sites by irradiation. These primary knock-on atoms will in turn displace other atoms in a cascade fashion, and the total number of atoms affected may be very much larger than the number displaced in primary processes. The number of primary knock-ons produced per unit volume in a bombardment, n_p, is given by

$$n_p = \phi t n_0 \sigma_d \tag{2-22}$$

where ϕ is the number of bombarding particles traversing unit area per unit time within the specimen (the flux density, commonly referred to as the flux), t is the duration of the bombardment, n_0 is the number of atoms per unit volume of the specimen, and σ_d is the cross section per atom for collisions which produce displacements (see preceding section). These primary knock-ons have a variety of energies, with a distribution in energy given by equations of the preceding section.

It is now necessary to consider in some detail the cascade process that is induced by each primary knock-on. We may anticipate the results by stating that a mean number of displaced atoms per primary knock-on, ν will be calculated (this is defined to include the primary knock-on as one of the displaced atoms). ν depends on the energy of the primary knock-on, and when averaged over the energy spectrum of primary knock-ons, will be denoted $\bar{\nu}$. The total number of displaced atoms per unit volume will then be given by

$$N_d = n_p \bar{\nu} \tag{2-23}$$

where n_p is given by equation 2-22. The primary knock-on moving through the lattice can be treated as a special case of a moving charged particle, which interacts with lattice atoms by screened Coulomb forces as already discussed. In order to make progress with this problem drastic simplifications are required. At a later stage the effects of these simplifications will be assessed. All collisions will be assumed to be binary, that is, the moving atom always will be assumed to interact with one target atom at a time. This assumption is possible because the range of the interaction forces is quite a bit shorter than the distance between atoms. Thus, the moving atom strikes lattice atoms one at a time, and these, if displaced, strike other atoms one at a time. It will be assumed that all collisions take place between a moving atom and an atom of the material which is initially at rest. The density of moving atoms generated by attainable bombardment fluxes is too small to expect many collisions between pairs of moving atoms, and thermal energies are so much lower than the energies important in displacement production that it is safe to assume that lattice atoms are always at rest when struck. It will also be assumed that the atoms are randomly located; that is, any effects of the regular lattice arrangement on the distribution of collisions will be overlooked.

The foregoing assumptions are common to all of the cascade calculations that have been made. In order to proceed without undue difficulty, further idealizations are necessary, and several models may be chosen. Snyder and Neufeld (24), Harrison and Seitz (11,25), Sampson, Hurwitz, and Clancy (26), Bruch, McHugh, and Hockenbury (27), and finally Kinchin and Pease (4) have all made calculations from slightly different assumptions. We follow the model of Kinchin and Pease, for which the specific additional assumptions are the following:

(*a*) The knock-on loses energy entirely by ionization until its kinetic energy falls below the limiting energy for ionization, E_i (see equations 2-1 and 2-2).

(*b*) All knock-ons with kinetic energies below E_i lose energy only by elastic collisions with lattice atoms, and in these collisions they behave as hard spheres.

(*c*) An atom will invariably be displaced from its lattice site if by collision it receives kinetic energy greater than some threshold energy E_d, and will never be displaced if it receives less than E_d.

(*d*) The striking atom will remain behind at the collision site if the struck atom receives energy greater than E_d *and* the incoming atom is left with energy less than E_d. Thus there will be a net increase in the number of displaced atoms only if both atoms have kinetic energies greater than E_d after the collision. All atoms will be assumed to be alike, so the theory as presented is strictly valid only for a monatomic substance.

It should be noted that, in this model, the struck atom is not required to climb out of a potential well before being in a position to make displacive collisions with other atoms. It moves away from the collision site with the full kinetic energy imparted in the collision. The models of Seitz and Harrison and of Snyder and Neufeld, on the other hand, assume that the struck atom loses energy E_d before moving off through the lattice to make other displacements. Also the latter models do not allow for the possibility that the incoming atom will be captured on the lattice site from which the knock-on was displaced. These two respects in which the models differ tend to compensate—introducing a binding energy reduces the net number of displacements, while ignoring the capture process increases the number. It thus turns out that the two models give nearly the same results for ν, but the model employed here leads to simpler mathematics.

Figure 2.1 shows a diagram in which the energy of the incident atom just after collision, E_1', is plotted as abscissa and the energy of the struck particle just after collision, E_2', is plotted as ordinate. Each point in the diagram represents a possible collision, the energy before collision being $E_1 = E_1' + E_2'$. Regions are marked out to show the results of each collision according to assumptions (*c*) and (*d*) above.

The assumption of hard-sphere behavior is very convenient for the mathematical analysis, but the energy distribution in actual collisions does not resemble that of hard spheres very closely, as has been noted in section 2.2. Fortunately the multiplication factor ν is not very sensitive to the form of this energy distribution, and this is the real justification of the use of the hard-sphere law. Neufeld and Snyder (24) have shown that the use of the Rutherford collision law in the higher energy ranges with their model scarcely changes the results. More extensive calculations with realistic collision laws would be highly desirable.

The mean number of displaced atoms, including the primary knock-on itself, produced by a primary knock-on of energy E_1 is defined as $\nu(E_1)$. This function obeys a rather simple integral equation, as will now be shown: Assume E_1 is less than the ionization threshold, E_i, but greater than $2E_d$. In its next collision the moving atom transfers energy to the struck atom, say E_2', retaining energy E_1', where $E_1' + E_2' = E_1$. By the hard-sphere assumption (*b*) the probability of this division of energy within unit range of energy is

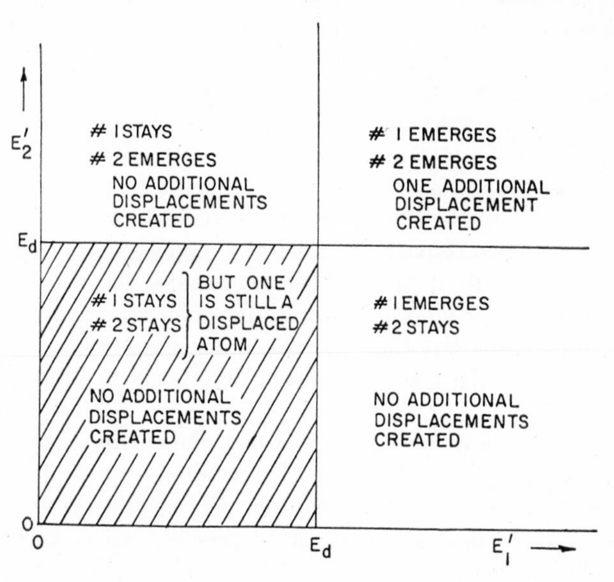

Figure 2.1 Diagram showing the assumptions of Kinchin and Pease for calculating the average number of displacements.

$1/E_1$ (this follows from equation 2-15 of section 2.2). There are now two atoms that may produce more displacements. The number expected to be produced by atom 1, including itself, is $\nu(E_1')$, if $E_1' \geq E_d$, zero if $E_1' < E_d$. The average number produced by atom 1 is found by multiplying this by the probability of the particular energy transfer and integrating to give

$$\int_{E_d}^{E_1} \frac{1}{E_1} \nu(E_1')\, dE_1'$$

The number of further displacements expected from atom 2 is $\nu(E_2')$ if $E_2' \geqslant E_d$, zero if $E_2' < E_d$. Multiplying this by the probability $1/E_1$ and integrating over the allowed range of E_2' gives

$$\int_{E_d}^{E_1} \frac{1}{E_1} \nu\,(E_2')\,dE_2'$$

which is the same as the first integral. Adding these and equating to $\nu(E_1)$ one finds the basic integral equation

$$\nu(E) = \frac{2}{E} \int_{E_d}^{E} \nu(E')\,dE' \qquad (2\text{-}24)$$

This is valid for $2E_d \leqslant E \leqslant E_i$. If $0 < E < 2E_d$ some of the collisions correspond to points in the shaded square of Figure 2.1, and the above bookkeeping is incorrect. However, it is clear from Figure 2.1 that $\nu(E) = 1$ for E in this range (no additional displacement can be created).

Equation 2-24 is easily solved by converting to a differential equation. Multiply both sides by E and differentiate with respect to E. This gives

$$E d\nu/dE = \nu, \qquad 2E_d < E < E_i \qquad (2\text{-}25)$$

which has the solution $\nu(E) = cE$. The constant c is determined by the requirement $\nu(2E_d) = 1$, thus matching this to the solution for $E \leqslant 2E_d$. One finds

$$\nu(E) = 1, \qquad 0 < E < 2E_d \qquad (2\text{-}26a)$$

$$\nu(E) = E/2E_d, \qquad 2E_d < E < E_i \qquad (2\text{-}26b)$$

Also,

$$\nu(E) = E_i/2E_d, \qquad E > E_i \qquad (2\text{-}27)$$

The result, equation 2-26b, is physically very reasonable, and says that on the average, just half of the energy of a moving atom is available for making displacements, at a cost of E_d per displacement; the other half is frittered away in sub-threshold collisions. The function $\nu(E)$ is shown in Figure 2.2. The results of the model of Seitz and Harrison, described above, are also shown for comparison. The two are appreciably different in the vicinity of $E = 2E_d$, but are in rough agreement at larger energies. For $E > 2E_d$ the Seitz-Harrison result is well approximated by the formula

$$\nu(E) \cong 0.561 + 0.561\ (E/E_d) \tag{2-28}$$

It must now be remembered that the number of knock-ons produced per unit volume in a bombardment is proportional to $\bar{\nu}$, that is to $\nu(E)$ averaged over the energy spectrum of primary knock-ons. For fission-neutron bombardment of elements of atomic weight greater than about 40 the great majority of the primary knock-ons have energies in the region where $\nu(E)$ is a linear function of E. Averaging this function over the energy spectrum is then precisely the same as replacing E in equation 2-26b or equation 2-28 by $\bar{E}$, the mean energy of primary knock-ons, and this is essentially $\bar{T}$, the mean energy transferred in neutron collisions. That is, one sets $\bar{\nu} = \nu(\bar{T})$. The calculation of $\bar{T}$ has been discussed in section 2.3.

For light elements some of the primary knock-ons have energies in the ionization range. The proper averaging of $\nu(E)$ in this case will be discussed below.

In the case of charged-particle bombardments the knock-on energies are sufficiently low that $\nu(E)$ is not quite linear, and it is not true that $\bar{\nu} = \nu(\bar{T})$. Still a very rough approximation is obtained from this relation, and $\bar{T}$ can be taken from equation 2-14 of section 2.2. To formulate the calculation properly, one defines $P(E)$, the probability that a primary knock-on received energy E, within unit range, when struck by a bombarding particle. If the differential cross section for energy transfer E by the bombarding particles is $\sigma(E)$, and the probability that a lattice atom is displaced when it receives energy E is $p(E)$, one has

$$P(E) = \frac{\sigma(E)\, p(E)}{\int_0^\infty \sigma(E)\, p(E)\, dE} \tag{2-29}$$

and then

$$\bar{\nu} = \int_0^\infty \nu(E)\, P(E)\, dE \tag{2-30}$$

The $\nu(E)$ to be used in this equation is that given by the Kinchin-Pease model. With the Seitz and Harrison model account must be taken of the energy E_d lost by the primary knock-on in climbing from its potential well. Thus one defines $P'(E)$, the probability that a primary knock-on emerges from its well with energy E, and finds $P'(E) = P(E + E_d)$. Finally, one writes

$$\bar{\nu} = \int_0^\infty \nu'(E)\, P'(E)\, dE$$

where $\nu'(E)$ is the Seitz-Harrison value for the mean number of displacements per primary knock-on. Because of this change the two models give nearly the same values of $\bar{\nu}$, even in the case of low-energy

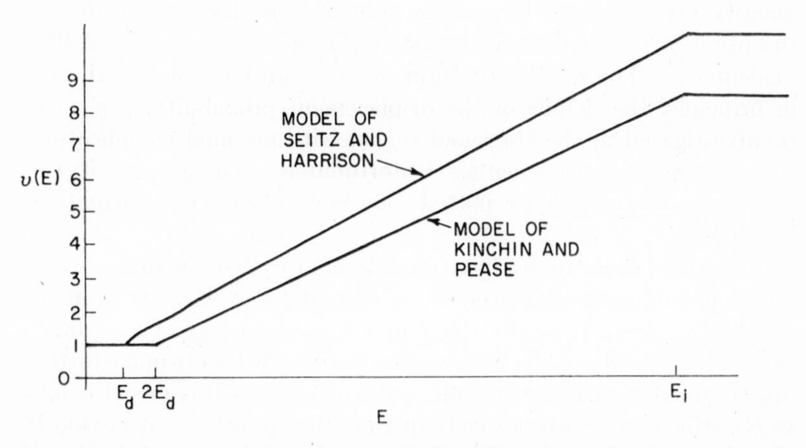

Figure 2.2 Average number of atoms displaced by primary knock-on of energy E, according to two simple models.

knock-ons, despite the appreciable difference in the $\nu(E)$ curve at low energies, as shown by Fig. 2.2.

In typical charged-particle bombardments (such as with deuterons in the Mev range) the primary knock-ons are created in Rutherford collisions, for which $\sigma(T) \propto 1/T^2$, $T < T_m$ (See equations 2-9 and 2-10 of section 2.2). Taking $p(E) = 1$, $E > E_d$, $p(E) = 0$. $E < E_d$, equation 2-29 gives

$$P(E) = \begin{cases} 0, & E < E_d \\ \left(\dfrac{T_m E_d}{T_m - E_d}\right) \dfrac{1}{E^2}, & E > E_d \end{cases}$$

and equation 2-30, assuming $T_m > 2E_d$, gives

$$\bar{\nu} = \frac{1}{2}\left(\frac{T_m}{T_m - E_d}\right)\left[1 + \ln\frac{T_m}{2E_d}\right] \qquad (2\text{-}31)$$

In the case of copper bombarded by 12 Mev deuterons, $T_m = 1.4$ Mev. Taking $E_d = 25$ ev, equation 2-31 gives $\bar{\nu} = 5.6$. This low value of $\bar{\nu}$ for charged-particle bombardments stands in sharp contrast to the much larger values of $\bar{\nu}$ obtained in neutron bombardments.

Finally, it should be noted that electron bombardment frequently involves such low-energy primary knock-ons that the assumption of a sharp threshold for displacement in equation 2-30 is inadequate. The relativistic form of $\sigma(T)$ must be employed, and, in principle, the details of the displacement probability, $p(E)$, can be investigated in the threshold region with minimal complications from cascade displacements. Unfortunately experiments of this sort have not yet been reported, nor have illustrative calculations been made.

Neufeld and Snyder have considered a cascade model in which replacements occur whenever $E_2' > E_d$ and $E_1' < E_d$, just as in the model of Figure 2.1, but in which an additional energy of E_d is taken from E_2' before atom 2 is considered to be in a position to make further displacements. The asymptotic value of $\nu(E)$ on this model is $0.35\ E/E_d$, which is slightly lower than the other results, as it obviously should be. This multiplicity of cascade models, all of which are about equally plausible *a priori*, emphasizes how unreliable these calculations are. On the basis of this and consideration of the assumptions common to all the models, one is not justified in expecting such calculations to be accurate to better than a factor of perhaps 2 or 3.

These models are oversimplified in assuming perfectly sharp thresholds for displacement. Sampson, Hurwitz, and Clancy (26) and Snyder and Neufeld (24) have considered the effect of a displacement probability which rises from zero to unity over a finite range of energy. As might be expected ν turns out to be not very different from that found by assuming an effective threshold at the energy for which the displacement probability is $^1/_2$ and using this in place of E_d in equations 2-26 and 2-27.

The models are also very much oversimplified in assuming a sharp threshold E_i at which ionization ceases and elastic collisions set in. In most bombardments the knock-ons have energies well below E_i in all substances of intermediate and high atomic weight, and so the nature of the ionization threshold is unimportant. For elements in the bottom fourth of the periodic table, however, fission-neutron bombardment produces many knock-ons above E_i and closer attention should be payed to the choice of this parameter. Also, the radiation damage produced by fission fragments occurs largely in the range above E_i. When secondary knock-ons also reach the ionization range the cascade theory becomes more complicated, and no ade-

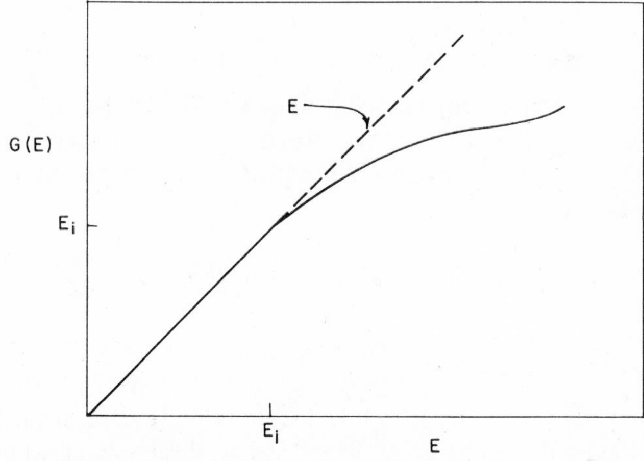

Figure 2.3 The energy of a knock-on that will be expended in elastic collisions, $G(E)$, as a function of the total energy of the knock-on, E.

quate calculation has been carried through. In most cases of concern, however, the elastic collisions made by a primary knock-on while its energy is above E_i are very weakly screened and produce a predominance of secondary knock-ons with very much lower energies than that of the primary. It is thus a good approximation to assume that the secondary knock-ons are always born with energies below E_i and therefore the elastic cascade considerations apply to them. The previous calculations (apart from the range $E < 2E_d$) gave a total number of displacements linearly dependent on the knock-on energy (equation 2-26b). Consequently the total number of displaced atoms becomes proportional to that part of the energy of the primary knock-on that is expended in elastic collisions, a quantity which will be denoted by $G(E)$. Equations 2-26 and 2-27 should thus be modified to read

$$\nu(E) = G(E)/2E_d, \qquad 2E_d < E \tag{2-32}$$

For $E < E_i$, $G(E) = E$, but for E exceeding E_i, $G(E)$ falls rapidly away from a linear function, as indicated in Fig. 2.3. $G(E)$ can be calculated in a straightforward way from the two functions $(dE/dx)_c$, the energy loss per centimeter of path by elastic collisions, and $(dE/dx)_e$ the energy loss per centimeter by ionization [see equation 2-3, section 2.2, and Seitz and Koehler (11)]. It is given by

$$G(E) = \int_0^E \frac{(dE/dx)_c}{(dE/dx)_c + (dE/dx)_e} \, dE \tag{2-33}$$

Hurwitz and Clark (28) have calculated $G(E)$ for Be, C, and Fe. They average over the uniform distribution of primary knock-on energies that would be produced in a neutron bombardment and find a quantity

$$\bar{G} = \frac{1}{T_m} \int_0^{T_m} G(E) dE$$

where T_m is the maximum energy transferred to the primary knock-on. Table 2.2 gives their values of $\bar{G}$ for 1-Mev neutron bombardment, together with $\bar{T}$, the mean energy of the primary knock-on, and E_i (computed according to the discussion of section 2.2).

Table 2.2. Energies associated with primary knock-ons produced by 1-Mev neutrons

Substance	$\bar{T}$ (ev)	$\bar{G}$ (ev)	E_i (ev)
Be	180,000	22,000	9,000
C	142,000	45,000	12,000
Fe	34,500	34,500	56,000

The best estimate of $\bar{\nu}$, the mean number of displacements per primary displaced atom then becomes

$$\bar{\nu} = \bar{G}/2E_d \tag{2-34}$$

From Table 2.2 it is evident that this formula gives appreciably higher results for light elements than do equations 2-26 and 2-27.

To summarize the results of this section, then, N_d, the mean number of atoms displaced per unit volume by heavy-particle bombardment, will be given by

$$N_d = \phi t n_0 \sigma_d \bar{\nu} \quad (2\text{-}34a)$$

where ϕ is the bombarding flux density, t the time of bombardment, n_0 the number of atoms per unit volume in the specimen, and σ_d the cross section per atom for collisions that produce displacements. The factor $\bar{\nu}$ is given by equation 2-34. As a first approximation, G in equation 2-34 may be set equal to T, the mean energy transferred by the bombarding particles in collisions that produce displacements. For proton, deuteron, and alpha-particle bombardment T is given by equation 2-14 (neglecting correction for energy loss in the sample); for fast-neutron bombardment it is given by equations 2–9 and 2-20, together with a correction factor f, becoming

$$\bar{T} = f[2M_1M_2/(M_1 + M_2)^2]\bar{E} \quad (2\text{-}34b)$$

Here M_1 is the mass of the neutron, M_2 the mass of an atom of the sample, $\bar{E}$ is the mean energy of the bombarding neutrons, and f is a factor correcting for anisotropy and inelasticity in fast-neutron scattering. When unmoderated fission neutrons are used, f may be taken from Table 2.1. For most reactor neutron bombardments, a nominal value of $f \cong {}^2/_3$ may be employed. For light elements undergoing neutron bombardment the replacement of $\bar{G}$ by $\bar{T}$ is inaccurate. The error becomes appreciable for elements of atomic mass about 45, and becomes very great for very light elements, for here $\bar{T}$ is well above the ionization threshold, E_i. Whenever $\bar{T} > E_i$, a much better approximation is achieved by setting $\bar{G} = E_i$ in equation 2-34 (for cases where $\bar{T} > E_i$ the correction represented by the factor f may be ignored). E_i was discussed in section 2.2. A further refinement is to calculate G by using equation 2-33 and then average over E. The only evaluations that have been made in this way are given in Table 2.2. Some estimates of $\bar{\nu}$ made according to these ideas are given in Table 2.3. A mean neutron energy of 1 Mev was assumed, and thus these values should apply to typical reactor irradiations in which the mean neutron energy is only a little less than that of the raw fission spectrum. For beryllium and carbon $\bar{G}$ was taken from Table 2.2. For the other substances $\bar{G}$ was set equal to $\bar{T}$ as given by equation 2-34b. For iron and copper f was

Table 2.3. Calculated mean number of displaced atoms per primary knock-on $\bar{\nu}$, for typical reactor irradiations in various substances.

Substance	Atomic weight	$\bar{\nu}$
Beryllium	9	440
Carbon (graphite)	12	900
Iron	56	390
Copper	64	380
Germanium	93	290
Gold	197	140

taken from Table 2.1; for germanium and gold f was assumed to be $^2/_3$. E_d was taken as 25 ev in every case; for Ge, in particular, this may be too high, and the resulting $\bar{\nu}$ may be too low (see chapter 3). Finally, it must be remembered that these values of $\bar{\nu}$ and the resulting calculated values of N_d are not highly accurate. Furthermore the possible disturbances of thermal spikes (see next section) and annealing during and after bombardment (see chapter 5) must always be kept in mind. Experimental efforts to check such calculations as these have been only moderately successful, the usual tendency being for equation 2-34 and 2-34a to predict more displacements than are observed. This matter is treated in detail in chapter 3.

2.5 Replacement Collisions

Besides displacing atoms to interstitial sites, irradiation can transfer atoms to new lattice sites by a process of interchanging moving atoms with lattice atoms. Of course this can only result in observable consequences in the case of polyatomic substances. An ordered alloy, for example, would be partially disordered by such a process. Experiments have in fact shown (29,30) that radiation is capable of disordering certain ordered alloys with greater efficiency than can be accounted for by the displacement calculations already discussed. One possible explanation of these results is that thermal or displacement spikes are producing further rearrangements. This will be discussed in the next section. A second possibility is that replacements of lattice atoms by moving atoms may occur very readily, more readily than the assumptions expressed in Figure 2.2 permit. A model which allows for this (31) retains assumptions (a) and (b) of the previous model but replaces assumptions (c) and (d) by the following:

(*c'*) An atom will invariably be displaced from its lattice site if by collision it receives kinetic energy greater than E_d. It will also be displaced if it receives energy between E_r and E_d (where $E_r < E_d$) and in addition the incoming atom is left with kinetic energy less than E_d. In this event the incoming atom remains behind in the lattice site, and is said to have replaced the struck atom.

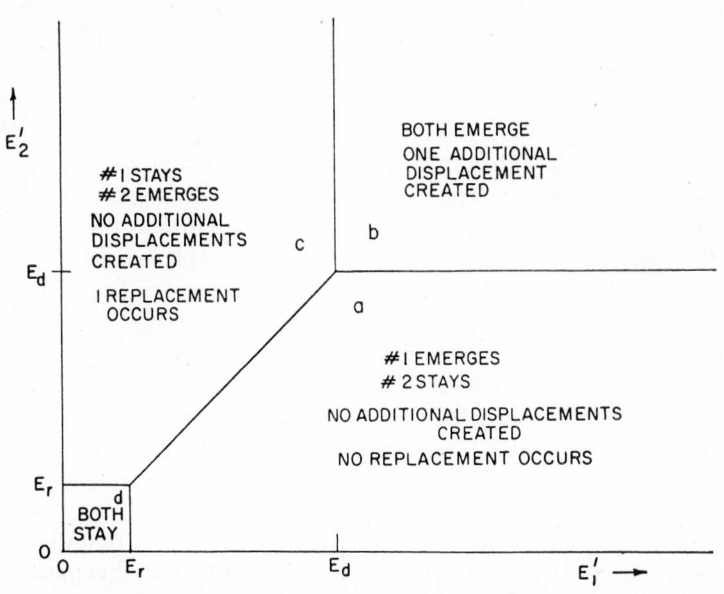

Figure 2.4 Diagram showing the assumptions of Kinchin and Pease for calculating the average number of replacements. Replacements occur in region *c*.

(*d'*) The incoming atom will also replace the struck atom if the latter receives energy greater than E_d and the incoming atom is left with energy less than E_d.

(*e*) The lattice atom will not be replaced or displaced in any other circumstances.

(*f*) All atoms will be assumed to be alike.

As in the earlier model, there will be a net increase in the number of displaced atoms only if both atoms have energy greater than E_d after the collision. Thus the total number of displacements will be the same in both models. However there will now be more replacement events than before, by an amount depending on the newly introduced replacement threshold E_r. The assumptions of the model are summarized in Figure 2.4, which is to be contrasted with Figure 2.1.

A calculation of the expected number of replacement collision can best be made by methods similar to those already employed in the displacement calculation. Let $\mu(E)$ be the average number of replacements generated by a moving atom of energy E. Let the probability that in a collision in which the incoming atom is left with energy E_1' and the struck atom receives energy E_2' the incoming atom emerges from the lattice site be $p(E_1', E_2')$. Let the probability that in the same collision the struck atom emerges be $q(E_1', E_2')$. Let the probability that in the same collision a replacement has occurred be $r(E_1', E_2')$. The number of replacements generated by an atom moving with energy E can now be calculated in this way: It is the sum of the average number of times a replacement occurs at the next collision of the moving atom, the average number of replacements subsequently generated by this atom after it emerges from the collision, and the average number of replacements subsequently generated by the atom that has been struck in this collision. Considering first a collision in which the incident and struck atoms end up with energies E_1' and E_2', respectively ($E_1' + E_2' = E$), for which the probability is $1/E$ per unit range of energy, and then averaging over the division of energy in the collision, one finds

$$\mu(E) = \int_0^E \frac{1}{E} r(E_1', E_2')\, dE_1' + \int_0^E \frac{1}{E} p(E_1', E_2')\, \mu(E_1')\, dE_1' + \int_0^E \frac{1}{E} q(E_1', E_2')\, \mu(E_2')\, dE_2' \quad (2.35)$$

This is the basic integral equation determining $\mu(E)$.

The coefficients p, q, and r can be evaluated for the present model by referring to Figure 2.4. $p(E_1', E_2')$ equals one in regions a and b, zero elsewhere. $q(E_1', E_2')$ equals one in regions b and c, zero elsewhere. Finally, $r(E_1', E_2')$ is one in region c, zero elsewhere. With this information equation 2.35 can be rewritten in the form

$$\mu(E) = 0, \qquad E_r \geq E \geq 0 \quad (2\text{-}36a)$$

$$\mu(E) = \left(\frac{E - E_r}{E}\right) + \frac{2}{E}\int_{E_r}^{E} \mu(E_1')\, dE_1', \quad 2E_r \geq E \geq E_r \quad (2\text{-}36b)$$

$$\mu(E) = \frac{1}{2} + \frac{2}{E}\int_{E/2}^{E} \mu(E_1') \, dE_1', \qquad 2E_d \geq E \geq 2E_r \quad (2\text{-}36c)$$

$$\mu(E) = \frac{E_d}{\mathrm{E}} + \frac{2}{\mathrm{E}}\int_{E_d}^{E} \mu(E_1') \, dE_1', \qquad E \geq 2E_d \quad (2\text{-}36d)$$

These relations can be converted to differential equations by multiplying through by E and differentiating with respect to E. The results are

$$E\mu'(E) = 1 + \mu(E) \qquad 2E_r \geq E > E_r \quad (2\text{-}37a)$$
$$E\mu'(E) = {}^1/_2 + \mu(E) - \mu(E/2), \qquad 2E_d \geq E > 2E_r \quad (2\text{-}37b)$$
$$E\mu'(E) = \mu(E), \qquad E > 2E_d \quad (2\text{-}37c)$$

Here $\mu'(E) = d\mu(E)/dE$. The first and third equations are immediately soluble, yielding

$$\mu(E) = (E/E_r) - 1 \qquad 2E_r \geq E \geq E_r \quad (2\text{-}38a)$$
$$\mu(E) = cE \qquad E \geq 2E_d \quad (2\text{-}38c)$$

Here c is an integration constant that must be determined by matching this function to the solution of equation 2-37b at $2E_d$. This mid-range solution can be found by first considering the range of E from $2E_r$ to $4\mathrm{E}_r$, in which range the term $\mu(E/2)$ is determined by equation 2.38a. Next the range of E from $4E_r$ to $8\mathrm{E}_r$ is considered, and the last solution determines $\mu(E/2)$. Thus by successive stages equation 2-37b can be solved in terms of elementary integrals. The result is a somewhat complicated function that fortunately can be approximated extremely accurately (to within $^1/_2\%$ for $32E_r > E > 2E_r$) by the formula

$$\mu(E) = 1.614 \ln \frac{\mathrm{E}}{2E_r} + 1, \qquad 2E_d \geq E \geq 2E_r \quad (2\text{-}38b)$$

Matching equation 2.38c to this, one finds

$$\mu(E) = \frac{\mathrm{E}}{2E_d}\left(1.614 \ln \frac{E_d}{E_r} + 1\right), \qquad E \geq 2E_d \quad (2\text{-}39)$$

For fast-neutron bombardment, the high-energy range is the only one of importance, and the calculation can be summarized by comparing this answer to the one previously obtained for the number of atoms displaced, $\nu(E)$ (see equation 2-26b). Taking the ratio, the result is

$$\frac{\text{number of atoms replaced}}{\text{number of atoms displaced}} = \frac{\mu(E)}{\nu(E)} = 1.614 \ln \frac{E_d}{E_r} + 1 \quad (2\text{-}40)$$

Kinchin and Pease (31), by an approximation scheme, obtained an answer differing only slightly from this.

Thus, if E_r is appreciably smaller than E_d a fairly large number of replacements would be expected for every displacement. No direct calculations of E_r have been made, unfortunately, but Kinchin and Pease have suggested that it is not unreasonable to expect $E_d/E_r = 10$. Equation 2-40 then predicts 4.7 replacements for every displacement, and this is about what is needed to explain the data of Aronin (30) on disordering of $MnNi_3$ by fast neutrons. Because of the logarithm in equation 2.40, the results are not very sensitive to the choice of E_d/E_r.

It must be remembered that the foregoing model is highly simplified. Hard-sphere collisions have been assumed, and this causes an overestimate of the number of replacements, since low-energy transfers are actually more probable than high ones. Also when the masses of the two constituents of an alloy are very disparate, low-energy transfers are favored and fewer replacements will occur. On the other hand, if the interstitials formed in the displacement process migrate by the interstitialcy mechanism during their annealing (see section 5.2A of Chapter 5), and if this takes place at quite low temperatures as seems to be the case in many metals, many additional replacements will occur. Furthermore, thermal- and displacement-spike effects have been ignored (see next section). Thus the foregoing calculation is not to be regarded as an accurate computation of the amount of disorder produced in irradiation but as an estimate that shows the general nature of a supplementary radiation effect of possible importance.

2.6 Spikes

A. General

The radiation effects considered in detail thus far have involved individual atomic displacements in undisturbed material. Actually the atoms are not affected singly, but in groups, and some distinct radiation effects arise because of this. Disturbances of small groups of atoms are even more difficult to encompass in a quantitative theory than disturbances of isolated atoms, and no entirely satisfactory treatment has been devised. Generally, a macroscopic approach that considers energy transfers in very large groups of atoms at not too rapid rates has been most fruitful. The subjects of these investigations are called temperature spikes.

Consider an atom moving through a lattice or an atom that has been hit just hard enough to vibrate with very large amplitude without being torn from its lattice site. Such an atom will rapidly transfer energy to its neighbors, which then become abnormally excited. These atoms give energy to their neighbors, and so on, and a localized excitation develops in the lattice and then dies out. The state of affairs is very much as if the lattice had been suddenly heated to a high temperature in a restricted region. One thus conceives of the spreading and dieing of the excitation as a form of heat conduction. This concept is very useful because it allows one to make a simple quantitative development in a situation that is exceedingly complex. In reality the excited region is never in equilibrium with itself and so is not strictly characterized by a temperature. Also, as will be shown, the distances and times involved are very small, so that the macroscopic laws of heat conduction are not strictly valid. Finally, the medium is not really homogeneous but atomic, and this must be ignored. Nevertheless the model is probably not bad, and although high quantitative reliability cannot be claimed, the qualitative features should be right.

Following Seitz and Koehler (11) we shall call all such excitations temperature spikes. These will be subdivided into two classes. When the excitation is high enough that many atoms in the spike are displaced from their lattice sites and wander about, the disturbance will be called a displacement spike. This includes the particular situation envisioned by Brinkman (see below). If the excitation is small so that few or none of the atoms leave their sites, the disturbance will be called a thermal spike. The theory of thermal spikes appears somewhat more firmly grounded than the theory of displacement spikes, which is still in a very speculative state.

When a moving atom or bombarding particle transfers energy Q to a lattice atom, where Q is from one to a few hundred electron volts, the spike model asks that one consider this energy to have been suddenly liberated as heat energy in a localized area of a continuous medium, and subsequently to spread according to the classical laws of heat conduction. The medium is considered to have a thermal diffusion coefficient D, and a temperature $T(r, t)$ at each point r and time t. D is related to the thermal conductivity C, the heat capacity c, and the density d by the equation

$$D = C/cd \tag{2-41}$$

In metals the ordinary heat conductivity is the sum of contributions from the lattice and the conduction electrons. Investigation shows that the coupling between lattice and electrons is sufficiently loose that the excitation in the spike,* which starts entirely in the lattice, will not be transferred to the conduction electrons during the important phase of the spike's existence. Consequently C in equation 2-41 should be the lattice thermal conductivity only. This makes D of the order of 0.001 cm^2/sec in most materials. D is actually temperature dependent, but this fact will be overlooked.

The temperature after initiation of the spike obeys the heat conduction equation

$$\nabla^2 T = (1/D)(\partial T/\partial t) \tag{2-42}$$

The solution of this corresponding to liberation of heat Q at a point at the origin at $t = 0$, with the temperature originally T_0 everywhere is

$$T(r, t) = T_0 + \frac{Q}{(4\pi)^{3/2}cd}\frac{1}{(Dt)^{3/2}}e^{-r^2/4Dt} \tag{2-43}$$

Here r is the distance from the origin. Figure 2.5 shows the temperature distribution at various times in a typical spike of this form. It is seen that the temperature rise extends to a distance of the order of r_e, where

$$r_e = 2(Dt)^{-1/2} \tag{2-44}$$

The temperature at any time has a maximum at the center of the spike, and this drops, as time increases, in proportion to $t^{-3/2}$.

If the moving atom that initiates the spike has high energy, its interactions with lattice atoms will be well separated and the individual spikes it produces can each be described by the foregoing distri-

* The transition metals are a possible exception. See section 27 of Seitz and Koehler (11).

bution. As the moving particle slows down, its interactions become more closely spaced and the individual spikes begin to overlap. The energy at which this sets in is higher with higher atomic numbers of moving particle and lattice (see discussion in section 2.2). When the interactions are closely spaced, one can idealize the situation by assuming that the initial burst of energy in the spike is uniformly dis-

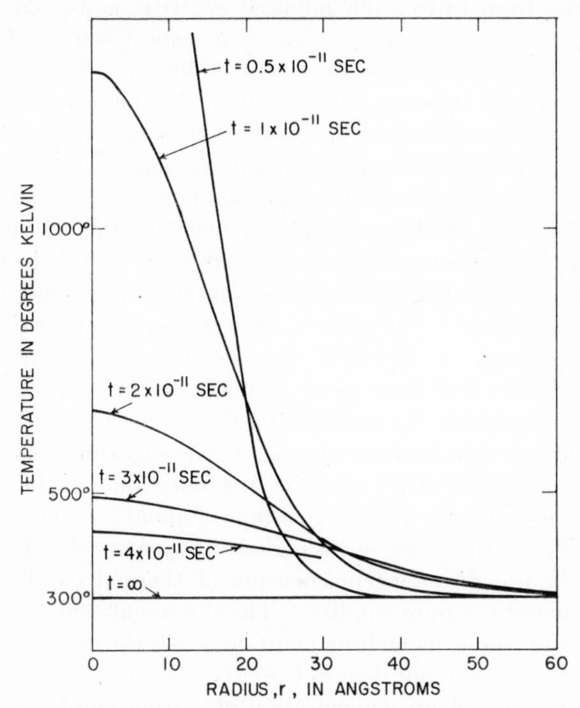

Figure 2.5 Temperature distributions in a typical thermal spike at various times. Taken from equation 2-43 with $D = 0.001$, $Q = 300$ ev, and other parameters suitable for copper.

tributed along the track of the particle and that the subsequent temperature distribution has cylindrical symmetry. If Q' is the energy released per unit length of the track, the corresponding cylindrical solution of the heat flow equation can be shown to be

$$T(\rho, t) = T_0 + \frac{Q'}{4\pi c d} \frac{1}{Dt} e^{-\rho^2/4Dt} \tag{2-45}$$

Here ρ is the perpendicular distance from the point of observation to the axis of the spike. Qualitatively this cylindrical spike is very much like the spherical spike (equation 2-43).

A few specific examples of temperature spikes will now be discussed to give a more concrete picture. In bombardments with light nuclei having energies of a few Mev, the typical energies imparted lie in the range from 10 to a few hundred ev, with occasional collisions transferring higher energies. Thus as a typical source of a spike, consider a knock-on atom with energy of 300 ev. This will have a range somewhere between 10 and 100 A, depending on the atomic number, and virtually all of its energy will be transferred to lattice vibrations. In simplest approximation one may regard this as the origin of a spherical spike with excitation energy $Q = 300$ ev. Actually the energy has been introduced over a region of appreciable size, and the excitation could more accurately be regarded as a superposition of smaller spikes centered at various points along the short track of the particle. This refinement is not necessary for the present rough assessment. Taking the case of copper for illustration, 300 ev is found to be sufficient energy to raise a spherical region 30 A in diameter from room temperature to the melting point, 1086° C. Such a region contains 1100 atoms. From equation 2-44, and the assumption that $D \cong 0.001$ cm²/sec, it is found that a spherical spike would spread over such a region in a time of about $r^2/4D \cong 5 \times 10^{-12}$ sec. This is of the order of 30 periods of atomic vibrations and is therefore in the range where concepts of thermal equilibrium are just beginning to acquire validity. The statement that this material is at or a little above its melting point describes the degree of thermal agitation in the spike but does not necessarily mean that it will have assumed the amorphous configuration of a true liquid. Because of the rapidity with which the temperature has risen and the confining effect of the surrounding material, the region is probably much more like a superheated solid, although genuine melting may also take place in the very center of the spike.

The newborn spike now spreads and cools. At 20×10^{-12} sec after initiation its diameter is 60 A, and the mean temperature in this region has fallen to about 150° C. This can be seen from equations 2-43 and 2-44. At about this time the spike has cooled sufficiently that it can no longer induce any permanent changes, and its subsequent decay is of no special interest. It is from considerations such as these that one arrives at the usual statements that typical thermal spikes endure for periods of the order of 10^{-11} sec and involve heating of the order of 10^3 atoms to the melting point or beyond. Individual spikes may differ from these in being either more or less intense.

Energetic knock-on atoms in light materials travel relatively large distances between elastic collisions, and thus become the sources of a number of individual spherical or approximately spherical spikes such as were discussed previously. Energetic knock-ons produced by neutron bombardment of heavy materials make collisions which are much more densely spaced, dissipating on the average one hundred to several hundred electron volts per Angstrom of path. These are better regarded as sources of cylindrical temperature spikes, of which a typical example would have a length of perhaps 1000 A and a diameter of 25 A about 10^{-12} sec after initiation. At this time the material inside this region would be at an average temperature of roughly 1000° C.

Fission fragments moving through uranium produce a more extreme case of a cylindrical temperature spike. A fragment having energy of 100 Mev has a range of about 4×10^{-4} cm. If it dissipated its energy uniformly along this line, and if all electronic excitation were transformed into lattice heat in this larger than normal spike, a cylindrical volume 4×10^4 A long and 100 A in radius would be heated to about 4000° C.

Many of the observable effects attributed to temperature spikes depend upon stimulation of diffusion, phase changes, and other activated processes by the local heating events. Although the heating can be rather intense, it is over small volumes and is always of brief duration (32). Consequently the actual extent of such stimulation demands careful quantitative consideration. Our ignorance of the kinetics of such processes is generally at least as great as our uncertainty about the energy distribution in the spikes themselves. Thus only rough estimates, suggestive but not definitive, can be made.

An example of such a calculation will now be given. Suppose each atom in a sample is capable of undergoing a rate process, such as interchanging with a neighbor or jumping to an interstitial site at an average rate

$$\nu = \nu_0 e^{-E'/kT} \qquad (2\text{-}46)$$

when the temperature is T. E' is the activation energy and ν_0 is the effective frequency, which is supposed to include any multiplicity and entropy factors necessary. Let there be n_0 atoms per unit volume. A spike will cause a certain number of atomic jumps, Δn, which can be computed by integrating the expression in equation 2-46 over time and over space, allowing T in the exponent to vary in the manner appropriate to the spike, and subtracting the number of jumps which would have occurred in the absence of the spike. Δn is then the *extra* number of jumps occurring in the entire crystal during the entire lifetime of the spike, and can be seen to be

$$\Delta n = n_0 \nu_0 \int_0^\infty dr\, 4\pi r^2 \int_0^\infty dt \left\{ \exp\left[-\frac{E'}{kT(r,t)} \right] - \exp\left[-\frac{E'}{kT_0} \right] \right\} \tag{2-47}$$

$T(r,t)$ is to be taken from equation 2-43. With N_0 spikes being produced per cm³ per sec, the augmentation of the atomic jump rate, in jumps/cm³/sec, is $N_0 \Delta n$.

Unfortunately the integrals in equation 2-47 are difficult and do not seem to have been investigated for finite T_0. Seitz and Koehler (11) have studied a simplified case, in which they assume the ambient temperature T_0 to be zero; they approximate the temperature distribution in the spike by the forms

$$T(r,t) \cong \begin{cases} \dfrac{Q}{(4\pi)^{3/2} cd} \dfrac{1}{(Dt)^{3/2}}, & 2(Dt)^{-1/2} > r \\ 0, & 2(Dt)^{-1/2} < r \end{cases} \tag{2-48}$$

They then find

$$\Delta n = 0.016\ (\nu_0 r_S^2/D)(Q/E)^{5/3} \tag{2-49}$$

where $r_S = [3/(4\pi n_0)]^{1/3}$.

The quantity $\nu_0 r_S^2/D$ affects the result in an essential way. It can be regarded as the ratio of an atomic diffusivity to a lattice thermal diffusivity, and might be expected to lie in the neighborhood of 1, although it may sometimes differ from this by rather large amounts and is not known accurately in any case. Measurements of the disordering of Cu_3Au at $-100°$ C by 9 Mev protons (33) show that about 125 atoms are disordered for every primary displaced atom. Seitz and Koehler (11) have considered whether thermal spikes could explain this and argue that each primary displaced atom should be accompanied by about six temperature spikes in each of which Q is about 50 ev. The excitation energy for interchange of adjoining atoms in Cu_3Au would be around 3 ev, and Seitz and Koehler suggest unity as the most plausible value of $\nu_0 r_S^2/D$. On this basis equation 2-49 predicts 10 disordered atoms per primary displaced atom, an order of magnitude less than the observed results. If one assumed $\nu_0 r_S^2/D$ to be 10, some of the atoms near the center of the spike would be contributing more than one jump to Δn, as can be seen from a calculation of the number of jumps for an atom in the hottest part of the spike. In this case equation 2-49 gives an overestimate of the disordering and must be diminished by a suitable correction. Making this correction Seitz and Koehler find that the number of atoms disordered is now 40, which is still too small.

The conclusion from these considerations is that some further mechanism is at work in the radiation disordering of ordered alloys, although the heating in temperature spikes could produce an appreciable acceleration of many rate processes. Of particular interest is the question of the production of Frenkel defects (vacancy-interstitial pairs) by temperature spikes and the subsequent annealing or rearrangement of these defects. A good deal of speculative discussion can be given, but the theory is unable to provide firm conclusions. The working hypothesis of most investigators in the field has been that such production is not an important source of Frenkel defects compared to the knock-on cascades.

Processes which are most likely to be affected by spikes are those which nearly go of their own accord at ambient temperature, and instances of nucleation and phase change have been attributed to spikes. Further discussion of experimental evidence along these lines will be given in subsequent chapters.

B. Plastic Deformation in Temperature Spikes

The heating in a temperature spike tends to expand the material in the spike, and this must generate a stress around the spike. Simple considerations allow one to estimate the magnitude of this stress. Consider a typical spike in which the material within a sphere of radius r_e is heated uniformly and the heating outside this region is neglected. If the flow of heat is proceeding at a rate slow compared to the velocity of elastic waves, a system of stresses is set up which obeys static elasticity theory. For simplicity it will also be assumed that the material is isotropic. One then finds a compressive stress in the radial direction having a magnitude (34)

$$p = \begin{cases} p_0, & r < r_e \\ p_0 r_e^3/r^3, & r > r_e \end{cases} \tag{2-50}$$

where r is the distance from the center of the spike and p_0 is given in terms of the shear modulus μ, Poisson's ratio σ, and the fractional linear expansion the heated material would have in the absence of pressure, $\Delta l/l$, by the expression

$$p_0 = \frac{4(1+\sigma)}{3(1-\sigma)} \mu \frac{\Delta l}{l} \tag{2-51}$$

In the directions perpendicular to the radial direction the stress is a pure tension of magnitude $\frac{1}{2}p$, for $r > r_e$.

These considerations may now be applied to the earlier example of a typical spike in copper, where a region 15 A in radius was melted. We take $\Delta l/l \cong 0.05$, $\mu = 10^{12}$ dynes/cm^2, and $\sigma = \frac{1}{4}$. Equation 2-51 then gives $p_0 \cong 10^{11}$ dynes/cm^2. This is well within the range where plastic deformation may occur in perfect crystals (35). On the other hand the stress drops rapidly with r. Assuming $r_e = 15$ A, at $r = 10r_e = 150$ A the stress is down to a value which can move existing dislocations but clearly cannot initiate plastic deformation in perfect material. In well annealed materials the average distance between existing dislocations is 10^4 to 10^5 A, so the typical spike will cause plastic flow only to the extent that it can produce dislocations in the high stress region near its center.

It is reasonable to suppose that dislocations will be formed within distances of the order of 10 A from the center of typical spikes. Since dislocation lines can terminate only on the surfaces of a crystal and we are considering those produced by a localized stress system on the interior of a crystal, it can be seen that any dislocation produced must have the form of a loop or system of loops. Such loops have a self-contracting tendency, since their energy content increases in proportion to their length. The thermal stress field overrides this and forces them to expand into the surrounding regions where the thermal stress is lower and can be balanced by the self-stresses of the loop. Since the self-energy of a dislocation is thought to be in the range of a few tenths ev per Angstrom of length and since the entire spike contains only a few hundred ev, it can be anticipated that the loops will not become very large. Calculation indicates that their equilibrium diameters will be of the order of ten or a few tens of Angstroms. As the spike subsequently cools, the stress system dies out and the loops contract again. If their contraction proceeds in exactly the inverse order of their formation all loops will contract to nothing and no plastic displacements will remain. However it is unlikely that the cooling will be in just the right pattern for this, and contraction in other sequences may leave dislocation loops entangled with one another, resulting in permanent plastic displacements.

Seitz and Koehler (11) have given an illustrative example of how this process might look, but no real calculations of the extent of such effects in actual materials have been made. It is probable that appreciable numbers of dislocations remain after bombardments, but the experimental evidence for this is equivocal. It should also be noted that such dislocations, if possessed of a Buerger's vector smaller than a superlattice vector, would produce considerable disordering in ordered alloys. This might be an explanation of the unaccountably large disordering effects of radiation, which have already been mentioned.

C. Displacement Spikes

A still more radical picture of the displacement spike has been developed by Brinkman (36,37). This author has made calculations of the separation of secondary displacements along the path of a primary knock-on and finds these rather more closely spaced than had been commonly believed. Brinkman estimates that the average spacing between secondary displacements in copper is less than one interatomic distance when the energy of the primary is anywhere between 50 and 23,000 ev. In heavier elements the close spacing would prevail over even larger ranges of energy. This would mean that as soon as the energy of the primary fell to some tens of kilovolts the atom would very rapidly be brought to rest (in a distance of the order of 100 A) amid such a dense shower of secondary displacements that it would be entirely incorrect to treat each secondary as independent of the others. Brinkman's figures indicate that 10^4 or more atoms in a cylindrical region would be brought rather violently to the molten state with considerable turbulent flow. He suggests that the pattern of rearrangement would be an inversion of the material in the spike, the atoms along the axis being driven outward most violently and ending up outside of those in the adjacent tubular region. Figure 2.6 shows this behavior.

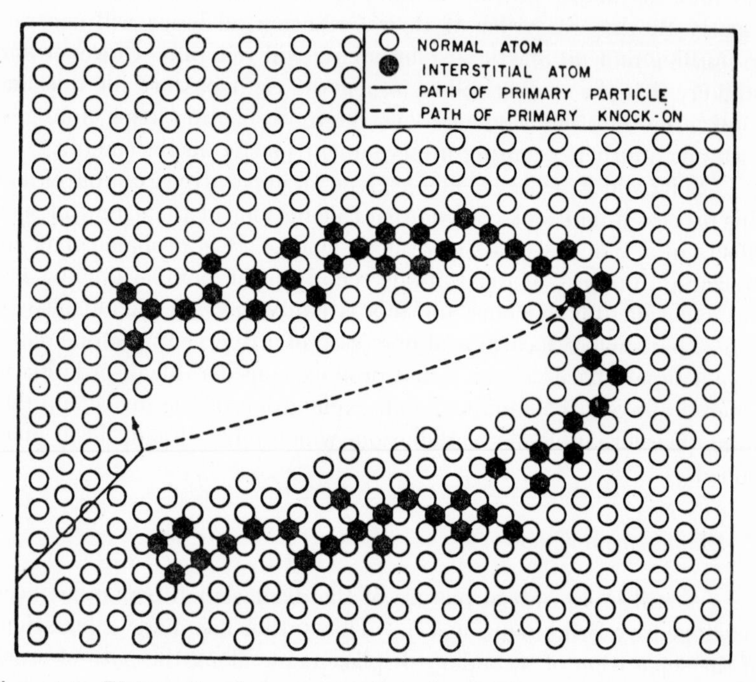

Figure 2.6 Picture of a displacement spike, after Brinkman (from reference 36). The configuration is unstable and will immediately collapse.

Immediately after this stage the molten zone would collapse and resolidify. Since freezing would start at the outside, the resolidified material would be expected to be largely in register with the original lattice. Most of the interstitials and vacancies would be expected to anneal, but an undetermined number of these, as well as small misoriented regions and entangled dislocation loops, would remain.

The key to this picture is the calculated close spacing between secondary knock-ons, to which the results are very sensitive, and it must be recognized that this is a difficult number to determine accurately. Brinkman assumes a stronger repulsive force between atoms than usual, and this enlarges his calculated collision frequency. He has also ignored recoil in his cross-section calculations, which again overestimates the frequency. On the other hand, criticism published by Seitz and Koehler (11), which maintains that the collisions are much less frequent, is not entirely free of objection either.

An important physical consequence of the Brinkman model is that the high degree of mixing that occurs in the spike and the large

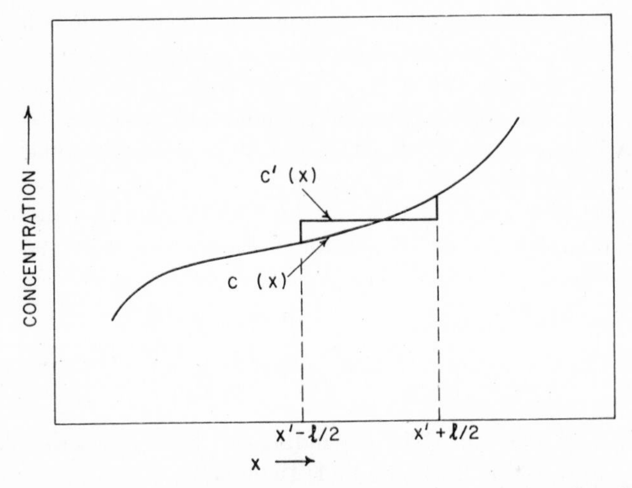

Figure 2.7 Alteration of concentration distribution by a single spike of length centered at x' (idealized).

size of the spike in heavy metals would enhance atomic diffusion in these materials. It is interesting to consider this quantitatively. The treatment of an idealized one-dimensional model is given here to show the essential features, and then the three-dimensional generalization is indicated. Suppose the concentration of one atomic species at x in a crystal is $c(x)$. Suppose that when a spike arrives at x' the composition is immediately modified by complete mixing over a length l centered on x'. The new concentration $c'(x)$ is given by

$$c'(x) = \begin{cases} \bar{c}(x'), & x' - l/2 < x < x' + l/2 \\ c(x), & \text{all other } x \end{cases} \qquad (2\text{-}52)$$

where $\bar{c}(x')$ is the average of $c(x)$ in the interval about x':

$$\bar{c}(x') = \frac{1}{l}\int_{x'-l/2}^{x'+l/2} c(x)\, dx \tag{2-53}$$

This mixing effect of a spike is shown in Figure 2.7.

Suppose spikes are being formed at random times and places but at an average rate N_0 per unit length per unit time. The concentration is then changing in a way which is very complicated in detail but which has an over-all resemblance to a diffusion process, as will now be shown. Consider the concentration as a function of position and time, and investigate the expectation value of its time derivative $< \partial c(x,t)/\partial t >$. The probability that a spike will arrive at time t to $t + dt$ with center in x' to $x' + dx'$ is $N_0\, dx'\, dt$. When such a spike arrives, the concentration at x changes by $\Delta c(x, t) = \bar{c}(x', t) - c(x, t)$, when $|x - x'| < l/2$, where $\bar{c}(x', t)$ is given by equation 2-53 with $c(x)$ replaced by $c(x, t)$. $\Delta c(x, t) = 0$ when $|x - x'| > l/2$. The expectation value of this, $<\Delta c(x, t)>$ is found by multiplying by the probability $N_0\, dx'/dt$ and integrating over x' from $-\infty$ to ∞. One then has

$$< \frac{\partial c(x, t)}{\partial t} > = \frac{<\Delta c(x, t)>}{dt} = N_0 \int_{x-l/2}^{x+l/2} dx' \{\bar{c}(x', t) - c(x, t)\} \tag{2-54}$$

One now evaluates $\bar{c}(x', t)$ by expanding $c(x)$ in Taylor series about x. Employing equation 2-53, one finds the result

$$\bar{c}(x', t) = \frac{1}{l}\int_{x'-l/2}^{x'+l/2} \sum_{n=0}^{\infty} \frac{1}{n!} c_n(x, t)(\zeta - x)^n d\zeta \tag{2-55}$$

where

$$c_n(x, t) = \partial^n c(x, t)/\partial x^n \tag{2-56}$$

Carrying out the integrations,

$$\bar{c}(x', t) = \sum_{n=0}^{\infty} \frac{c_n(x, t)}{l(n+1)n!}\left[\left(x' - x + \frac{l}{2}\right)^{n+1} - \left(x' - x - \frac{l}{2}\right)^{n+1}\right]$$

Inserting this in equation 2-54 and integrating again, one finds

$$< \frac{\partial c(x, t)}{\partial t} > = \sum_{m=1}^{\infty} \frac{2N_0 l^{2m+1}}{(2m+2)!} c_{2m}(x, t) \tag{2-57}$$

If it is assumed that $c_{2m}(x, t)$ is also the $2m$th derivative of the expectation value of $c(x, t)$, equation 2-57 amounts to a differential equation of infinite order governing the evolution of the concentration under the stochastic mixing effect of the spikes. Under conditions of interest l is very small and the concentration changes relatively slowly with x. Thus it may be assumed that only the initial term on the right of equation 2-57 is necessary. One then has

$$\frac{\partial}{\partial t} < c(x, t) > = \left(\frac{N_0 l^3}{12}\right) \frac{\partial^2}{\partial x^2} < c(x, t) > \tag{2-58}$$

This is the diffusion equation and shows that the concentration, in this approximation, evolves in accord with Fick's law with a (one-dimensional) coefficient of diffusivity $N_0 l^3/12$.

A precisely similar development is possible in three dimensions, and this development shows at once that the diffusivity is given by

$$D_s = N_0 l^5/12 \tag{2-59}$$

where l^3 is the volume of the spike.

Essentially the same result has been given by Bleiberg, Jones, and Lustman (38) and by Konobeevsky (39) by arguments from more specialized situations. The latter finds the numerical factor in equation 2-59 to be $^1/_{24}$ instead of $^1/_{12}$. It is felt that the present derivation gives a more reliable number, although this part of the equation cannot be put to any very severe experimental test. The computed diffusivity is exceedingly sensitively dependent on the linear dimensions of the spike, and this is not at all accurately known. If one takes Brinkman's value of 10^{-6} cm for l and considers a bombardment in which 10^{14} spikes are produced per cm^3 per sec, as would be the case in uranium in a reactor, equation 2-59 gives $D_s \cong 10^{-17}$ cm^2/sec. This is a small value, but it would be capable of causing observable effects in some cases. Thus Bleiberg, Jones, and Lustman suggest this process to explain the homogenization of uranium-molybdenum alloys containing very finely grained precipitates.

2.7 Gamma Irradiation

Gamma-rays and x-rays produce ionization in all solids, and this is their most important effect. In insulators, chemical reactions may be promoted, some of which cannot be induced by other means.

Further discussion of such effects will be found in Chapter 6. In metals, ionization produced by radiation is very rapidly neutralized by the conduction electrons, and no structural changes result from this process. There is also evidence that gamma-rays can produce displaced atoms in solids; the efficiency is low but occasionally detectable. In the present section the theoretical basis of gamma-ray displacement effects will be considered.

Gamma-ray dosages are commonly expressed in roentgens,* a unit that measures intensity of ionization produced. It must be remembered that the energy or photon density in the radiation depends on the wavelength as well as on the number of roentgens. In reactor irradiations a strong γ-ray flux is usually present, but its intensity and energy distribution depend very much on the type of reactor and the conditions of irradiation. Most experimental work to date has been done with rather meager knowledge of the γ-ray conditions. The justification has been that the γ-ray effects are expected to be small compared with neutron effects, but this is a matter which should be given more attention. The γ-rays originate chiefly in the fission products in the fuel elements and thus possess a broad spectrum of energies, from kilovolts to perhaps 10 Mev. As with the neutrons, the average energy is somewhere around 1 Mev.

In the Brookhaven reactor (natural uranium, graphite moderated, air cooled) the γ-ray intensity near the center of the reactor is around 3,000,000 roentgens/hour, which can also be expressed as a flux density of about 1.6×10^{12} photons/cm^2/sec of mean energy about 1 Mev. The photon flux density in this reactor is about 40% of the slow-neutron flux density, or perhaps twice as large as the fast-neutron flux density.

In the Materials Testing Reactor (enriched uranium, water moderated) the gamma-ray intensity reaches the astonishing level

* A roentgen is defined as the amount of x- or γ-radiation that liberates one statcoulomb of ions in one cubic centimeter of dry air at 0° C and 760 mm Hg. One roentgen liberates 0.11 erg per cubic centimeter in standard air, forming about 2×10^9 ion pairs per cubic centimeter. In denser materials the ionization and energy liberation *per unit volume* is greater than the above by the ratio of the density of the material to the density of air, if the atomic weight is the same as air, and is somewhat different in materials of other atomic weights. It is useful to know that, for 1-Mev γ-rays, 1 roentgen consists of 1.9×10^9 photons/cm^2. For further discussion of these matters see chapter 25 of Evans (12) and reference (46).

of 10^{10} roentgens/hour, or approximately 5×10^{15} photons/cm²/sec. This may well be the cause of some of the differences found between irradiations to identical neutron exposures in this reactor and in other reactors.

Primak (45) has published calculations of gamma-ray dosage in Oak Ridge and Chicago reactors, and discusses the problem for inhomogeneous reactors in general.

The interaction of γ-rays with matter occurs principally by means of three mechanisms: the photoelectric effect, the Compton

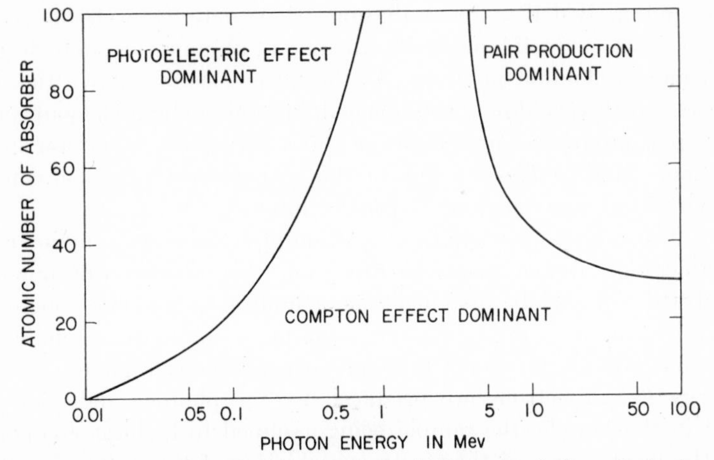

Figure 2.8 Diagram showing energies at which each of the principal γ-ray processes becomes dominant (after Evans).

effect, and pair production. The first predominates at low energies, the second at intermediate energies, and the third at quite high energies. For a given energy the atomic cross section for each process depends solely on the atomic number, Z, of the absorber, and so the dividing lines between the processes can be given on a diagram of Z *vs* photon energy, as shown in Figure 2.8. The separating lines are drawn so that the atomic cross sections are equal for neighboring processes along the lines. From Figure 2.8 it is seen that for ordinary x-rays the photoelectric effect has the largest cross section, except in the very lightest elements. For reactor γ-rays, and also for γ-rays from cobalt and fission-product sources, the Compton effect has the largest cross section, except for the case of very-high-Z materials, where the low-energy tail on the spectrum produces photoelectrons and the high-energy tail causes some pair production.

In all three processes electrons are ejected with energies comparable with the original γ-ray energy, and thus γ-ray irradiation inevitably causes a substance to be internally bombarded by fairly energetic electrons. The processes by which these electrons lose energy have already been discussed. Most of their energy is dissipated in causing further ionization, but occasionally they displace atoms by elastic collisions. In typical x-irradiations, these electrons are below threshold energies for displacement production, but in pile and activated-source radiations they may be well above it. There is also a recoil imparted to the parent atom in the photoelectric and pair-production processes; in the latter energies above the displacement threshold may be imparted, but only in light elements, and here pair production at energies of a few Mev has a very low cross section. It thus does not appear that pair-production recoil can be important at γ-ray energies of present interest.

The internal β-irradiation by Compton electrons remains as a producer of atomic displacements, and this process will now be analyzed. It will be assumed that a uniform γ-ray flux consisting of ϕ_γ photons/cm^2/sec traverses the sample, suffering no attenuation. The flux will be considered to be monoenergetic, each photon having energy E_γ. Electrons are produced by the photons and come to rest in the sample, the sample being assumed to be large compared to the mean range of the electrons, which is of the order of 1 mm. There is then a polyenergetic β-ray flux in the sample of density $\phi_\beta(E)$ electrons/cm^2/sec, at energy E, per unit range of energy. Let the number of atoms per unit volume in the sample be n_0, and let the cross section per atom for the production of a Compton electron at energy E be $\sigma_c(E)$. Then the number of electrons produced per cm^3 per second at energy E, within unit range, by Compton processes is

$$\phi_\gamma \, n_0 \, \sigma_c(E) \qquad (2\text{-}60)$$

The number of electrons passing from energies above E to energies below E by slowing-down processes in the medium, per cm^3 per second is

$$\phi_\beta(E)(-dE/dx) \qquad (2\text{-}61)$$

where $(-dE/dx)$ is the energy loss per cm of path for electrons.

Conservation of the total number of electrons now requires that the derivative of expression 2-61 with respect to energy equal the negative of expression 2-60

$$\frac{d}{dE}\left[\phi_\beta(E)\,\frac{dE}{dx}\right] = \phi_\gamma\, n_0\, \sigma_c(E) \tag{2-62}$$

This differential equation allows one to determine the electron flux density, $\phi_\beta(E)$. If E_{max} is the maximum energy that electrons can receive from photons of energy E_γ, $\phi_\beta(E_{max}) = 0$, and equation 2-62 yields

$$\phi_\beta(E) = \phi_\gamma\, n_0\,(-dE/dx)^{-1} \int_E^{E_{max}} \sigma_c(E')\, dE',\ 0 < E \leqslant E_{max} \tag{2-63}$$

If the cross section for an atom to be displaced by an electron of energy E is $\sigma_d{}^\beta(E)$, the number of atoms displaced/cm^3/sec, $R_d{}^\beta$, can be written

$$R_d{}^\beta = \int_0^{E_{max}} n_0\, \sigma_d{}^\beta(E)\, \phi_\beta(E)\, dE =$$

$$\phi_\gamma n_0{}^2 \int_0^{E_{max}} dE\, \sigma_d{}^\beta(E)\, (-dE/dx)^{-1} \int_E^{E_{max}} \sigma_c(E')\, dE' \tag{2-64}$$

The Compton cross section of an atom is given by the formula [Bethe and Ashkin (5)]

$$\sigma_c(\epsilon) = \sigma_0 \left\{\frac{1}{1-\epsilon} + 1 - \epsilon + \frac{\epsilon}{\gamma^2(1-\epsilon)}\left[\frac{\epsilon}{1-\epsilon} - 2\gamma\right]\right\} \tag{2-65}$$

where $\epsilon = E/E_\gamma$, $\gamma = E_\gamma/mc^2$, and $\sigma_0 = \pi r_0{}^2\, Z_2\, mc^2/E_\gamma{}^2$. Here e and m are electronic charge and mass, respectively, c is the velocity of light, r_0 is the classical electron radius, $r_0 = e^2/mc^2$, and Z_2 is the atomic number of the sample. The energy loss per cm, $-dE/dx$, can be written (12)

$$-dE/dx = a[(1 + E/mc^2)/E] \tag{2-66}$$

where $a = 2\pi e^4 n_0 Z_2 L$, and L is a coefficient depending only weakly on the electron energy and the nature of the stopping material. For present purposes L may be set equal to 10.

The cross section for an atom to be displaced by an electron of energy E, assuming a sharp displacement threshold energy E_d, has been given by Seitz and Koehler (11) (see also the discussion in the preceding section 2.2). With this information, equation 2-64 can be evaluated to find R_d^β. $\sigma_c(E)$ increases with increasing Z_2. $\sigma_d^\beta(E)$ is zero for E below a threshold, and the threshold rises with Z_2. For energies well above threshold $\sigma_d^\beta(E)$ increases with Z_2. As a result of these conflicting tendencies the dependence of R_d^β on gamma-ray energy is complicated. For gammas of 1 Mev or less R_d^β is a maximum in the very light elements and declines rapidly with increasing atomic number, becoming zero, for 1-Mev gammas and a displacement threshold of 25 ev, at atomic weight about 125. For higher energy gammas R_d^β is a maximum with intermediate or heavy elements. Table 2.4 gives some representative values of $R_d^\beta/(\phi_\gamma n_0)$, which may be considered an effective atomic cross section for atomic displacement by gamma-rays by the Compton-electron mechanism. In these calculations the threshold energy for displacement has been assumed to be 25 ev.

By similar methods the effective cross section for displacement by photoelectrons can also be computed. For example, for copper, the photoelectrons contribute an effective cross section of 0.005×10^{-24} cm² at 1 Mev and 0.013×10^{-24} cm² at 2 Mev. From the calculations available it does not appear that this mechanism makes an appreciable contribution in comparison with that of the Compton process.

Table 2.4. Calculated values of the effective cross section for atomic displacement by gamma-rays through the Compton mechanism, $R_d^\beta/(\phi_\gamma n_0)$ (in units of 10^{-24} cm²).

Element	Gamma-ray energy (Mev) R_d^β	$R_d^\beta/(\phi_\gamma n_0)$
Carbon	0.5	0.02
	1.0	0.14
	2.0	0.43
Copper	0.5	0
	1.0	0.046
	2.0	1.40
Gold	0.5	0
	1.0	0

In reactor irradiations the total number of displacements produced by the gamma-rays by the Compton process can now be estimated if the spectrum and flux of the gammas are known. For purposes of orientation, it will be assumed that the mean gamma energy is between 1 and 2 Mev, and that there is approximately one photon for every fast neutron. From Table 2.4 it is seen that the effective cross section for the gammas is of the order of 1 barn for copper. The collision cross section for fast neutrons is about 3 barns in this element, and each fast-neutron collision, by cascade processes, produces approximately 400 displaced atoms. Thus the neutrons should produce, in this substance, two to three orders of magnitude more displacements than the gamma-rays. This margin of effectiveness of neutrons over gammas would be equalled or exceeded in other materials, except that in many insulating materials additional displacement mechanisms exist for gammas. These will be discussed below.

In irradiations by pure gamma-rays, such as obtained from a cobalt source, the Compton displacement mechanism may be important. Cleland, Crawford, and Holmes (40) have observed displacement of atoms in germanium irradiated in a Co^{60} source. Their measurements indicate an effective cross section for atomic displacement by photons of 1.5×10^{-26} cm^2, which is in rough agreement with the above theory.

Beside the effect of internal β-ray bombardment and the direct recoils from γ-ray events, two other possible mechanisms by which γ-rays may produce atomic displacements have been suggested. Both of these mechanisms involve conversion of electronic excitation energy to displacement energy, and should be especially effective in insulators. The first was suggested by Seitz (41). According to this proposal excitons (localized regions of electronic excitation) are produced by radiation and travel through the crystal until they encounter a lattice irregularity, at which point the energy is discharged into the lattice, producing a local hot spot. Jogs in dislocation lines are likely sites for such discharges, and the temporary heating of the lattice at a jog can induce dislocation climb, which is to say vacancies can be "boiled off" at the jog. The energies available are of the order of 10 ev, which is sufficient to create a vacancy. It is also possible that free electrons and holes created by ionizing radiation recombine and liberate energy at these sites. Excitons can be produced by irradiation with light in the fundamental absorption band, that is with wavelengths in the ultraviolet, as well as by x-rays and γ-rays. Also the migration of point defects away from their point of origin may be caused by further absorptions of excitons on the defect. The proposal offers an attractive explanation of the production of color centers in ionic crystals by ultraviolet light at low temperatures. Unfortunately no quantitative development has been published, and calculations of the extent of vacancy production by this mechanism in typical radiation damage experiments have not been made.

The second displacement mechanism was suggested by Varley (42,43,44) and applies to substances with highly ionic binding. Varley pointed out that in irradiation by charged particles, γ-rays, x-rays, or possibly even ultraviolet light, some negative ions will be deprived of two or more electrons, becoming temporarily positively charged. The stripped electrons move away through the crystal, and the positive ion remaining behind finds itself in a highly unstable position since it is on a site surrounded by other positive ions. This instability may lead to ejection of the ion to an interstitial site, where it will ultimately capture enough electrons to be neutralized. The vacant lattice site may capture an electron to become an F-center. The interstitial atom will remain in its new position, or, if the temperature is high enough, it will diffuse about and eventually become trapped at a defect. The operation of this mechanism requires that (*a*) the lattice be largely ionic, (*b*) the cross section for multiple ionization be sufficiently great, (*c*) the recombination time for electrons and stripped atom be long enough to allow ejection (which requires a time of the order of 10^{-13} seconds), and (*d*) the ejected atom go far enough to be stable against immediate return upon neutralization. It is plausible that all these conditions can be satisfied in many materials, and experiments on coloration of alkali halides by electron bombardment are in general agreement with the model (43). In this case the experimentally observed cross section for displacement is about 30 times larger than that for direct collision between electron and atom (relativistic Rutherford scattering), and could be explained by the proposed mechanism. The cross sections for multiple ionization have not been much studied. Existing evidence indicates that, for electrons in the kilovolt range the atomic cross section for $a(p + 1)$-fold ionization event is about one order of magnitude smaller than that for a p-fold event, $p = 1, 2, 3, \ldots$. For megavolt electrons the $(p + 1)$-fold cross section may be two orders of magnitude smaller than the p-fold cross section. These numbers are consistent with the expectation that in electron bombardment of ionic materials the Varley mechanism provides an important number of atomic displacements. Threshold energy studies in such materials, which unfortunately have not been made, would test this conception. These numbers also suggest that the Varley process may be an important secondary effect in the bombardment of ionic materials by charged particles and neutrons. In the case of electromagnetic radiation, multiple ionization may occur through direct interaction with more than one outer electron or through an Auger cascade effect. Quantitative investigations of this, of the recombination time for ionized atoms, and of the return probabilities for ejected atoms have not yet been carried out. They would be most valuable in assessing the effectiveness of the Varley mechanism.

References

1. R. Smoluchowski, "Irradiation of Ionic Crystals," *Proceedings of the International Conference on the Peaceful Uses of Atomic Energy*, United Nations, 1956, Vol. 7, p. 682 (Paper No. 748).
2. N. Bohr, "The Penetration of Atomic Particles Through Matter," *Kgl. Danske Videnskab. Selskab, Mat.-fys. Medd.*, **18,** 8 (1948) (particularly Ch. IV).
3. F. Seitz, "On the Disordering of Solids by Action of Fast Massive Particles," *Discussions Faraday Soc., No.* **5,** 271 (1949).
4. G. H. Kinchin and R. S. Pease, "The Displacement of Atoms in Solids by Radiation," *Rept. Progr. in Phys.*, **18,** 1 (1955).
5. H. A. Bethe and J. Ashkin, in *Experimental Nuclear Physics*, Vol. I, E. Segre, Ed., John Wiley, New York, 1953.
6. E. Everhart, G. Stone, and R. G. Carbone, "Classical Calculation of Differential Cross Section for Scattering from a Coulomb Potential with Exponential Screening," *Phys. Rev.*, **99,** 1287 (1955).
7. H. B. Huntington, private communication.
8. N. F. Mott, "The Scattering of Fast Electrons by Atomic Nuclei," *Proc. Roy. Soc. (London)*, **A124,** 426 (1929).
9. N. F. Mott, "Polarization of Electrons by Double Scattering," *Proc. Roy. Soc. (London)*, **A135,** 429 (1932).
10. W. A. McKinley, Jr. and H. Feshbach, "The Coulomb Scattering of Relativistic Electrons by Nuclei," *Phys. Rev.*, **74,** 1759 (1948).
11. F. Seitz and J. S. Koehler, "Displacement of Atoms during Irradiation," in *Solid State Physics* (editors F. Seitz and D. Turnbull), Academic Press, New York, 1956, Vol. 2, pp. 307–442.
12. R. D. Evans, *The Atomic Nucleus*, McGraw-Hill, New York, 1955.
13. B. E. Watt, "Energy Spectrum of Neutrons from Thermal Fission of U^{235}," *Phys. Rev.*, **87,** 1037 (1953).
14. D. J. Hughes, *Pile Neutron Research*, Addison-Wesley Publishing Co., Cambridge, 1953, pp. 58–61.

15. W. Primak, "Fast Neutron Damaging in Nuclear Reactors: Its Kinetics and the Carbon Atom Displacement Rate," *Phys. Rev.*, **103,** 1681 (1956).
16. M. Walt and H. H. Barschall, "Scattering of 1 Mev Neutrons by Intermediate and Heavy Elements," *Phys. Rev.*, **93,** 1062 (1954).
17. M. Walt and J. R. Beyster, "Interaction of 4.1 Mev Neutrons with Nuclei," *Phys. Rev.*, **98,** 677 (1955).
18. Allen, Walton, Perkins, Olson, and Taschek, "Interaction of 0.5 and 1.0 Mev Neutrons with Some Heavy Elements," *Phys. Rev.*, **104,** 731 (1956).
19. H. Feshbach and V. F. Weisskopf, "A Schematic Theory of Nuclear Cross Sections," *Phys. Rev.*, **76,** 1550 (1949).
20. E. T. Jurney, "Inelastic Collision and Transport Cross Sections for some Light Elements," *U. S. Atomic Energy Comm.*, Document LA-1339 (1951).
21. D. T. Keating, "X-ray Measurements of Pile-Irradiated LiF," *Phys. Rev.*, **97,** 832 (1955).
22. M. Lambert and A. Guinier, "Étude par les Diagrammes de Diffusion des Rayons x du Fluoride de Lithium Irradié," in *Action des Rayonnements de Grande Energie sur les Solides* (editor: Y. Cauchois), Gauthier-Villars, Paris, 1956.
23. J. W. Cleland and J. H. Crawford, Jr., "Radiation Effects in Indium Antimonide," *Phys. Rev.*, **93,** 894 (1954).
24. W. S. Snyder and J. Neufeld, "Disordering of Solids by Neutron Irradiation," *Phys. Rev.*, **97,** 1636 (1955); **99,** 1326 (1955); **103,** 862 (1956).
25. W. A. Harrison and F. Seitz, "Theory of Radiation Damage," *Phys. Rev.*, **98,** 1530 (1955) (A).
26. J. B. Sampson, H. Hurwitz, Jr., and E. F. Clancy, "Sensitivity of Radiation Damage to the Displacement Probability," *Phys. Rev.*, **99,** 1657 (1955) (A).
27. C. A. Bruch, W. E. McHugh, and R. W. Hockenbury, "Variations in Radiation Damage to Metals," *J. Metals*, **8,** 1362 (1956).
28. Unpublished calculations quoted in ref. (27).
29. S. Siegel, "Effect of Neutron Bombardment on Order in the Alloy Cu_3Au," *Phys. Rev.*, **75,** 1823 (1949).
30. L. R. Aronin, "Radiation Damage Effects on Order-Disorder in Nickel-Manganese Alloys," *J. Appl. Phys.*, **25,** 344 (1954).
31. G. H. Kinchin and R. S. Pease, "The Mechanism of the Irradiation Disordering of Alloys," *J. Nuclear Energy*, **1,** 200 (1955).
32. C. W. Tucker, Jr., and P. Senio, "On the Nature of Thermal Spikes," *J. Appl. Phys.*, **27,** 207 (1956).
33. J. A. Brinkman, C. E. Dixon, and C. J. Meechan, "Interstitial and Vacancy Migration in Cu_3Au and Copper," *Acta Met.*, **2,** 38 (1954).
34. A. E. H. Love, *Theory of Elasticity*, Dover, New York, 1944, p. 142.
35. S. S. Brenner, "Tensile Strength of Whiskers," *J. Appl. Phys.*, **27,** 1484 (1956).
36. J. A. Brinkman, "On the Nature of Radiation Damage in Metals," *J. Appl. Phys.*, **25,** 961 (1954).
37. J. A. Brinkman, "Production of Atomic Displacements by High Energy Particles," *Am. J. Phys.*, **24,** 246 (1956).

38. M. L. Bleiberg, L. J. Jones and B. Lustman, "Phase Changes in Pile-Irradiated Uranium Base Alloys," *J. Appl. Phys.*, **27,** 1270 (1956).
39. S. T. Konobeevsky, "On the Nature of Radiation Damage in Fissile Materials," *J. Nuclear Energy*, **1,** 356 (1956).
40. J. W. Cleland, J. H. Crawford, Jr., and D. K. Holmes, "Effects of Gamma Radiation on Germanium," *Bull. Am. Phys. Soc.*, II **1,** 135 (1956).
41. F. Seitz, "Color Centers in Alkali Halide Crystals, II," *Rev. Mod. Phys.*, **26,** 1 (1954), particularly Section 37.
42. J. H. O. Varley, "A Mechanism for the Displacement of Ions in an Ionic Lattices," *Nature*, **174,** 886 (1954).
43. J. H. O. Varley, "A New Interpretation of Radiation-Induced Phenomena in Alkali Halides," *J. Nuclear Energy*, **1,** 130 (1954).
44. J. H. O. Varley in "Metallurgy and Fuels," Series V of *Progress in Nuclear Energy* (Editors: H. M. Finniston and J. P. Howe), Pergamon Press, London, 1956, Vol. 1, Chapter 8-4.
45. W. Primak, "Gamma-Ray Dosage in Inhomogeneous Nuclear Reactors," *J. Appl. Phys.*, **27,** 54 (1956).
46. Report of the International Commission on Radiological Units and Measurements (ICRU), Handbook 62, National Bureau of Standards, Washington, D. C. (1957).

CHAPTER 3

Basic Experiments

3.1 Introduction

The theoretical treatment of Chapter 2 permits one to calculate, although in a rather approximate manner, the number of displaced atoms produced by a given high-energy irradiation. An experimental test of the theory is difficult mainly because most physical properties depend in a complicated, and theoretically poorly understood, way on the number of crystalline defects. Consequently, although most physical properties are altered by the presence of displaced atoms only a few properties are well enough understood to serve as a quantitative measure of the concentration of displaced atoms. Such basic experiments are discussed in this chapter.

It was shown in the previous chapter that an important parameter which enters the theory of displacement production is the threshold energy for displacement, E_d, which is the energy required to displace an atom permanently from a stable site in the lattice. Thus, for a proper comparison of theory and experiment, one must know E_d as well as the concentration of defects. The threshold energy has been studied both theoretically and experimentally in recent years and is the first topic taken up in this chapter.

3.2 The Threshold Energy for Displacement

A. *Theoretical Calculations*

Seitz (1) estimated the magnitude of E_d qualitatively as follows. The energy required to remove a typical atom from a lattice site in a solid and place it in an interstitial position in an adiabatic or reversible manner is about $2E_c$, where E_c is the energy of sublimation. If, however, the process is carried out dynamically, as in a fast collision, the process is highly irreversible and the energy required should be roughly twice as large, or approximately $4E_c$. Since E_c in tightly bound solids is of the order of 5–6 ev, Seitz suggested 25 ev as a reasonable value for E_d.

More detailed theoretical calculations have been carried out recently by Huntington (2) for copper and Kohn (3) for germanium. Huntington has considered low-energy collisions and has assumed that the principal interaction between colliding atoms in a typical close-packed metal, such as copper, is the repulsion of the closed ion shells. This interaction he approximated by a Born-Mayer type function

$$V(r) = A \exp \left[\frac{-(r - r_0)}{r_0} \rho \right] \tag{3-1}$$

where r_0 is the equilibrium separation of two adjacent ions and ρ and A are constants. Since this force law is short range, a hard-sphere model was used for the collision calculations. For copper the value of ρ can be bracketed (4) between 13 and 17. For $\rho = 13$, an energy of 18.5 ev is required to move an atom to an interstitial position in the (111) direction through the triangle formed by its three nearest neighbors, and 17.5 ev is required for displacement in the (100) direction. In the latter case the original fast atom moves to another lattice site, displacing its nearest neighbor into an interstitial position. For $\rho = 17$, the corresponding energies were found to be 43 and 34 ev. The experimental value for copper, to be discussed in the next section, lies well inside these rather wide theoretical limits.

Kohn (3) has carried out similar calculations for germanium and found that some of the nearest interstitial positions can be reached by substantially smaller energies, of the order of 10 ev. The main reason for the lower theoretical value is the open structure of the Ge lattice in contrast to the close-packed face-centered-cubic structure of Cu. Kohn's calculations also show that the energy required to displace an atom in the diamond lattice may vary substantially with direction. For example, it is found that an atom can escape more easily in the $(-1, -1, -1)$ direction than in a direction close to (111) that is blocked by a nearest neighbor. The discrepancy between the theoretical and experimental values and its implications will be discussed in the next section.

With a working value of 25 ev for the displacement energy it is of interest to calculate for various types of radiations the minimum energy required to produce displacements. In the case of massive particle irradiation

$$E_m = 4M_1M_2E/(M_1 + M_2)^2 \tag{3-2}$$

where E_m is the maximum energy transferred by a moving particle of mass M_1 and energy E to a stationary atom of mass M_2. For electron bombardment, relativistic effects must be taken into account and the maximum energy transfer is

$$E_m = 2E(E + 2Mc^2)/M_2c^2 \tag{3-3}$$

where m is the electron mass and c is the velocity of light (see equations 2-9 and 2-17). In the case of γ-rays the radiation effect is primarily caused by the Compton or photoelectrons, permitting one to use the electron thresholds. The results of such calculations are presented in Table 3.1

Table 3.1. Threshold radiation energy for producing displacements with E_d = 25 ev

Atomic weight of stationary atoms	10	50	100	200
Neutrons, protons (ev)	76	325	638	1263
Electrons, γ-rays (Mev)	0.10	0.41	0.68	1.10
α-particles (ev)	31	91	169	325
Fission fragments of mass 100 (ev)	76	28	25	28

B. *Experimental Determinations*

The first published result on threshold energy determination came from the work of Klontz [as discussed by Lark-Horovitz (5)] on germanium bombarded with high-energy electrons at room temperature. In these experiments n-type Ge was bombarded with electrons of various energies with the total number of incident particles per bombardment kept constant. The change in conductivity was observed as a function of the energy of the incident particles. The conductivity *vs* electron energy curve showed a level portion, indicating no change in conductivity, followed by a sharp decrease in the conductivity. Extrapolation to the level portion gave a threshold energy of about 0.65 Mev.

Klontz (6) followed up this study with a detailed investigation of conductivity changes in germanium as a function of electron energy.

These later experiments were done at liquid-nitrogen temperature in order to minimize annealing. The sample was subjected to electron bombardment in a Van de Graaff machine at various well defined energies. Typical curves are shown in Figure 3.1. The initial hori-

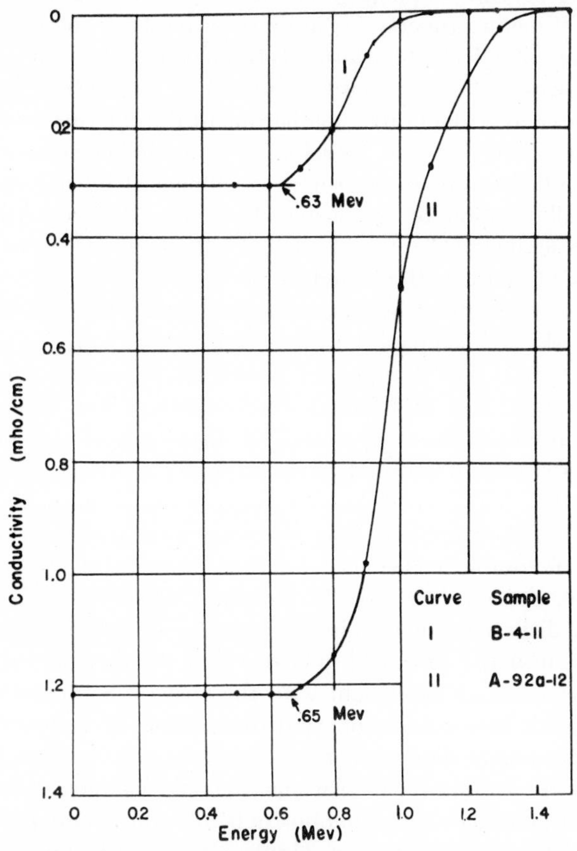

Figure 3.1 Extrapolation curves used in determination of threshold for lattice displacements in Ge (from reference 6).

zontal line (up to about 0.6 Mev) is followed by a large decrease in conductivity, the extent of which depends on the original conductivity and the number of electrons incident at each energy. The threshold is obtained by extrapolating the region of large change to its intersection with the initial horizontal portion. For the two samples of

Figure 3.1, thresholds of 0.63 and 0.65 Mev are observed. Klontz concludes that the most probable value of the threshold is 0.63 ± 0.02 Mev. By equation 3-3 this corresponds to a threshold energy, E_d, of 30 ± 1 ev.

Loferski and Rappaport (7) have used changes in minority carrier lifetime, a property far more sensitive than the resistivity to the presence of defects, to measure threshold energies. In this experiment changes in the short-circuit current of an electron voltaic cell are measured as a function of bombardment time at various bombarding energies. In this case, therefore, a transient phenomenon due to the incident electrons is measured as influenced by defects created by a small fraction of the same electrons. By an extrapolation procedure similar to that used by Klontz, these investigators conclude that E_d is 13 ev for both Ge and Si.

These two sets of experiments are in disturbing disagreement, with Loferski and Rappaport's values being closer to Kohn's theoretical predictions. The discrepancy is difficult to resolve. Sensitivity may have been lost in Klontz's experiments at low bombardment energies since both the cross section for displacement and the volume of suitably irradiated material decrease rapidly with decreasing energy. On the other hand, Loferski and Rappaport, because of the high sensitivity of their method, may well have measured the results of a few very favorable collisions. Further, because of the very high sensitivity, these values may be structure sensitive, e.g., they may depend on dislocation density in the crystal. The gradual appearance of damage near the threshold indicates that the threshold is actually quite spread out, in agreement with the ideas of Sampson *et al.* (8). It is not clear which value or what distribution of values should be used in theoretical displacement calculations. It is clear, however, that the cross section for displacement should be determined experimentally in great detail as a function of bombarding energy. Further, because of the indications from Huntington's and Kohn's theoretical work, the displacement energy also has to be studied as a function of crystalline direction (see also section 2.4).*

* The dependence of damage rate on crystalline direction has been observed recently by W. L. Brown and W. Augustyniak (*Bull. Am. Phys. Soc.* **II**, 2, 156 (1957) (A)) using electron irradiation near the energy threshold. These workers found that the damage rate was 40% higher with the electrons bombarding in the (111) direction than in either the (110) or (100) direction.

The threshold energy for graphite was determined by similar methods by D. T. Eggen (9). He found a value near 25 ev for E_d in this material.

Eggen and Laubenstein (10) have determined the threshold energy for copper using low-temperature electron irradiation. In this experiment thin Cu specimens were mounted on a heavy copper plate which was immersed in liquid air during the irradiation and measurements. The rate of change of resistance was determined as a function of electron energy in the 0.45 to 1.0 Mev range. Extrapolation to zero damage gave 0.49 ± 0.02 Mev for the threshold electron energy, corresponding to E_d for copper of 25.0 ± 1.0 ev. This value falls well within the theoretical limits obtained by Huntington.

Denney (11) has found that irradiation of a metastable alloy of iron in copper (2.4 weight-% Fe) initiates the transformation of the face-centered-cubic iron to the stable ferromagnetic body-centered-cubic structure. Upon bombarding with electrons of varying energy and measuring the saturation magnetization, Denney was able to deduce the threshold energy for the production of displaced atoms. This occurred at 0.45 Mev. Denney concludes that the displaced

Table 3.2 Theoretical and experimental threshold energies

Bombarded material	Property measured	Threshold energy, ev		Reference
		Experiment	Theory	
n-Germanium at −196° C	Resistivity	30		6
n-Germanium at room temp.	Minority carrier lifetime	13		7
p-Silicon at room temp.	Minority carrier lifetime	13		7
Germanium			~10	3
Graphite	Resistivity	25		9
Copper	Resistivity	25		10
Copper			17–34	4
Iron-copper alloy, Fe displaced	Saturation magnetization	27		11
Cu_3Au	Ordering	~10		12

iron atoms are responsible for initiating the transformation. Thus, 0.45 Mev corresponds to an E_d of 27 ev in iron.

Dugdale (12) has found that ordering in $AuCu_3$ can be induced at temperatures where thermal ordering rates are unobservably low by bombarding with electrons of about 0.3 Mev energy. Dugdale interprets this low-temperature ordering as due to the formation of vacancies and interstitials which are sufficiently mobile to allow the necessary micro diffusion for ordering to take place. If this interpretation is correct the threshold energy in $AuCu_3$ is about 10 ev.

The experimental and theoretical results on threshold energy determinations are summarized in Table 3.2. For the present it appears quite satisfactory to use a value of 25 ev for E_d in theoretical calculations of the number of displaced atoms produced by irradiation. Much work remains to be done in determining more clearly and precisely the probability of displacement as a function of bombarding energy and crystalline direction.

3.3 Experimental Determination of the Number of Displaced Atoms

In this section those experiments which lead to rather clear cut estimates of the number of displaced atoms in solids will be discussed in some detail. Different methods have been used with different solids, and the material of this section is organized around the different types of solids involved.

A. Metals

The electrical resistivity of pure metals is increased upon irradiation with massive fast particles (13). Ionizing radiation alone has no effect. The increase in resistance is mainly due to an increase in the residual resistivity, although some changes in the thermal part of the resistivity have been observed (14). The residual (or very low temperature) resistivity of metals is very sensitive to the presence of impurities and imperfections in the crystal. Any disturbance of the ideal periodic potential leads to scattering of the conduction electrons and thereby to an increase in the resistance. At low concentrations there should be very little interference among the various defects, and the increase in resistivity is expected to be proportional to the number of defects introduced into the material. The proportionality constant has to be calculated theoretically and will be discussed in detail in conjunction with the interpretation of the experimental data.

It is clear from the discussion so far that the resistivity measurement must be made at low temperature in order to determine the residual resistivity. The irradiation itself must be done at low temperature because the radiation induced defects in metals are known to

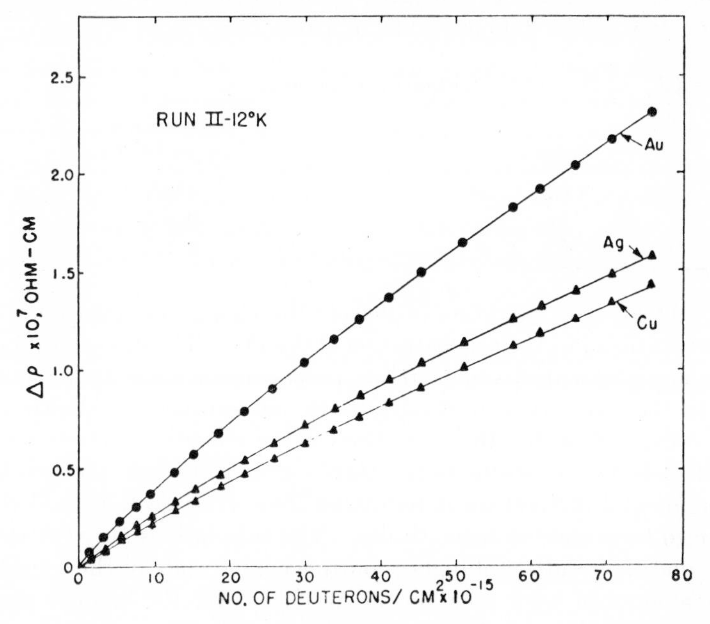

Figure 3.2 Resistivity increase as a function of integrated deuteron flux (from reference 15).

anneal out at quite low temperatures. The experiments of Cooper, Koehler, and Marx (15) satisfied the above requirements. These investigators irradiated 5-mil (0.13 mm) wires of pure Cu, Ag and Au with 12-Mev deuterons. The samples were mounted on a liquid helium cryostat, and the temperature was maintained near 10° K. The range of 12-Mev deuterons in Cu is 8 mils (0.20 mm) so that the particles penetrated through the wires.

Figure 3.2 shows the changes in the resistivity of Cu, Ag and Au as a function of the time-integrated flux for specimens irradiated near 10° K. The curves start linearly from the origin but have a slight negative curvature. The resistivity change, $\Delta\rho$, obtained after a given amount of irradiation near 10° K is stable at the bombardment temperature. The negative curvature, therefore, is due to an annealing process associated with bombardment. This process is generally termed radiation annealing. For the present discussion it is the initial slope of the curve that is pertinent in giving the number of displaced atoms to be compared with the theory of displacement production. The data are given in Table 3.3.

Table 3.3. 12-Mev deuteron irradiation data at 12° K

Sample	Initial slope ($\mu\Omega$-cm per $10^{17}d/\text{cm}^2$)
Cu	0.221
Ag	0.263
Au	0.379

At low concentration of defects the change in resistivity, $\Delta\rho$, is proportional to the concentration of defects. The interpretation is now straightforward provided the proportionality constant relating $\Delta\rho$ to the concentration of interstitials and vacancies is known, i.e., the cross section for the scattering of the conduction electrons by such defects. Unfortunately, there is no obvious independent experimental method for determining these cross sections and they have to be evaluated theoretically. The calculations are very intricate and the results still highly controversial in spite of the considerable amount of work done on this problem over the last few years. The theoretical work is briefly summarized in the following paragraphs since it is central to the interpretation of the experimental results.

Dexter (16) approximated the scattering potential associated with the imperfections by a shielded Coulomb interaction and computed electronic transition matrix elements by the Born approximation. The shielding constant was adjusted so as to yield the experimental values when applied to substitutional impurities having adjacent atomic numbers. Dexter took into account the effect of lattice distortions around the defects and concluded that they represent only a minor correction. His result for Cu, Au and Ag was that one atomic per cent of vacancies would give an extra resistivity of about 0.4 $\mu\Omega$-cm. A similar calculation for interstitials gave about 0.6 $\mu\Omega$-cm.

Jongenburger (17, 18) suggested that the Born approximation was inadequate in this problem. He carried out detailed calculations for vacancies based on the free-electron approximation and using for the scattering potential the negative of the Hartree potential of a free copper ion. This potential was adjusted to take care of the screening of the conduction electrons, which was approximated by creating in the electron gas a spherical hole of unit charge and of radius r_s, where r_s is defined by $(4\pi/3)r_s^3$ = atomic volume. On calculating the phase shifts he found that they gave good agreement with the Friedel (19) sum rule. He also confirmed Dexter's conclusion that distortion around the defects can be neglected. For one per cent vacancies in Cu, Ag and Au, Jongenburger obtained the following $\Delta\rho$ values; 1.3, 1.5 and 1.5 $\mu\Omega$-cm., respectively.

Jongenburger (20) also estimated by the same method the extra resistivity caused by interstitial atoms. For the contribution of the interstitial scattering potential alone a value of 1–2 $\mu\Omega$-cm was found. An additional resistivity of 3.5 $\mu\Omega$-cm is contributed by the nearest neighbor displacements, leading to a final value of about 5 $\mu\Omega$-cm per per cent interstitials.

More recently Blatt (21) has calculated the resistivity associated with one atomic per cent of interstitials by assuming that the effect of the associated displacements can be neglected. He derived the scattering potentials for the imperfections from the appropriate Hartree self-consistent fields and employed the partial wave method in evaluating the scattering cross sections. The potentials were adjusted until the phase shifts satisfied the Friedel sum rule. The calculated resistivities do not appear to depend critically on the choice of potential. Blatt (22) finds, however, that the choice of potential is important for the calculation of thermoelectric power. His calculation of thermoelectric power leads to good agreement with experiment in the case of substitutional arsenic in copper. Blatt's final value for the estra resistivity due to one per cent interstitial atoms in copper is 1.4 $\mu\Omega$-cm, which is practically the same as that due to vacancies. For substitutional impurities approximate agreement was obtained with resistivity changes measured by Linde, although the calculated resistivities were consistently too high. In view of this Blatt suggests that his, as well as Jongenburger's calculations, overestimate the resistivity increase due to vacancies and interstitials by about a factor of two.

Overhauser and Gorman (23) have reexamined the whole problem of scattering by imperfections. In particular, they have studied in detail the contribution of the elastic displacement of atoms near the imperfections to the increase in the residual resistivity. They found that for interstitials scattering from the strained regions is an order of magnitude greater than that from the defect itself. The effect is smaller for a vacancy but not negligible. Interference terms were found to be small. In the Overhauser-Gorman treatment unknown parameters, such as effective mass and electron-lattice interaction constant, are eliminated by comparing the final formula with the theoretical resistivity associated with lattice vibrations. The residual resistivity of the strained lattice is obtained then from the experimental lattice resistivity. The final results for $\Delta\rho$ are: 10.5 $\mu\Omega$-cm per per cent of interstitials and 1.5 $\mu\Omega$-cm per per cent of vacancies.

The results of the various theoretical investigations are summarized in Table 3.4.

Table 3.4. Theoretical residual resistivity of interstitial atoms and vacancies in Cu, Ag and Au. The units are $\mu\Omega$-cm per atomic per cent of the imperfection

Material	Interstitials	Vacancies	Reference
Copper	0.6	0.4	16
		1.3	68
	5.0	1.3	17,18,20
	1.3	1.4	21,22
	10.5	1.5	23
Silver	0.6	0.4	16
		1.45	68
	—	1.5	17
Gold	0.6	0.4	16
		1.45	68
	—	1.5	17

It is clear from the large discrepancies among the various theoretical values that the experiments cannot yet be interpreted in a precise way. The proportionality constant required to derive the number of displaced atoms from the experimental measurements is apparently only known within an order of magnitude. Seitz and Koehler (24) adopted the value of 2.7 $\mu\Omega$-cm per vacancy-interstitial pair in Cu, based essentially on Blatt's calculation. The number of displaced atoms per 10^{17} d/cm^2 is, then, 0.082% using the experimental number in Table 3.3. The theoretical value corresponding to the experiments of Cooper, Koehler and Marx is 0.43%. Equations 2-23 and 2-31 were used in this calculation. The discrepancy between simple displacement theory and experiment is, therefore, about a factor of 5, with the theory apparently overestimating the number of displaced atoms. The discrepancy is less if Dexter's numbers are used; it becomes very large, of the order of a factor of 20, if Overhauser's number are used for the theoretical value of the residual resistivity (see Table 3.4). Similar results have been obtained recently by Blewitt and coworkers (25) using neutron irradiation at 17° K.

Recent work by Denny and coworkers (26, 27, 28) using electron irradiation on copper at 10° K led to somewhat different results. These workers found that upon irradiation with 1.35-Mev electrons the increase in resistivity observed experimentally agrees with that calculated theoretically within a factor of two provided Blatt's numbers are used for the resistivity increment per per cent defect (see Table 3.4). From preliminary annealing experiments, however, it appears that Blatt's value is too low while that calculated by Overhauser and Gorman is too high. It was assumed here that all the interstitials anneal out below 80° K. Thus, while it is likely that the simple defects formed by electron irradiation conform to theory better than those produced by massive particles, the question is by no means resolved at the present time.

B. Graphite

Antal, Weiss and Dienes (29) used the scattering of very slow neutrons by interstitials and vacancies to determine the defect concentration. This technique is limited to materials of low neutron capture cross section. Detailed experimental studies have been carried out on graphite. Neutrons of sufficiently long wavelength are scattered isotropically by isolated point defects, and the scattering can be measured when crystalline effects (Bragg scattering) are absent. Babinet's principle may be applied under such conditions and, therefore, vacancies and interstitials scatter in exactly the same manner. The cross section for this nuclear type of scattering is accurately known from other measurements. Thus, if the scattering from the defects is measurable, an absolute method is at hand for determining their concentration. While the physics of the situation is quite analogous to the scattering of conduction electrons by defects in metals, the great advantage of the neutron technique is the accurate knowledge of the corresponding nuclear cross sections.

Let slow neutrons in the wavelength region of several Angstroms, i.e., the energy region of 0.001 ev, be incident on a crystal. For such low-energy neutrons the solution of Schrödinger's equation is the sum of an incident plane wave and a radially scattered wave from each nucleus. The scattered radiation at unit distance, for unit incident intensity, is

$$\psi = \sum_{p} a\, e^{i\mathbf{k}\cdot\mathbf{r}_p} \tag{3.4}$$

where $\mathbf{k} = \mathbf{k}' - \mathbf{k}_0$ = wave number difference, $\mathbf{r}_p$ = vector distance between origin and pth scatterer in the crystal, and a is the scattering length.

Let a monatomic crystal contain m point scatterers per unit volume in the form of interstitial atoms and vacant lattice sites and a total of N atoms per unit volume. The scattering is then described by

$$\psi = \sum_{j=1}^{N} a\, e^{i\mathbf{k}\cdot\mathbf{r}_j} + \sum_{i=1}^{m} a_i e^{i\mathbf{k}\cdot p_i} \tag{3.5}$$

where the first term is the sum over the perfect crystal and the second one is that over the defects. In the second term $a_i = +a$ for interstitial atoms and $-a$ for vacancies.

For wavelength beyond the Bragg cut-off, the first term is zero. The intensity scattered is then the square of the second term, and for random location of defects cross terms in this square may be omitted. The resulting total cross section is

$$\sigma = 4\pi m a^2 \tag{3.6}$$

The cross section per atoms is

$$\sigma_d = \sigma/N = 4\pi a^2 m/N = 4\pi a^2 f \tag{3-7}$$

where f is the atomic fraction of scatterers in the material and σ_d is the cross section for scattering by defects alone. The scattering process is fully described, therefore, by $4\pi a^2$ which is the scattering cross section, σ_b, for the atoms of the crystal. It should be noted that distortion around the defects has been neglected in this derivation. This point is discussed later in evaluating the accuracy of the experiments.

It is not practical to attempt to measure directly the isotropically scattered neutron intensity. Instead, the attenuation of a long-wavelength neutron beam during its passage through the material is measured in a transmission experiment. There are other sources of attenuation which have to be taken into account and whose cross sections should be small compared to the cross section for defect scatterings.

In the absence of defects and past the last Bragg cut-off ($\lambda > 2d_{max}$), the transmitted intensity, I_s, is given by

$$I_s = I_0 \exp\left[-NX(\sigma_a + \sigma_i + \sigma_{dis})\right] \quad (3\text{-}8)$$

where I_0 = incident intensity, N = number of nuclei per cm^3, X = path length traversed through the sample, σ_a = cross section for absorption, σ_i = cross section for inelastic scattering, and σ_{dis} = cross section for disorder scattering other than defects (isotopic, spin, etc.).

If m defects are present the transmitted intensity, I_d, is

$$I_d = I_0 \exp\left[-NX(\sigma_a + \sigma_i + \sigma_{dis} + \sigma_b f)\right] \quad (3\text{-}9)$$

A direct comparison of a crystal containing a fraction, f, of defects to a control crystal gives

$$I_d/I_s = e^{-NX\sigma_b f} \quad (3\text{-}10)$$

Measurement of the ratio I_d/I_s immediately gives then a value for f.

Graphite was chosen for study because of inherent interest in this material and because it fulfilled very well the theoretical and experimental requirements. Samples were available which were estimated to contain of the order of a few per cent defects. This concentration should be easily measurable. For graphite

$$\sigma_b = 4.7 \text{ barns}$$

$$\sigma_a + \sigma_i \simeq 0.9 \text{ barn at 8 A}$$

and there is no spin or isotopic incoherence. The graphite specimen served also as a neutron filter, which resulted in a most economical use of the very low intensity available in a long-wavelength neutron beam.

The slow-neutron beam was obtained from the Brookhaven reactor by filtering the thermal-neutron spectrum. This spectrum of flux has a Maxwellian energy distribution peaked near 1 A. If a polycrystalline material of sufficient length is placed in such a beam, Bragg scattering removes all neutrons from the incident beam except those having $\lambda > 2d_{max}$, where d_{max} is the largest interplanar spacing for which diffraction is possible. In these experiments the graphite specimens were made long enough (approximately 9 inches) to constitute efficient filters by themselves. A typical spectrum of the neutrons transmitted by a 9-inch graphite specimen is shown on Figure 3.3 as the "unirradiated" curve. The "cut-off" wavelength is clearly marked by an abrupt increase in transmitted intensity at $\lambda = 2d_{(002)} = 6.70$ A.

In order to avoid spurious effects due to the increase in the *c*-axis of graphite upon pile irradiation, a plot of transmitted intensity *vs* wavelength was obtained using a crystal spectrometer. Any irrelevant change in intensity could then be disregarded and the transmitted intensity obtained by measuring the area under the curves for $\lambda > 7.30$ A (see Figure 3.3). The beam intensity is too weak, to be used past 12 A. Care was taken to accept all small-angle-scattered neutrons, thus eliminating effects of small particle size in the sample.

Several spectra were obtained from the spectrometer for the irradiated and standard (unirradiated) specimen run alternately and averaged. Figure 3.3 shows the results. The areas under each curve give

$$I_d / I_s = 0.607$$

The estimated accuracy of this figure is about $\pm 10\%$. By equation 3-10, $f = 0.0526$. The fraction of displaced atoms is $f/2 = 0.0263$.

The f value obtained by the above method may now be compared to the number of displaced atoms expected theoretically using equation 2-27. For 1-Mev neutrons in graphite, using $E_d = 25$ ev and $E_i = 10^4$ ev, equation 2-27 gives for the number os atoms displaced per 1-Mev neutron*

* Table 2.3 of Chapter 2 gave $\bar{\nu} = 900$. This large value arose from the value of G calculated by Hurwitz and Clark, whereas $\bar{\nu} = 200$ comes from using $E_i = 10^4$ ev (equation 2-2). At present it is not certain which value is more reliable.

$$\bar{\nu} = 200$$

The fraction of displaced atoms which corresponds to 1.1×10^{20} nvt (neutrons per cm^2) of 1-Mev neutrons† is, therefore, 0.055 or 5.5% using for σ_s, the collision cross section for the carbon atom, the value 2.5×10^{-24} cm^2. This value is an overestimate because the effective neutrons were assumed to be of 1-Mev energy. Further, the value of E_i is rather uncertain (equation 2-2 of Section 2.2 was used to estimate E_i). The number to be used for nvt is rather uncertain since the fast flux and its energy distribution are not known with any accuracy. Our best estimate of the effective nvt for the graphite sample used in these experiments is 1.1×10^{20} neutrons/cm^2 (total integrated neutron flux of about 5×10^{20} n/cm^2). The uncertainty in this number is of the order of 50%.

The experimentally determined value of f is known, therefore, with greater accuracy than any theoretically derived value, partly

† The expression nvt is frequently used to specify neutron irradiation exposures, which is to say, integrated neutron flux densities. In this n means the density of neutrons in and near the sample (neutrons per cubic cm), v is their mean velocity (cm per second), and t is the time of exposure (seconds). nv is thus the neutron flux density (neutrons per cm^2 per sec), which has previously been denoted by ϕ (see section 2.4 of Chapter 2). If nv is the flux density of *all* neutrons, slow and fast, the number expressing the exposure should be labelled nvt (total); if nv is the flux density of the slow or fast component alone, the labelling should be nvt (slow) or nvt (fast), respectively. It may be noted that the integrated flux density is the number of neutrons of the specified type (fast, total, etc.) that traverse an imaginary sphere of cross sectional area one cm^2 (radius $1/\pi^{-1/2}$ cm) in the sample during the bombardment. It is *not* the number which cross a flat surface of area 1 cm^2, but in the usual case of isotropic flux is twice the latter number, as can be seen by elementary integrations. The reason for specifying an exposure as, say, 10^{20} neutrons/cm^2 nvt (total), instead of simply 10^{21} neutrons/cm^2 (total) is to preserve this distinction. When an exposure is known only to order-of magnitude precision, the distinction can be ignored.

In some cases, exposures have been reported in megawatt-days per adjacent ton of uranium (MWD/T). This unit is defined as the irradiation exposure received by the sample during the period required for the (2000-lb) ton of uranium metal in the immediate vicinity of the sample to generate one megawatt-day of fission heat. For irradiations in cooled test holes at Hanford, 1 MWD/T of exposure is considered to involve an integrated neutron flux density of 6.5×10^{17} neutrons/cm^2 nvt (total). Other conversion factors apply to other facilities.

because of uncertainties in the value of nvt. Consequently, the theory itself cannot be judged too critically. The fraction of displaced atoms determined experimentally by this method is in good agreement with the theory within the limitations mentioned above.

The value of f determined in these experiments may be in error. One reason is that if the defects are aggregated into pairs or larger clusters their scattering will not be equivalent to those of isolated

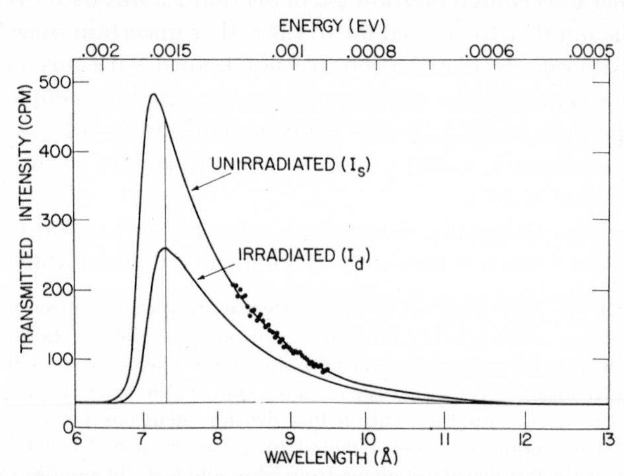

Figure 3.3 Slow-neutron intensity transmitted by an irradiated and unirradiated graphite specimen. For clarity, only a typical group of experimental points have been reproduced along one curve to indicate their number and spread. Only intensities to the right of the vertical line at 7.30 A were considered in computing I_s and I_d (from reference 29).

interstitials and vacancies. Another reason is that the inelastic cross section may be altered by the irradiation. It has been assumed that this effect is unimportant. It has also been assumed that there is negligible inhomogeneous distortion (i.e., distortion rather than just displacement of the graphite planes) in the neighborhood of the defect. An outward inhomogeneous distortion around the interstitial can be shown to reduce the effective cross section of the interstitial (a similar distortion would increase the cross section of the vacancy). Theoretical estimates of this correction are at present unreliable, but it is probably not greater than 20 per cent. In principle the occurrence of pairs is detectable by examining the wavelength dependence of the attenuation. These preliminary experiments are not sufficiently accurate past 9 A to establish the existence of a wavelength dependence. The fact that no wavelength dependence which would be outside experimental error is observable indicates that only a small fraction of the displaced atoms may be present in the form of pairs. More refined experiments will be necessary to establish this point definitely.

Some annealing undoubtedly has occurred during irradiation near room temperature since it is known that about one-third of the

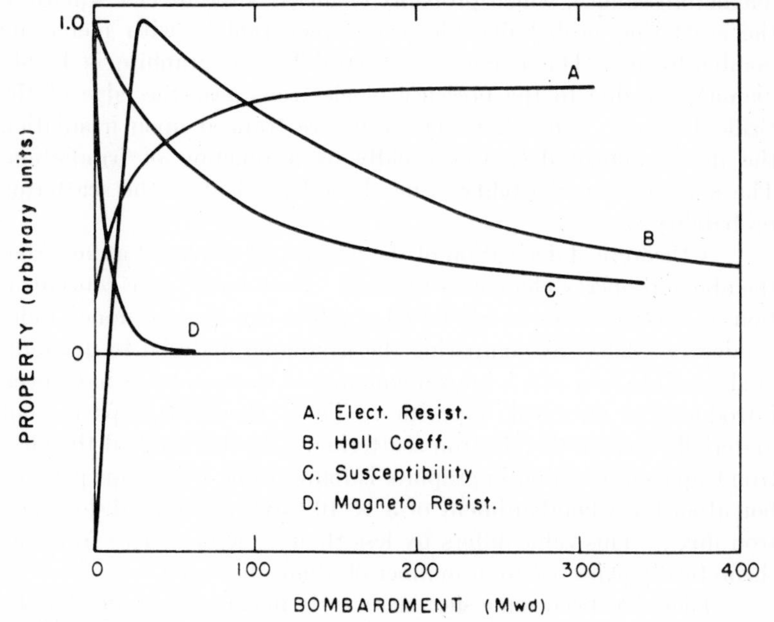

Figure 3.4 Electrical properties of graphite after bombardment (from reference 31).

damage introduced at about $-190°$ C anneals out in warming to room temperature (30). Because of all these uncertainties one cannot claim a better agreement between theory and experiment than within a factor of two or three. Because of annealing one expects the experimental value to be smaller than the theoretical one.

Changes in electrical properties can also be used to determine the fraction of defects, or rather the fraction of electron traps (31). Typical experimental curves as a function of reactor exposure are shown in Figure 3.4. The damage centers are both electron traps and electron scatterers.

Changes in electrical properties must be separated into contributions from each of these two effects. Electron traps actually increase the number of carriers by lowering the Fermi energy to a region of higher density of states, as indicated by the Hall coefficient data. The electrical resistance nevertheless increases upon irradiation because of the large increase in scattering probability. The magnetoresistance, which probably changes as the inverse square of the scattering probability, decreases very rapidly with increasing bombardment. The magnetic susceptibility of graphite is highly diamagnetic due to the presence of electrons near the edge of the Brillouin zone. Since these electrons are trapped upon irradiation the diamagnetism decreases rapidly as a function of irradiation. The magnetic susceptibility is nearly independent of the scattering probability.

A theoretical derivation of the number of displaced atoms from the above property changes is difficult. Fortunately, the concentration of electron traps in irradiated graphite can be determined independently (32,33) by comparing the irradiated material to unirradiated graphite into which known amounts of electron traps have been introduced as chemical impurities. These chemical traps do not materially change the electron scattering. By this method the electron trap concentration in graphite is found to be 10^{-4} traps per carbon atom for a bombardment of 5×10^{17} nvt. (integrated slow-neutron flux). This value differs by less than a factor of two from the theoretically expected total number of atoms displaced.

There has been some success recently in calculating directly the number of trapped electrons from changes in magnetic susceptibility (34,35). A value of 1.4×10^{-4} electrons trapped per carbon atom is obtained after a bombardment of 1.7×10^{17} nvt of fast neutrons. This value is in good agreement with the figure quoted above, which was determined by the use of bromine-graphite residue compounds. Similar calculations based on radiation-induced changes in the Hall coefficient appear to be far less successful (36). A value of 10^{-5} electron traps per carbon atom is derived for a neutron irradiation of 5×10^{17} nvt of integrated slow-neutron flux. This value is a factor of 10 below that obtained by a number of different methods described earlier. The number of traps produced by neutron bombardment still has to be converted into the number of displaced atoms. Unfortunately, the number of electron traps per displaced atom is not known with any accuracy. It is likely that the number of traps per interstitial plus vacancy, i.e., per displaced atom, is near two (31). With this value, generally satisfactory agreement is observed among the determinations of the number of displaced atoms based on neutron transmission and those based on changes in electronic properties (with the exception of the theoretical change in Hall coefficient).

One can also estimate the number of displaced atoms from measurements of stored energy. The heat content of a sample is raised by the production of interstitials and vacancies. If their energies of formation are known their concentration is immediately calculable from total stored energy values, determined calorimetrically as an increase in the heat of combustion. A value for the stored energy of 100 cal/gm for an irradiation at room temperature of 10^{20} total integrated neutron flux appears to be representative (37). Dienes (38) has calculated theoretically the energy of formation of an interstitial and a vacancy in graphite and obtained the values 420 kcal/mole and 120 kcal/mole, respectively. Hennig (39) has pointed out that some of the attractive terms were neglected unjustifiably in the Van der Waals potential employed in the interstitial calculation. For the interstitial 320 kcal/mole is a better value, giving 440 kcal/mole of displaced atoms. Use of this figure leads to 0.27% displaced atoms per 10^{20} nvt of total flux. The neutron transmission experiments, which gave a value of 2.6% were carried out on samples which had received 1.1×10^{20} nvt of fast neutrons, or about 5×10^{20} nvt of total integrated neutron flux. The corresponding value from stored energy is, therefore, 1.35%. The agreement is not too bad, particularly if it is recalled that the irradiations were not carried out in the same reactor or on the same samples.

There is also evidence of a higher damage rate at liquid-nitrogen than at room temperature (30,40). The extra damage anneals out below room temperature. The amount of energy stored below room temperature is about the same as that stored above (40) and, therefore, the number of displaced atoms calculated from this measurement should be approximately doubled. However, corresponding neutron transmission experiments are not yet available, and it is impossible at this point to say whether some of the defects have annealed out or found energetically more favorable places in the lattice.

The various experiments on graphite are summarized in Table 3.5 and compared with theory. The conclusion from this table is that the various experimental methods agree quite well among themselves, well within the large uncertainties in the flux. The only exception is the value derived from a theoretical analysis of Hall coefficient measurements; this value is unreasonably low. The experiments also agree quite well with theory, although the theory cannot be judged too critically because of large uncertainties both

Table 3.5. Number of displaced atoms produced in graphite by reactor irradiation

	Per cent of displaced atoms						
Exposure in nvt	Theory[a]	Neutron transmission	Electronic properties + chem. traps[b]	Magnetic susceptibility + theory[b]	Hall coeff. + theory[b]	Stored energy + theory[c]	Per cent of displaced atoms per 10^{20} nvt total
1×10^{20} fast or $\sim 4.5 \times 10^{20}$ total	5.0						1.11
1.1×10^{20} fast or $\sim 5 \times 10^{20}$ total		2.6					0.52
5×10^{17} total			5×10^{-3}				1.0
1.7×10^{17} fast or $\sim 7.5 \times 10^{17}$ total				7×10^{-3}			0.93
5×10^{19} total					5×10^{-2}		.10
10^{20} total[d] (room temp)						0.27	.27
10^{20} total[d] (liquid nitrogen temperature)						~ 0.50	~ 0.50

[a] Calculated using 1 Mev for neutron energy.
[b] Assuming two trapped electrons per displaced atom.
[c] Using 440 kcal per mole of displaced atoms.
[d] From initial rise of stored energy with exposure.

in the theory and in the exposures. The agreement, which is of the order of a factor of two, is considerably better than in the case of metals. The results suggest that the simple collision theory is reasonably adequate for a material like graphite and that E_d is not spread out over a wide range of values.

C. Semiconductors

The electrical properties of semiconductors are generally very sensitive to bombardment with energetic particles that produce displaced atoms in the crystal (5,41). The reason is that the concentration of charge carriers is extremely small in a semiconductor and the introduction of a very few traps or donors can lead to very large changes in the carrier concentration.

It is now generally agreed that in specimens of n-type germanium of high conductivity (42,43) the displaced atoms introduce acceptor levels, at least initially, that are sufficiently low for electrons to be removed from the conduction band. In the early stages of irradiation the Fermi level remains almost unaltered and the decrease in number of carriers is directly proportional to the increase in the number of acceptor levels. At higher irradiations the Fermi level drops and the situation is far more complex (43). Eventually the sample becomes p-type. The initial rate of loss of conductivity of n-type Ge should give a good measure of the rate of production of displaced atoms.

Klontz's work (6,44) carried out at liquid nitrogen temperature on 0.35 mm thick samples showed that in n-type germanium bombardment with 1.5 Mev electrons results in the loss of 0.065 carriers per bombarding electron. Similar experiments with 4.5 Mev electrons gave 6.15 times more damage. Recent work with neutron bombardment (45) shows that two types of electron traps are produced by both electron and neutron bombardment. This is compatible with the model suggested by James and Lark-Horovitz (42) provided two traps are associated with each Frenkel pair. This means that two acceptors are produced per displacement. On this basis the above experiments give 0.032 displacements per electron at 1.5 Mev and 0.196 displacements per electron at 4.5 Mev. The corresponding theoretical values (24) are 0.06 and 0.156, respectively. The calculations were made using $E_d = 30$ ev and equations 3-11 through 3-14 given below.

In the case of bombardment with fast electrons, relativistic formulas have to be used. The range of charged particles becomes nearly proportional to the energy in the relativistic region. Below 2.5 Mev the range of electrons satisfies the relation (46)

$$R(\text{mg/cm}^2) = 412\ E^{(1.265 - 0.0954 \ln E)} \tag{3-11}$$

where E is in Mev. Above 2.5 Mev the linear relation

$$R(\text{mg/cm}^2) = 530\ E - 106 \tag{3-12}$$

becomes satisfactory. A convenient approximation may be used for specimens thin enough so that E remains larger than the threshold value E_d. In this case, the cross section may be expressed as

$$\sigma(R) = \sigma(R_1)\ (R - R')/(R_1 - R') \tag{3-13}$$

where $\sigma(R)$ is the cross section when the range is R, R_1 is the initial range and $\sigma(R_1)$ the corresponding cross section for the incident particles of energy E_1. R' is to be adjusted to give the best fit of the $\sigma_d(E)$ curve over the range of interest. Whenever equation (3-13) is valid the number of primary atoms displaced per electron can be calculated from

$$n = n_0 \int_{R_0}^{R_1} \sigma(R)\ dR = n_0\ \sigma(R_1)\ (R_1 - R_0) \left[\frac{R_1 + R_0 - 2R'}{2(R_1 - R')}\right] \tag{3-14}$$

where R_0 is the residual range after penetration, so that $R_1 - R_0$ is the thickness.

Brown, Fletcher and Wright (47) bombarded Ge with 3-Mev electrons at room temperature. They found a cross section of 30×10^{-24} cm² for the production of traps. This corresponds to 0.106 displacements per electron in their samples ($^1/_{16}$-inch thick), assuming two traps per displacement. The corresponding theoretical figure is about a factor of four bigger (24), 0.424 displacements per electron (using 30 ev for E_d). However, in this case some annealing has occurred (47).

Similar results are obtained from alpha-particle bombardments at room temperature. Brattain and Pearson (48) bombarded layers of n-type Ge with 5.3-Mev alpha particles which were stopped in the specimens. They found that each alpha particle introduces about

78 acceptors or 39 displaced atoms. Lark-Horovitz and colleagues obtained a value of 95 acceptors (47 displaced atoms) under similar conditions (43). The corresponding theoretical value (24) is 123 displaced atoms per alpha particle. Again, some annealing has undoubtedly occurred. A similar result is obtained upon deuteron bombardment (9.5 Mev) at 200° K (43). The calculated (24) number of displaced atoms per incident deuteron is found to be 31 and the experimentally observed value is 8 (17 acceptors).

For neutron bombardment at liquid nitrogen temperature (45) an average of 5 acceptor levels per unit of fast effective nvt was found. This corresponds to about 2.5 displaced atoms per fast neutron. The theoretical values are higher by about a factor of six. The discrepancy may actually be larger than this since some of the resistivity change may be due to changes in mobility (49).

The above results for semiconductors are summarized in Table 3.6. The conclusion from this table is that the agreement between theory and experiment is about the same as in the case of metals

Table 3.6. Number of displaced atoms produced in germanium by various irradiations[a]

Experimental technique	Experimental value for number of displaced atoms, N_e	Theoretical value for number of displaced atoms, N_{th}	N_{th}/N_e	Reference
1.5-Mev electrons at 90° K	0.032 per incident electron	0.06 per incident electron	2.3	6,44,24
4.5-Mev electrons at 90° K	0.196 per incident electron	0.156 per incident electron	0.8	6,44,24
3-Mev electrons at 25° C	0.106 per incident electron	0.424 per incident electron	4.0	47,24
5.3-Mev α at 25° C	39 per incident alpha particle	123 per incident alpha particle	3.1	48,24
5-Mev α at 25° C	47 per incident alpha particle	123 per incident alpha particle	2.6	43,24
9.5-Mev deuteron at 200° K	8 per incident deuteron	31 per incident deuteron	3.9	43,24
Neutron bombardment at 90° K	2.5 per incident fast neutron	15 per incident fast neutron	6.0	45,49

[a] Two acceptors per displaced atom are assumed throughout (estimates, therefore, differ by a factor of 2 from those in ref. 24).

and is not as good as in the case of graphite, particularly for neutron bombardment. The number of displaced atoms is apparently overestimated theoretically.

D. Corundum and Fused Silica

It is attractive to study the number and nature of displaced atoms produced by fast-particle bombardment by means of changes in optical properties, e.g., color centers, trapping centers, etc. The

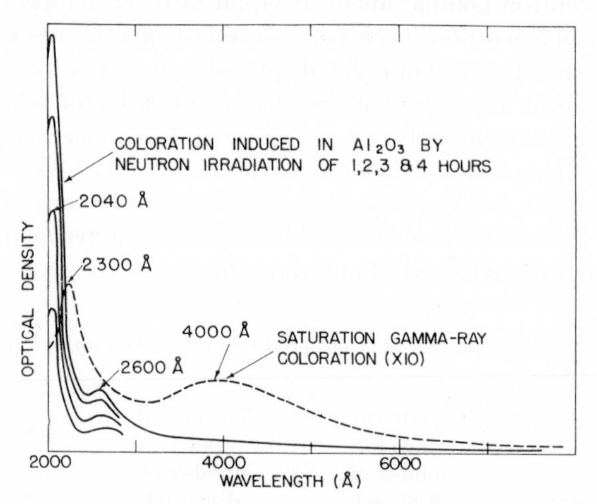

Figure 3.5 Optical absorption bands induced by reactor and gamma-ray irradiation in Al_2O_3. All these measurements were made with the Beckman DU spectrophotometer. The optical density scale for γ-coloration has been multiplied by 10 (from reference 50).

optical methods are generally very sensitive and can be rendered absolute by independent measurement of the oscillator strength involved in any given absorption band. In order to use such methods, however, it is necessary to separate unequivocally the effects due to displaced atoms from those produced by ionizing radiation. Such a separation of displacement and ionizing effects is difficult, particularly in the case of the otherwise very attractive simple ionic crystals.

A clear-cut separation of the two effects has been reported by Levy and Dienes (50,51) for alpha aluminum oxide (Al_2O_3). This material turns out to be very resistant to coloration by ionizing radiation and the slight coloration due to such radiation saturates at a very low exposure. Upon reactor irradiation α-Al_2O_3 was found to show two optical absorption bands in the 2000–8000 A region, one at approximately 2040 A and one at 2600 A (there appears to be an additional band at 1650 A which has not yet been studied). Typical experimental data are shown in Figure 3.5. The neutron irradiations were carried out in the same pneumatic tube facility at the Brookhaven reactor with flux constant to 10% and at a temperature of $100 \pm 5°$ C. The optical absorption spectrum is independent of any further exposure to ionizing radiation.

The growth of the absorption bands as a function of irradiation was studied. It was found that the growth may be resolved into a linear part and an initial part which saturates exponentially. The linear part is interpreted as due to the steady rate of production of defects by fast neutrons. Theory and experiment may now be compared in terms of this steady rate of defect production.

The theoretically expected number can be calculated from equation 2-27. For Al_2O_3 the following numbers were used: $E_i = 3.72 \times 10^4$ ev ($I = 8$ ev), $M_1 = 20.4$ (average atomic mass), $E_d = 25$ ev. With these numbers equation 2-27 gives

$$\bar{\nu} = 744$$

The number of nuclei per cm^3 is 1.2×10^{23} and the average cross section for primary neutron collision in the neighborhood of 1 Mev is 3 barns. The calculation was made for a sample that was exposed in a flux of 2.8×10^{12} nv total corresponding to a fast flux of about 0.7×10^{12} nv. Under these conditions the expected rate of production is

$$n = 6.6 \times 10^{17} \text{ displaced atoms per cm}^3 \text{ per hour}$$

The number of color centers times the oscillator strength, $n_0 f$, was calculated from the optical absorption band at 2040 A using the measured half-width and Smakula's equation (52,53). The corresponding number is

$$n_0 f = 6.0 \times 10^{15} \text{ color centers per cm}^3 \text{ per hour}$$

It is evident that n_0 can be made equal to n if the oscillator strength, f, is chosen to be 0.011. This is an unreasonable value. A value of 0.2 for f was deduced by Crawford and Wittels (54) from a comparison of optical absorption bands and magnetic susceptibility in vitreous SiO_2 colored by reactor irradiation. If f is taken to be 0.1, a reasonable value, the number of color centers is less than the theoretically expected number of displaced atoms by a factor of 10. Further work is needed before this discrepancy can be interpreted.

Early experiments by Levy (55) and more detailed experiments by Mitchell and Paige (56) have shown that similar results obtain in the case of crystalline and vitreous silica. In crystalline quartz two absorption bands have been found, at 5.7 and 7.6 ev respectively, and these are associated with atomic displacements. The bands occur at about the same energies in fused quartz indicating that the short range atomic arrangement determines the energy of the transition. Mitchell and Paige (56) suggest that the defects are responsible for the 5.7 and 7.6 ev bands and oxygen vacancies and interstitials, respectively. A comparison with collision theory calculation shows that the lower limits to the oscillator strengths are 0.05 (5.7 ev band) and 0.2 (7.6 ev band). Thus, the results are qualitatively similar to those for aluminum oxide; i.e., agreement with collision theory calls for very low values of the oscillator strength.

Various experimental and theoretical methods have been described in this section for determining the concentration of displaced atoms produced by exposure to fast neutrons in a nuclear reactor. It is concluded that theory and experiment are in essential agreement in the case of graphite (i.e., within about a factor of two). For other types of solids the number of displaced atoms appears to be overestimated theoretically and agreement with experiment can be claimed only within an order of magnitude. It is not possible to decide at this time whether the discrepancies are caused by inadequacies in the theory of displacement production or in theories linking changes in physical properties to the concentration of lattice defects.

3.4 Order-Disorder Systems

Order-disorder alloys are generally sensitive to fast-particle irradiation, and are, therefore, very suitable for studies of radiation effects. These alloys differ from random alloys and from pure metals in two important respects:

(*a*) Changes that result from displaced atoms may be observed even after the displaced atoms have returned to lattice sites, since they are expected to return in a random manner and leave the degree of order altered. Similarly, any radiation-induced exchange of atoms, a process unobservable in a pure metal or random alloy, leads to an altered degree of order.

(*b*) Several physical properties of these alloys are very sensitive to the state of order, and quantitative studies of radiation effects are rather easily carried out. Some of these studies, as they relate to thermal spikes and replacement collisions, are discussed in this section.

A. *Disordering Experiments*

It has been found in general that radiation produces atomic rearrangements in metals that are more extensive than can be accounted for by displaced atoms alone. Early observations by Siegel (57) on the disordering of $AuCu_3$ indicated quite clearly that the number of displaced atoms was insufficient to account for the amount of disordering observed upon neutron irradiation by about an order of magnitude. Cook and Cushing's data (58) led to the same conclusion.

Quantitative experiments were carried out by Aronin (59) on the disordering of $MnNi_3$ by fast-neutron bombardment. He found that about 5000 atoms are disordered per fast-neutron collision (neutron energy over 0.5 Mev) while only about 1300 displacements could have been produced. Similar results have been obtained by Brinkman, Dixon and Meechan (60,61) for $AuCu_3$ using 9-Mev protons and 33-Mev alphas for bombardment. The number of disordered atoms per primary was found to be about a factor of 10 higher than the calculated number of displaced atoms per primary.

B. *Thermal Spikes and Replacement Collisions*

Several theoretical models have been proposed to account for these large disordering effects. The two most important ones are thermal spikes and replacement collisions. These already have been treated theoretically in Chapter 2, and only their comparison with experiment will be covered here.

A detailed calculation of the rate of disordering induced by thermal spikes is difficult. Seitz and Koehler (24) take the thermal spike as made up of separate spikes of 50 ev each for the disordering of $AuCu_3$ by deuterons and conclude that the number of disordered atoms per deuteron is about 10. This is much smaller than the 125 observed experimentally. They conclude that it seems unlikely that the thermal spike mechanism can account for the observed disordering. As an alternative Seitz (24,62) suggested that the irreversible plastic strain, which originates in thermal stesses about thermal or displacement spikes, is the source of the disorder.

An alternative interpretation of these experiments has been suggested by Kinchin and Pease (63,64) in terms of replacement collisions. These are the collisions in which a moving atom that does not have enough energy to cause displacement, has enough energy to substitute for an atom and push it into an interstitial position. Kinchin and Pease show that for a reasonable choice of the energy parameters the number of replacement collisions can become large enough to explain Aronin's (59) experimental results on the disordering of $MnNi_3$. However, in order to account for the experimental results on $AuCu_3$ a rather low value has to be assumed for the threshold energy of a replacement collision.

C. *Phase Reversal and Thermal Spikes*

The above experiments apparently do not lead to a clear-cut decision as to the existence of thermal or displacement spikes. The best evidence for the existence of such irradiation effects has come from irradiation studies of the uranium-molybdenum system. The first studies were reported by Konobeevsky and coworkers (65) who found that reactor irradiation dispersed the precipitated phases in the stable two-phase system of a U-9% Mo alloy and rendered the alloy homogeneous. The metastable single-phase alloy showed no precipitation.

A much more detailed study has been carried out by Bleiberg, Jones and Lustman (66) on phase changes in reactor irradiated uranium alloys. These workers studied U-9, −10.5 and −13.5% Mo (by weight) and U-10%Nb (by weight) alloys which were irradiated at maximum temperatures less than 200° C. They measured changes in electrical resistivity, temperature coefficient of resistivity, hardness, density and x-ray diffraction patterns. It was found that the phases stable at room temperature reverted to the metastable gamma phase during irradiation, in full agreement with Konobeevsky's early observations. The x-ray results, particularly the line-broadening studies, showed clearly that essentially complete homogenization had taken place. The irradiation was, therefore, effective in causing phase reversion as well as in eliminating the concentration gradient which existed in the stable two-phase system.

It would be very difficult to explain these results on the basis of replacement collisions, because a very large number of them would be required. A far more satisfactory explanation is found in thermal or displacement spikes, and this is the way that Bleiberg, Jones and Lustman (66) interpreted their results. They have considered spike-induced diffusion according to the model discussed in section 2.6C of Chapter 2, assuming six spikes per fission, with each spike homogenizing a region 1.5×10^{-6} cm on a side. This spike contains about 1.7×10^5 atoms. The above experiments and their interpretation furnish strong support for the existence of thermal or displacement spikes. It appears that either thermal or displacement spikes can explain the results; no obvious differentiation between the two is apparent.

The conditions under which thermal or displacement spikes are effective are not yet entirely clear. For example, Tucker and Senio (67) investigated the U-2%Cr system both in the α- and β-phases (transformation temperature = 640° C). They reasoned that heated or melted zones corresponding to the spikes would cause an alloy initially in the α-phase to transform to the β-phase as a result of rapid quenching. X-ray diffraction patterns of the irradiated samples (irradiated up to about 10^{18} nvt) showed no evidence of β-phase in the initially α-phase specimens or α-phase in the initially β-phase material. In this case apparently the duration of a spike is not sufficient to initiate the transformation.

References

1. F. Seitz, "On the Disordering of Solids by Action of Fast Massive Particles," *Discussions Faraday Soc., No.* **5,** 271 (1949).
2. H. B. Huntington, "Creation of Displacements in Radiation Damage," *Phys. Rev.,* **93,** 1414 (1954).
3. W. Kohn, "Bombardment Damage of Ge Crystals by Fast Electrons," *Phys. Rev.,* **94,** 1409 (1954) (A).
4. H. B. Huntington, "Mobility of Interstitial Atoms in a Face-Centered Metal," *Phys. Rev.,* **91,** 1092 (1953).
5. K. Lark-Horovitz, "Nucleon Bombarded Semiconductors," *Reading Conference on Semiconducting Materials,* Butterworth's Scientific Publications, London, England, pp. 47–78 (1951).

6. E. E. Klontz, "Production of Lattice Defects in Germanium by Electron Bombardment," *U. S. Atomic Energy Comm.*, Report AECU-2664 (1952), Thesis, Purdue Univ.; see also *Phys. Rev.*, **82,** 763 (1951) (A); **86,** 643 (1952) (A).
7. J. J. Loferski and P. Rappaport, "Electron Voltaic Study of Electron Bombardment Damage and Its Threshold in Ge and Si," *Phys. Rev.*, **98,** 1861 (1955); **100,** 1261 (1955) (A).
8. J. B. Sampson, H. Hurwitz, Jr. and E. F. Clancy, "Sensitivity of Radiation Damage to the Displacement Probability," *Phys. Rev.*, **99,** 1657 (1955) (A).
9. D. T. Eggen, Unpublished work. See: G. R. Hennig and J. E. Hove, "Interpretation of Radiation Damage to Graphite," *Proceedings of the Conference on the Peaceful Uses of Atomic Energy*, United Nations, 1956 (Paper No. 751).
10. D. T. Eggen and M. J. Laubenstein, "Displacement Energy for Radiation Damage in Copper," *Phys. Rev.*, **91,** 238 (1955) (A).
11. J. M. Denney, "Radiation Damage Energy Threshold in a Face Centered Cubic Alloy," *Phys. Rev.*, **92,** 531 (1953) (A); "Displacement Energy of Face Centered Cubic Iron," *U. S. Atomic Energy Comm.*, Report NAA-SR-271 (1954).
12. R. A. Dugdale, "Recent Experiments at Harwell on Irradiation Effects in Crystalline Solids," *Report of the Bristol Conference on Defects in Crystalline Solids*, The Physical Society, London, 1955, p. 246.
13. For a review see: T. Broom, "Lattice Defects and the Electrical Resistivity of Metals," *Phil. Mag. Suppl.*, **3,** 26 (1954).
14. D. Bowen and G. W. Rodeback, "The Influence of Cold Work and Radiation Damage on the Debye Temperature of Copper," *Acta Met.*, **1,** 649 (1953).
15. H. G. Cooper, J. S. Koehler and J. W. Marx, "Irradiation Effects in Cu, Ag and Au Near 10°K," *Phys. Rev.*, **97,** 599 (1955).
16. D. L. Dexter, "Scattering of Electrons from Point Singularities in Metals," *Phys. Rev.*, **87,** 768 (1952).
17. P. Jongenburger, "The Extra Resistivity Owing to Vacancies in Copper," *Phys. Rev.*, **90,** 710 (1953).
18. P. Jongenburger, "The Extra Resistivity Due to Vacancies in Copper, Silver, and Gold," *Appl. Sci. Research*, **B3,** 237 (1953).
19. J. Friedel, "The Distribution of Electrons Round Impurities in Monovalent Metals," *Phil. Mag.*, **43,** 153 (1952).
20. P. Jongenburger, "Extra Resistivity Due to Interstitial Atoms in Copper," *Nature*, **175,** 545 (1955).
21. F. J. Blatt, "Effect of Point Imperfections on the Electrical Properties of Copper, I. Conductivity," *Phys. Rev.*, **99,** 1708 (1955).
22. F. J. Blatt, "Effect of Point Imperfections on the Electrical Properties of Copper, II. Thermoelectric Power," *Phys. Rev.*, **100,** 666 (1955).
23. A. W. Overhauser and R. L. Gorman, "Resistivity of Interstitial Atoms and Vacancies in Copper," *Phys. Rev.*, **102,** 676 (1956).
24. F. Seitz and J. S. Koehler, "Displacement of Atoms during Irradiation," in *Solid State Physics* (editors F. Seitz and D. Turnbull), Academic Press, 1956, Vol. 2, pp. 307–442.
25. J. K. Redman, T. S. Noggle, R. R. Coltman and T. H. Blewitt, "Very Low

Temperature Irradiation of Metals," *Bull. Am. Phys. Soc.*, **1**, 130 (1956) (A).
26. Fiske, Walker, Corbett and Denney, "Electron Irradiation of Copper below 100°K, I," *Bull. Am. Phys. Soc.*, II, **1**, 334 (1956) (A).
27. Walker, Corbett, Denney and Fiske, "Electron Irradiation of Copper below 10°K, II," *Bull. Am. Phys. Soc.*, II, **1**, 335 (1956) (A); see also *Phys. Rev.*, **104**, 851 (1957).
28. J. M. Denney, "Resistivity of Interstitials and Vacancies in Cu," *Bull. Am. Phys. Soc.*, II, **1**, 335 (1956) (A).
29. J. J. Antal, R. J. Weiss and G. J. Dienes, "Long Wavelength Neutron Transmission as an Absolute Method for Determining the Concentration of Lattice Defects in Crystals," *Phys. Rev.*, **99**, 1081 (1955).
30. D. T. Keating, "X-Ray Measurements on Low-Temperature Neutron Irradiated Graphite," *Phys. Rev.*, **98**, 1859 (1955).
31. G. R. Hennig and J. E. Hove, "Radiation Damage to Graphite," *Proceedings of the International Conference on the Peaceful Uses of Atomic Energy*, United Nations, 1956, Vol. 7, p. 666 (Paper No. 751), see also special article by M. Burton, T. J. Neubert, *et al.* on "Neutron-Induced Decomposition in Graphite," *J. Appl. Phys.*, **27**, 557–572 (1956) in which the early work in this field is covered.
32. G. Hennig, "The Properties of the Interstitial Compounds of Graphite I, II, III," *J. Chem. Phys.*, **19**, 922 (1951); **20**, 1438 (1952); **20**, 1443 (1952).
33. G. R. Hennig and J. D. McClelland, "Magnetic Susceptibility and Free Energy of Graphite Bromide," *J. Chem. Phys.*, **23**, 1431 (1955).
34. John E. Hove, "Theory of the Magnetic Susceptibility of Graphite," *Phys. Rev.*, **100**, 645 (1955).
35. John E. Hove, "Magnetic Susceptibility of Neutron-Damaged Graphite," *Phys. Rev.*, **100**, 106 (1955) (A).
36. D. F. Johnston, "A Calculation of the Density of Electron-Trapping Defects in Neutron-Irradiated Graphite from Measurements of the Temperature Variation of the Hall Coefficient," *J. Nuclear Energy*, **1**, 311 (1955).
37. W. K. Woods, L. P. Bupp and J. F. Fletcher, "Irradiation Damage to Graphite," *Proceedings of the International Conference on the Peaceful Uses of Atomic Energy*, United Nations, 1956, Vol. 7, p. 455 (Paper No. 746).
38. G. J. Dienes, "Mechanism for Self-Diffusion in Graphite," *J. Appl. Phys.*, **23**, 1194 (1952).
39. G. R. Hennig, private communication, 1955.
40. S. B. Austerman, "Stored Energy Release in Graphite Irradiated at Low Temperatures," *Phys. Rev.*, **100**, 1807 (1955) (A).
41. J. W. Cleland, J. H. Crawford, K. Lark-Horovitz, J. C. Pigg, and F. W. Young, "The Effect of Fast Neutron Bombardment on the Electrical Properties of Germanium," *Phys. Rev.*, **83**, 312 (1951).
42. The first attempt at a systematic model was given by: H. M. James and K. Lark-Horovitz, "Localized Electronic States in Bombarded Semiconductors," *Z. physik. Chem. (Leipzig)*, **198**, 107 (1951).
43. H. Y. Fan and K. Lark-Horovitz, "Fast Particle Irradiation of Germanium

Semiconductors," *Report of the Bristol Conference on Defects in Crystalline Solids*, The Physical Society, London, 1955, pp. 232–245.
44. E. E. Klontz, R. R. Pepper and K. Lark-Horovitz, "Electrical Properties of Electron Bombarded Ge," *Phys. Rev.*, **98,** 1535 (1955) (A).
45. J. W. Cleland, J. H. Crawford, Jr., and J. C. Pigg, "Fast Neutron Bombardment of n-Type Ge," *Phys. Rev.*, **98,** 1742 (1955).
46. L. Katz and N. Penfold, "Range-Energy Relation for Electrons," *Rev. Mod. Phys.*, **24,** 28 (1952).
47. W. L. Brown, R. C. Fletcher, and K. A. Wright, "Annealing of Bombardment Damage in Germanium: Experimental," *Phys. Rev.*, **92,** 591 (1953).
48. W. H. Brattain and G. L. Pearson, "Changes in Conductivity of Germanium Induced by Alpha-Particles Bombardment," *Phys. Rev.*, **80,** 846 (1950).
49. H. Brooks, "Nuclear Radiation Effects in Solids," *Ann. Rev. Nuclear Sci.*, **6,** (1956).
√ 50. P. W. Levy and G. J. Dienes, "Colour Centers Induced in Al_2O_3 by Reactor and Gamma-Ray Irradiation," *Report of the Bristol Conference on Defects in Crystalline Solids*, The Physical Society, London, 1955, pp. 256–260.
51. P. W. Levy and G. J. Dienes, "Research on Radiation Effects in Insulating Materials at Brookhaven National Laboratory," *Conference on Effects of Radiation on Dielectric Materials*, Washington, 1954, ONR Symposium Report ACR-2.
52. F. Seitz, *The Modern Theory of Solids*, McGraw-Hill, New York, 1946, Eq. (8), p. 664.
53. D. L. Dexter, "Absorption of Light by Atoms in Solids," *Phys. Rev.*, **101,** 48 (1956).
54. J. H. Crawford, Jr. and M. C. Wittels, "Radiation Effects in Crystals," *Proceedings of the International Conference on the Peaceful Uses of Atomic Energy*, United Nations, 1956, Vol. 7, p. 654 (Paper No. 753).
55. P. W. Levy, "Reactor and Gamma-Ray Induced Coloring in Crystalline Quartz and Corning Fused Silica," *J. Chem. Phys.*, **23,** 764 (1955).
56. E. W. J. Mitchell and E. G. S. Paige, "Optical Effects of Radiation Induced Atomic Damage in Quartz," *Phil. Mag.*, **1,** 1085 (1956).
57. S. Siegel, "Effect of Neutron Bombardment on Order in the Alloy Cu_3Au," *Phys. Rev.*, **75,** 1823 (1949).
58. L. G. Cook and R. L. Cushing, "The Effects of Neutron Irradiation in the NRX Reactor on the Order-Disorder Alloy Cu_3Au," *Acta Met.*, **1,** 539 (1953), **1,** 549 (1953).
59. L. R. Aronin, "Radiation Damage Effects on Order-Disorder in Nickel-Manganese Alloys," *J. Appl. Phys.*, **25,** 344 (1954).
60. J. A. Brinkman, C. E. Dixon and C. J. Meechan, "Interstitial and Vacancy Migration in Cu_3Au and Copper," *Acta Met.*, **2,** 38 (1954).
61. See article by S. Siegel in *Modern Research Techniques in Physical Metallurgy*, ASM, Cleveland, 1952, p. 319.
62. F. Seitz, "Source of Disordering of Alloys during Irradiation," *Phys. Rev.*, **98,** 1530 (1955) (A).
63. G. H. Kinchin and R. S. Pease, "The Mechanism of the Irradiation Disordering of Alloys," *J. Nuclear Energy*, **1,** 200 (1955).

64. G. H. Kinchin and R. S. Pease, "The Displacement of Atoms in Solids by Radiation," *Rept. Progr. in Phys.*, **18,** 1 (1955).
65. S. T. Konobeevsky, N. F. Pravdyuk and V. I. Kutaitsev, "Irradiation of Fissionable Materials," *Proceedings of the International Conference on Peaceful Uses of Atomic Energy*, United Nations, 1956, Vol. 7, p. 433 (Paper No. 681).
66. M. L. Bleiberg, L. J. Jones and B. Lustman, "Phase Changes in Pile-Irradiated Uranium-Base Alloys," *J. Appl. Phys.*, **27,** 1270 (1956).
67. C. W. Tucker, Jr. and P. Senio, "On the Nature of Thermal Spikes," *J. Appl. Phys.*, **27,** 207 (1956).
68. F. Abeles, "Résistance électrique et pouvoir thermoélectrique supplémentaires dus aux lacunes dans les métaux," *Compt. rend.*, **237,** 796 (1953).

CHAPTER 4

Nature and Properties of the Defects

4.1 Introduction

In most of the discussion so far it has been assumed that the interstitials and vacancies produced by fast-particle irradiation are distributed at random in the solid. The order-of-magnitude agreement between theory and experiment outlined in the previous chapter indicates that this assumption is not too bad as a first approximation. However, since the mean free path of a knock-on is generally considerably less than that of a fast bombarding particle, the displaced atoms are expected to be produced in a rather small volume around each primary collision. The primary collisions themselves are distributed at random if the sample is sufficiently thin; they are concentrated in surface layers if the sample is thick compared with a mean free path. For fast neutrons the mean free path is of the order of 10 cm. The end result of this process is that there is some clustering of the defects at the time of their production. The associated thermal spikes may act in the opposite direction and tend to disperse the clusters. In any given situation it is not yet possible to estimate the fraction of isolated and clustered defects.

In this chapter the physical property changes expected from the presence of isolated defects are discussed. Not enough is known about clusters of defects to extend the discussion to them. Simple clusters of defects, namely pairs, have been studied some in the last few years, mainly theoretically. This work is discussed below.

Seitz (1) suggested that, as in the case of salts (2,3), vacancies in metals will tend to associate in pairs, and that the migration of such a pair may require a lower activation energy than that of an isolated vacancy. The first theoretical estimate for metals was carried out by Bartlett and Dienes (4) who showed, on the basis of a very simple model, that the dissociation energy of a pair of vacancies in copper is between 0.23 and 0.59 ev. They also showed, using a Morse function for the interatomic potential, that the activation energy for the motion of a double vacancy through any face-centered-cubic metal crystal is about one-half that for a single vacancy. A more refined calculation by Seeger and Bross (5) gave 0.3 ev for the dissociation energy of a pair of vacancies in the noble metals.

The nature of the long-range interaction between defects has been investigated by various workers (6,7,8). The picture is far from complete at the present stage, but there are good arguments for believing that two vacancies are attracted to one another at large separations, probably with a potential proportional to the inverse sixth power of the separation. In the case of two interstitials or a vacancy and an interstitial, and for all pairs at intermediate distances, the net interaction is uncertain. A further discussion of these matters will be found in section 5.2 of Chapter 5.

Some experimental evidence for the existence and the high mobility of pairs of vacancies has appeared very recently. Li and Nowick (9) suggest that the high mobility defect is the divacancy in their experiments on quenched and neutron irradiated Cu-Al alloy and in the experiments of Kauffman and Koehler (10) on quenched gold. Letaw (11) suggests, in a detailed examination of the nature and mobility of thermal acceptors in germanium, that the first step in the annealing of excess thermal acceptors is the formation of divacancies. He further suggests that, at low temperatures, the second annealing step may be the migration of divacancies to the surface or their aggregation into larger clusters.

4.2 Point Defects and Changes in Physical Properties

One of the most important aspects of research in the field of radiation effects is the determination, both experimentally and theoretically, of the relation between the defects introduced by radiation and the associated changes in physical properties. Such investigations are also of general importance in modern solid-state physics, which is increasingly concerned with the properties of imperfect crystals (12). Fast-particle irradiation is a new technique that permits one to introduce a relatively large number of defects into crystals under reasonably well controlled conditions. It is clear, however, from the previous section that it is premature to expect that the relations between imperfections and physical properties can be described quantitatively. Not enough is known either about crystal defects or about the physical properties themselves to accomplish this except in a very few cases. The exceptions have already been treated in the previous chapter in connection with the quantitative measurement of the number of displaced atoms. In this section illustrative and representative examples will be given of this field of research. The coverage is not intended to be exhaustive.

A. *Electrical Properties*

Changes in electrical properties are easily measured with high precision at almost any desired temperature. This physical property has been used a great deal for studying radiation effects. Changes in electrical properties due to the introduction of defects arise from either changes in the number or in the mobility of the current carriers or both. Some illustrative examples are discussed in the following paragraphs.

(*a*) *Metals.* Changes in the electrical resistivity of irradiated metals have already been discussed in the previous chapter since they form the basis of one of the quantitative comparisons between theory and experiment. Suffice it to say that in good metallic conductors an increase in resistivity is observed upon fast-particle irradiation. This increase in resistivity is primarily an increase in the residual resistivity, although some changes in the thermal part of the resistivity have been observed (13). Since the number of conduction electrons is not altered to any significant extent in a good metallic conductor by the introduction of a very low concentration of defects, the increase in resistivity must be ascribed to the scattering of conduction electrons by the defects. The difficulties of determining the proportionality constant relating the increase in residual resistivity to the concentration of defects have been dealt with fully in the preceding chapter.

Order-disorder alloys should be mentioned briefly since they show very large changes in resistivity upon irradiation (14,15,16,17). In these cases the change in resistivity comes from the change in degree of long-range order and not directly from introduction of defects.

(*b*) *Semiconductors.* Semiconductors represent the opposite case to that of the good metallic conductors insofar as they have only a very small number of conduction electrons. In these materials, therefore, very large changes in electrical properties can be expected upon irradiation if the defects can serve as trapping centers for the current carriers. This is indeed the case, as many studies have shown

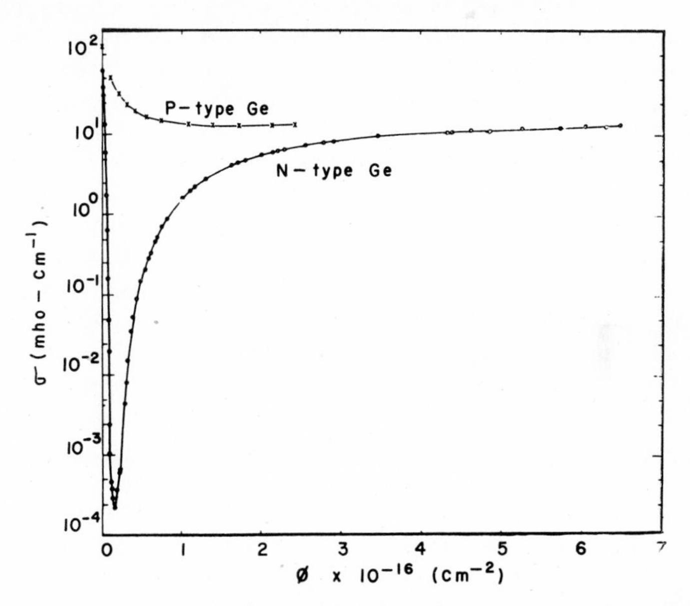

Figure 4.1 Conductivity *vs* flux density curves for an initially *p*-type and an initially *n*-type sample. Irradiation by 9.6-Mev deuterons at 200°K (from reference 20).

(18,19,20,21). Many of the quantitative measurements have already been discussed in the preceding chapter.

Typical resistivity data for deuteron-irradiated germanium are shown in Figure 4.1 taken from a recent article by Fan and Lark-Horovitz (20). Similar results are obtained upon neutron irradiation. The results may be described as follows. Bombardment of *n*-type Ge results in a decrease of conductivity, initially at a uniform rate. On further irradiation a minimum is reached, followed by an increase in the conductivity. Hall-coefficient measurements prove that near the conductivity minimum the sample has been converted to a *p*-type semiconductor. Bombardment of a *p*-type Ge sample leads generally to a steady increase in conductivity, with the rate of increase decreasing monotonically, although decreases in conductivity had been observed in bombarded high-conductivity p-type Ge as shown in Figure 4.1. Thus, at high hole concentrations the introduction of donors is apparently of importance.

These results can be interpreted qualitatively on the basis of a very simple model, although full quantitative interpretation calls for a complex and intricate picture (20). Only the simple model is described here, based on the production of isolated vacant lattice sites and interstitial atoms by the radiation. If one assumes that the vacancies and interstitials act like substitutions from the next columns of the period system, then vacancies produce empty acceptor states above the full band and interstitials produce donor states below the conduction band. If these were produced in the same way as in chemical substitution, and if they were equal in number, there would be no change in conductivity since they would cancel each other. In the case of chemical impurities, the ionization energies are so small that practically all donors and acceptors are ionized at room temperature. The ionization energies of irradiation defects, however, are distributed over a wide range of energies. In germanium acceptors appear to be the most important; the donors presumably lie near the top of the filled band and are not effective in releasing electrons or trapping holes. In silicon both types of centers appear to be equally important.

The effects of bombardment on Ge may now be pictured as follows. As vacant acceptor states are introduced in n-type Ge they will trap electrons from the conduction band and from the original donors, thereby decreasing the conductivity. Both deep-lying and high-lying acceptors will be filled, and the resistivity of an n-type sample will increase most rapidly during initial irradiation. As further acceptors are introduced, the low-lying vacant states begin to act as acceptors, leading to hole conduction. Thus, the material becomes p-type. Bombardment of a p-type sample leads to increased conductivity by augmenting the concentration of holes in the full band. This latter process is expected to be considerably less efficient than the initial electron removal since only sufficiently deep-lying vacant states can act as acceptors for electrons from the full band.

(*c*) *Ionic crystals.* In the alkali halides the electrical conduction is ionic and occurs by the motion of positive-ion vacancies (22). Radiation may now have several effects on the resistivity depending on just what happens to the concentration of positive vacancies. Purely ionizing radiation may neutralize a vacancy by providing a hole to be trapped at the positive-ion vacancy. Irradiation with neutrons may produce vacancies and interstitials without extensive ionization effects and in this case, then, an increase in the number of carriers and hence an increase in the conductivity may be expected. By means of the Varley mechanism (23) one may also produce an overabundance of negative-ion vacancies accompanied by an equivalent number of interstitial atoms. Both of the first mentioned effects have been observed in early experiments. Mapother (24) had shown that self-diffusion in NaCl is slowed down during irradiation by X-rays. The first experiments on the influence of nuclear irradiations were reported by Nelson, Sproull and Caswell (25). These workers found that γ-ray irradiation decreased the conductivity while long irradiation with neutrons led to an increase in the conductivity.

Smoluchowski and coworkers (26) have studied NaCl and KCl in considerable detail using 400-Mev protons for the irradiation. They find that a simple interpretation in terms of increased number of vacancies does not account for the observed effects and particularly for the observed annealing behavior. This is perhaps not surprising since in addition to displacing atoms the fast protons provide heavy local ionization, particularly when nuclear stars are formed. Annealing experiments carried out after irradiation show a striking increase of resistivity during the initial part of the heating curve and a return to normal resistivity at higher temperatures. An interpretation, based on Varley's mechanism, may be suggested (26). According to this picture the primary effect of ionizing radiation is to ionize the halogen ions until they become positive and are spontaneously displaced into an interstitial position. An overabundance of negative-ion vacancies can be produced this way which may be an order of magnitude higher than the normal low-temperature concentration. Upon increasing the temperature high enough to provide sufficient mobility, neutral clusters of positive and negative ion vacancies will form. Consequently, the concentration of positive-ion vacancies decreases, leading to an increase in resistivity. At increasingly higher temperatures the clusters tend to dissociate and the defects tend to anneal out.

(*d*) *Graphite.* The electrical properties of this material are quite sensitive to the presence of displaced atoms. The details have already been discussed in the previous chapter, and graphite is mentioned here only because it is a substance in which both the number and the mobility of the carriers are altered by fast-particle irradiation.

B. Thermal Conductivity

One might expect that thermal waves, or phonons, would be scattered by lattice imperfections analogously to the scattering of

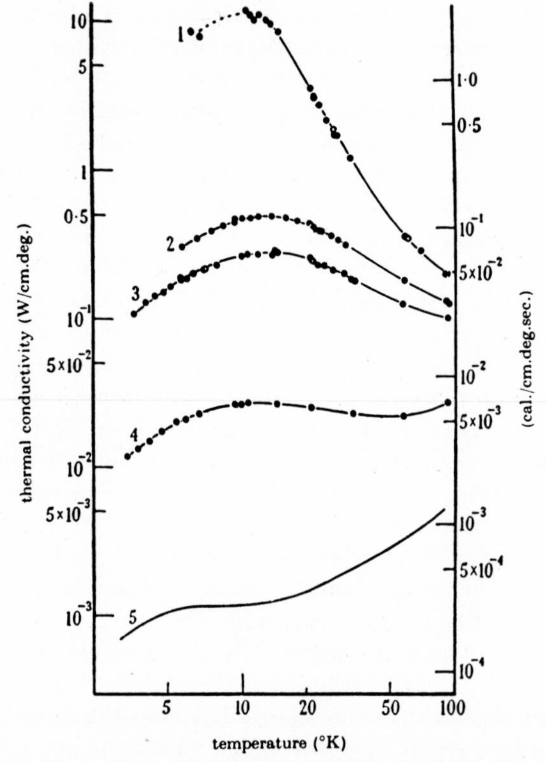

Figure 4.2 Thermal conductivity of quartz crystal, irradiated quartz crystal, and quartz glass: (1) quartz crystal perpendicular to axis 5 mm square cross section: ● length measured 3.05 cm, O length measured 2.15 cm; (2) after first irradiation—1 unit; (3) ● after second irradiation—1.4 units, O after subsequent heating at 100° C for three weeks; (4) after third irradiation—16.5 units; (5) quartz glass (from reference 28).

conduction electrons. Hence, large changes in the thermal conductivity of crystals can be expected upon irradiation. Theory indicates that the thermal conductivity is particularly sensitive to impurities and imperfections in the temperature region where the conductivity is a maximum (27). For most dielectric solids the relevant temperature region is below 50° K. Detailed studies have been published for a few crystals and are discussed in the following paragraphs.

Berman (28,29) and Klemens (30) have studied the low-temperature thermal conductivity of irradiated quartz crystals. Typical results are shown in Figure 4.2. To a first approximation the thermal resistance produced by the irradiation can be regarded as additive to the normal lattice resistance. This extra resistance has a minimum at about 15° K and increases roughly linearly with the temperature above 15° K. Below this temperature the extra resistance increases more rapidly than the inverse of the temperature. It is suggested that the extra resistance above 15° K is to be attributed to the presence of single lattice defects. The required defect concentration was found to be of the same order of magnitude as that calculated from the radiation exposure.

It is necessary to assume that large defects are also present to explain the increasing resistance at lower temperatures. These larger defects are probably clusters of interstitials and vacancies formed in the neighborhood of a primary knock-on.

Berman, Foster and Rosenberg (31) carried out thermal conductivity experiments on synthetic sapphire and diamond with similar results. In the case of sapphire the results can be interpreted in terms of regions of damage containing about 4000 atoms, each region arising from a primary neutron collision. From the fact that the resistance was found to be constant over an appreciable temperature range, one may deduce that the scattering is due to a long thin obstacle rather than a sphere (31). This experiment, therefore, gave the first indication that the damaged regions are nonspherical, in agreement with theoretical expectations.

Gamma-radiation had a rather similar effect, but the damage appeared to saturate at a rather low level, in agreement with optical observations in this material (32). In diamond gamma-radiation gave no effect, but a large reduction in thermal conductivity was observed after neutron irradiation (31).

In graphite the thermal conductivity maximum is in the neighborhood of room temperature (33,34) and, therefore, large changes in the thermal conductivtiy may be expected in this temperature range. This expectation is fully verified experimentally. Some typical data are shown in Figure 4.3. The thermal conductivity is seen to decrease by a large factor upon irradiation. The temperature dependence of the conductivity is also altered with an apparent shift of the maximum to higher temperature. In some instances the

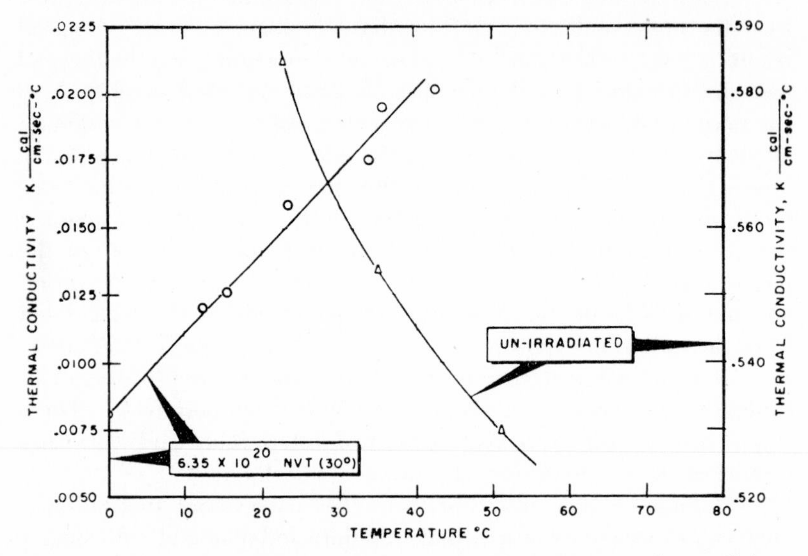

Figure 4.3 Variation of thermal conductivity with temperature for parallel cut KC graphite (from reference 35).

conductivity has been reduced by as much as a factor of 50 by irradiation. The radiation effects are markedly reduced by increasing the temperature of exposure.

C. Stored Energy

Irradiation of a crystal increases the energy content of the lattice. This increase in energy is referred to as the stored energy. In many ways this is perhaps the most basic physical change accompanying the production of defects. If the energy of formation of the defects is known theoretically and if the total stored energy is measured, then the number of defects is immediately calculable. This method of determining the fraction of displaced atoms has been used for graphite and has already been described in the preceding chapter.

For simplicity of interpretation it is essential that the increase in enthalpy be measured by starting and terminating an experiment in well defined thermodynamic states. This was done in the graphite experiments referred to above, where the stored energy was measured as an increase in the heat of combustion (36). This extra heat content is clearly the total energy content of the defects. If the irradiation is done at low temperature so that no annealing of the defects has taken place, then the above energy change is simply the total energy of formation of a given fraction of defects. If, say, aggregation has already taken place via annealing, the corresponding stored energy is no longer interpretable in such a simple way. Stored-energy experiments have also been done on diamond (37), and the results for this substance are very similar to that for graphite.

The authors are not aware of any other experiments in which the total stored energy has been measured in an unambiguous way. The release of stored energy over limited temperature ranges has been studied in various materials (38,39,40,41). From such experiments important information is often obtainable concerning the annealing of radiation damage, particularly if other physical properties are measured and correlated with the release of energy. More work in this field would be welcome since suitable measurements are clearly interpretable, and, in principle, interstitials and vacancies can be distinguished since their energy contents are expected to differ by a factor of 2 to 5.

The release of stored energy in certain irradiated materials can cause large temperature increases, and technical importance attaches to this fact. A case in point is graphite (87), and recent measurements of Kosiba *et al.* (117) demonstrate this in a simple way. An irradiated sample of graphite is placed suddenly in a furnace held at 200° C, and the temperature of the graphite is observed as a function of time. It is found that the graphite rises rapidly to a temperature considerably above that of the furnace, then returns to equilibrium at 200° C. The sample is next removed, cooled to room temperature, and returned to the furnace. The temperature rise for this annealed sample is monotonic, and the excess temperature achieved in the first run compared to the second is a measure of the stored energy released. Figure 4.4 shows results for a sample which had been irradiated at 55° C to an exposure of about 1.2×10^{20} neutrons/cm^2 (nvt) (total).

To a first approximation it can be assumed that the stored energy, in calories per gram, that will be released during warming from temperature T to $T + dT$ will be a function of T, nearly independently

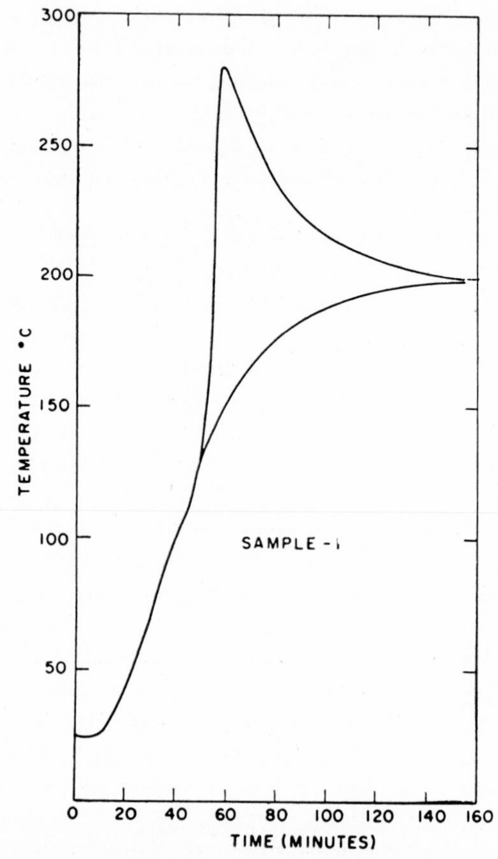

Figure 4.4 Time *vs* temperature plot of graphite placed in furnace held at 200° C. Upper curve, sample previously irradiated at 55° C. Lower curve, same sample after annealing (from reference 117).

of the rate of warming (see section 5.3 of Chapter 5). Let this function be $q(T)dT$. If heat is supplied to the sample from outside at a rate R calories per second and the specific heat of the substance is C (assumed unaffected by the annealing), the temperature rise during time dT is given by the energy balance relation

$$C\,dT = R\,dt + q(t)\,dT \tag{4-1}$$

$$dT/dt = R/[C - q(T)] \tag{4-2}$$

From this, it is seen that if the heat release per degree q is nearly as large as the specific heat, a very rapid heat rise will occur; an instability, which is not properly covered by equation 4-1, will occur if $q \geq C$. Q, the total stored energy released between temperatures T_1 and T_2, is found by integrating equation 4-1,

$$Q = \int_{T_1}^{T_2} q(T)\,dT = \int_{T_1}^{T_2} C\,dT - \int_{t_1}^{t_2} R\,dt \tag{4-3}$$

The temperature during the warming of the irradiated sample departs from that of the annealed sample at a temperature T_1, at which energy release commences, and reaches a maximum at approximately the temperature T_2, at which energy release ceases. If the temperature rise is rapid, the heat input from the furnace

$$\int_{t_1}^{t_2} R\,dt$$

is negligible during the rise, and Q can be found from the relation

$$Q \cong \int_{T_1}^{T_2} C\,dT = \bar{C}(T_2 - T_1) \tag{4-4}$$

Analyzed in this manner Figure 4.4 gives $Q = 45$ cal/gm. A more exact analysis (J. Chernick, unpublished) taking account of the heat input term gives $Q = 54$ cal/gm in this case. Analysis of a series of samples irradiated to about the same exposure at a variety of temperatures shows that the energy release in this low-temperature stage declines very rapidly as the temperature of irradiation rises. This is not all of the stored energy, however, and further release occurs at much higher temperatures. The reader is referred to Woods, *et al.* (35).

D. *Elastic Properties*

The first observation of a change in elastic properties upon irradiation came from early work on graphite (35,42). Reactor irradiation of graphite was found to produce a stronger, harder and more brittle material. Young's modulus was increased by about a factor of three upon an exposure of 10^{20} nvt.

Theoretical interpretation of these changes is difficult because of the complicated structure of graphite. The first theoretical calculations were carried out for metals by Dienes (43,44,45), who investigated the effect of vacancies and interstitials on the elastic constants of simple close-packed metallic crystals. In such substances the elastic constants are determined primarily by the repulsive interactions of the closed ion shells. This potential is of an exponential nature and varies extremely rapidly with interatomic distance. As the interaction distance is shortened by creating an interstitial, the energy of the system increases sharply on the repulsive side of the potential curve. The creation of vacancies results essentially in the destruction of some normal interactions. Thus, one expects the influence of the interstitials to outweigh heavily the effect of vacancies.

Detailed calculations, in which relaxation of nearest neighbors was taken into account, led to the following conclusions: The presence of a small fraction of interstitials and vacancies results in large increases in the elastic moduli of copper, of the order of 5–7 per cent per 1 per cent interstitial. Lattice vacancies alone were found to decrease the moduli by essentially a bulk effect. Consequently, increases in the elastic moduli are to be attributed primarily to the presence of interstitial atoms. There is a complicating factor arising from modulus changes which may occur by a mechanism of dislocation pinning (46). A proper experimental test of this theory has not yet been carried out. It is essential, because of annealing, to make pre- and post-irradiation measurement at very low temperatures (below 30° K) on low-temperature irradiated crystals. It would also be advantageous to do the experiments on a low-concentration alloy so as to eliminate the dislocation contribution to the modulus by pinning the dislocations. It should also be mentioned that the theory indicates that the above effect would be absent in a soft body-centered cubic crystal such as sodium. In this case the relaxation around the interstitial is large enough to eliminate essentially the crowding upon which the modulus increase depends.

A rather large increase in modulus has been observed experimentally by Thompson and Holmes in copper single crystals after reactor irradiation (47,48,49). These workers found that the modulus increase, which may be as high as 15–20%, is not proportional to the amount of irradiation and saturates (i.e., no further change in modulus occurs) at a very low irradiation level, namely of the order of 4×10^{12} nvt of fast flux. During this process the logarithmic decrement, which also saturates, decreases by almost an order of magnitude. It is quite clear that this effect cannot be due to the production of defects in the bulk as calculated by Dienes, for two reasons. First, the required flux is orders of magnitude too small. Second, no appreciable internal friction effects are to be expected from the presence of isolated interstitials and vacancies. The pinning of dislocations by the radiation-produced defects is a very reasonable explanation, and this is the interpretation advanced by Thompson and Holmes. They show that this interpretation leads to generally accepted values for the dislocation densities and average segment lengths.

A change in modulus without an accompanying change in attenuation has been observed in silicon by Truell, Teutonico, and Levy (50). These workers carried out ultrasonic-velocity and double-refraction measurements on a single crystal of silicon that had been bombarded with a beam of approximately collimated fast neutrons. The neutrons were incident along a [100] direction of the crystal. It was found that the ultrasonic velocities were lowered by the irradiation, and that acoustic double refraction was observable with waves propagated perpendicular to the neutron beam. Double refraction was not observed with waves propagated parallel to the beam. Since there was no observable change in attenuation it is reasonable to attribute the velocity changes to changes in the elastic moduli without any change in the dislocation network. If an analogy to Dienes' calculation for close-packed metals is valid for the diamond structure, the results suggest, since the moduli decreased, that vacancies are responsible for the observed effects. This is not unreasonable for a room-temperature irradiation, since the interstitials may have annealed out. The double refraction then is due to a clustering of defects along the path of the primary knock-on, since the recoiling atom is expected to produce a region of damage roughly ellipsoidal in shape with the long direction oriented, on the average along the direction of the incident particle.

Modulus changes have also been observed in quartz (51) upon pile irradiation. The modulus (measured as the frequency of a BT-cut crystal oscillator) decreases rapidly at first and then more or less linearly as a function of exposure. The early part may well be due to ionization, while the steady decrease in frequency is probably associated with the production of displaced atoms. More detailed studies by Mayer (52) indicate that different moduli in quartz behave differently. Mayer's preliminary results show that S_{11} decreases and S_{33} increases upon irradiation, while the piezoelectric constant d_{11} decreases. He found a simultaneous increase in the electrical conductivity.

E. Optical Properties

Ionization effects become observable as the electrical conductivity of the medium is decreased. Thus, ionization effects are important in insulating crystals, where they lead to more or less permanent phenomena. The nonequilibrium distribution of electrons often becomes observable as a color center in these materials. The effect of ionizing radiation on insulating crystals, particularly ionic crystals, has been studied for many years, and it is not the purpose of this section to review this field (53). Attention will be focussed on those color centers which may be clearly attributed to displaced atoms.

Diamond is known to color upon exposure to high-energy particles, but no color is produced by ionizing radiation alone (54,55,56, 57). The absorption spectrum is drastically altered in the 1.6–2.5 ev region, where the absorption is greatly increased. The spectrum is complex, however, and a detailed interpretation is not yet at hand. However, since particle irradiation is required, it is clear that the phenomena involve interstitials and vacancies or their aggregates. Paramagnetic resonance data, reviewed in the next section, indicate the same conclusion.

Another example, namely the coloring of α-Al_2O_3 has already been discussed quite fully in the previous chapter as a quantitative method for determining defect concentrations (32). The color centers in crystalline and fused silica have been studied in considerable detail (57–68). In most specimens the optical absorption spectrum is quite complex, primarily because of the presence of impurities. The sensitivity to radiation appears to depend to a great extent on small amounts of impurities. However, one band produced by irradiation, at 214–220 mμ (5.7 ev), is common to all specimens and is the only band in some highly purified fused silicas. This band is found to be far more sensitive to reactor than to pure ionizing radiation, particularly for short irradiations (65). Recent work by Mitchell and Paige (69) showed that there is another band in the ultraviolet, at 7.6 ev, which is introduced by reactor irradiation. Both of these are probably due to the presence of displaced atoms, most likely oxygen vacancies and interstitials (see also the discussion is section 3.3).

The band at 465 mμ that is observed in most irradiated crystalline silicas should be discussed briefly, since a concrete model has been proposed for this center (70), namely that of an aluminum atom in place of a silicon atom in the quartz lattice. Since no paramagnetism is observed prior to irradiation, it is further postulated that a Li (or H or Na) atom has been simultaneously incorporated which would reside in the crystal as a positive ion, having lost an electron to the aluminum. Irradiation with ionizing radiation removes the electron from the Al center, making it light absorbing and paramagnetic. The evidence for this model may be summarized as follows:

(*a*) The intensity of the 465-mμ band is approximately proportional to the Al content in synthetic quartz crystals doped with Al (57). This proportionality also obtains in a series of bleached smoky quartz samples irradiated with X-rays (71).

(*b*) The optical anisotropy of the band indicates that the Al has substituted for a Si without appreciably disturbing the geometry of the oxygen atom with which the unpaired electron is associated (71,72).

(*c*) Synthetic quartz samples show paramagnetic electron resonance intensities proportional to the Al content (70,73). The fine structure of the electronic resonance showed that the paramagnetic electrons are associated with nuclei of spin $^5/_2$. Aluminum is monoisotopic and has nuclear spin $^5/_2$.

F. Paramagnetic Resonance

As another consequence of the nonequilibrium distribution of electrons after irradiation an increase in paramagnetism can be expected. This effect was observed first by McClelland and Donoghue (74) in several pure oxides as a decrease in the diamagnetic susceptibility. Similar studies on vitreous SiO_2 (66) led to a correlation of magnetic susceptibility and the ultraviolet optical absorption (around 215 mμ, see previous section). From these two measurements the oscillator strength of the optical absorption band has been estimated as approximately 0.2.

The simple susceptibility measurements, however, are of rather limited usefulness since one cannot distinguish in this way between ionization of impurity atoms and paramagnetic lattice defects. Far more information can be obtained from the paramagnetic resonance spectra. Two such studies, one dealing with irradiated diamond and the other with irradiated quartz, are discussed briefly in the following paragraphs. The paramagnetism due to the presence of ionized Al in quartz has already been discussed in the previous section.

(*a*) *Diamond.* In diamond irradiated with fast neutrons two main types of resonance absorption lines have been found (73): (*a*) a single isotropic line with *g*-value close to 2 (2.0028), and (*b*) many less intense anisotropic lines which appear to arise from centers with an electronic spin of one. The intensity of the isotropic line can be greatly reduced by heating to 1000° C, while the anisotropic lines are not much affected by heat treatment. Other lines have also been found but have not been subjected to detailed analysis. The magnetic centers are only found in samples subjected to high-energy particle irradiation and are, therefore, associated with displaced atoms. The line width indicates that the centers are not distributed evenly and that there is some interaction between them.

O'Brien and Pryce (75) suggest an interpretation based on the presence of displaced atoms. Their calculations indicate that a vacancy would show a single isotropic line in resonance absorption with the free-spin *g*-value. The experimentally observed line (*a*) above is then probably due to vacancies. For the interstitial carbon atoms, the ground state is probably a singlet and hence nonmagnetic, although the lowest level may be a triplet with the lines so much broadened by local strains that they are unobservable. The type (*b*) lines discussed above may arise from simple aggregates of interstitials and vacancies, such as divacancies or interstitial C_2 molecules. The details of the anisotropy are not fully explained by such a model.

(*b*) *Quartz.* Weeks (76) has studied various types of silica glass and natural and synthetic quartz crystals irradiated with fast neutrons at 250–300° C. Two groups of resonance lines were found in the natural crystals after irradiation. In the glasses two asymmetric resonance lines have been found, which are apparently associated with the crystalline lines since they can be represented as the envelopes of the crystalline lines when the latter are summed over random orientations with respect to the magnetic field. The two lines in the glasses have g-values of 2.0013 and 2.0090. Weeks interprets these results as due to defects in the basic SiO_4 tetrahedra generated by the fast neutrons and the associated knock-ons. He suggests that the resonance line with $g = 2.0013$ is due to an electron paramagnetic center while the other one is due to a trapped hole. He further suggests that the electron resonance center corresponds to the optical center that has its absorption at 218 mμ. Reliable values for the oscillator strength of the optical center have not yet been established.

G. *Effects Observable by Diffraction*

Lattice imperfections caused by irradiation influence the X-ray diffraction pattern of a substance, and this was indeed one of the early ways in which radiation damage was observed. The characteristic sharp Bragg reflections in the X-ray diffraction pattern of a good crystal are generally displaced, weakened, and eventually broadened when the crystal is irradiated. Also, diffuse background scattering appears, and sometimes extra crystalline reflections as well. These effects are much more pronounced in some materials than in others. In general metals show the least effect, while covalent and ionic crystals are more strongly affected. This difference seems to be partly due to the greater ease with which displaced atoms in metals anneal at ordinary temperatures. Organic crystals show a disruptive influence from ionizing radiation alone, while the covalent and ionic materials generally require heavy-particle irradiation before their X-ray patterns will be appreciably influenced. Very heavy irradiation can completely disrupt the crystalline lattice of susceptible materials.

With low exposures the X-ray effects can be attributed to isolated point defects. With very heavy exposures the X-ray pattern of some susceptible materials comes to resemble that of an amorphous substance, all crystalline features of the pattern having disappeared. Usually the external crystalline form is not disturbed, and so one finds a specimen having the superficial appearance of a crystal with none of its internal architecture. This is the so called metamict state, which has been known to mineralogists for many years (77) because it is occasionally found in natural crystals that contain radioactive elements and have thus irradiated themselves over very long periods.

The diffraction effects of interstitials and vacancies in low concentration can be fairly well calculated. In the first place an interstitial atom in an otherwise perfect lattice gives extra scattering that is distributed in angle according to the atomic structure factor. Similarly, a vacancy in a perfect lattice is identical with an extra center of scattering having precisely the negative of the scattering power of one atom. At scattering angles other than the Bragg angles the scattering of the perfect lattice vanishes, while that of the imperfections remains. If the imperfections are in small concentration they will scatter with incoherent phases at angles away from the Bragg angles. Thus between the Bragg peaks a background scattering will appear. If there are n_I interstitials and n_v vacancies in the sample the background scattered intensity, in electron units, will be

$$I \cong (n_I + n_v)f^2 \tag{4-5}$$

where f is the atomic structure factor. The intensity in the Bragg peaks will be lowered by a corresponding amount. This is precisely the scattering that is being utilized in the neutron-transmission method of determining defect concentration (see section 3.3).

The foregoing discussion is only a first approximation. Interstitials and vacancies also distort the lattice, and this causes further diffraction effects. In general the atoms neighboring an interstitial are pushed outward, while those neighboring a vacancy are moved outward or inward depending on the lattice and its type of binding. In metals the neighbors of a vacancy move inward by small amounts; in strongly ionic materials they move outward. The displacements of the second and third neighbors may be opposite to that of the first neighbors (78), and consequently the details of the displacements near the imperfection are complicated and have not yet been extensively investigated [see also Kanzaki (113,114)]. Nevertheless, as an approximation, the interstitial atom may be regarded as a center of pressure that produces a predominantly outward displacement around itself; the vacancy, in the case of metals, may be regarded as a center of contraction. For purposes of computation the situation is further idealized by treating the medium around the imperfection as an isotopic elastic continuum. Classical elasticity theory then shows that the displacement of an atom at a distance r from an imperfection is radial and of magnitude

$$\delta_r = c/r^2 \tag{4-6}$$

where c is a constant characterizing the "strength" of the imperfection. Equation 4-6 can only be realistic for $r \geq \rho_0$ where ρ_0 is a limiting distance of the order of the interatomic spacing.

Huntington (79) has calculated the displacements around an interstitial atom in copper and finds that the constant c of equation 4-6 should be about 0.16 v, where v is the volume per atom and the estimated accuracy is about 20 per cent. The relaxation around a vacancy in copper is inward, and the displacements are about one-fifth as large as around an interstitial (80,81). Thus, for a vacancy in this metal the constant c should be about $-0.03\ v$. These numbers are probably representative of the behavior of close-packed metals, although no other cases have yet been calculated. In highly anisotropic materials (e.g., graphite) the strains are quite different (see below).

Eshelby (82) has shown that n point imperfections randomly located in an isotropic elastic medium of finite volume V and producing strains according to equation 4-6 cause a volume expansion of the material ΔV given by

$$\Delta V = 12\ \pi \left(\frac{1 - \sigma}{1 + \sigma}\right) nc \tag{4-7}$$

where σ is Poisson's ratio.

From this one finds that the lattice parameter a_0 of a crystal would be altered by point imperfections by an amount Δa_0 where

$$\Delta a_0/a_0 = \frac{1}{3}\frac{\Delta V}{V} = 4\pi \left(\frac{1 - \sigma}{1 + \sigma}\right) (n/V)c \tag{4-8}$$

The work of Eshelby (82) has also shown that, contrary to some earlier predictions, the lattice parameter as revealed by x-ray diffraction should be in accord with the over-all expansion of the crystal caused by the elastic fields of point imperfections.

If several species of imperfections are present, for example n_I interstitials and n_v vacancies, nc in equation 4-8 should be replaced by $(n_I c_I + n_v c_v)$, where c_I and c_v are the strength constants of interstitials and vacancies, respectively. In the case of copper the previously quoted results show that $c_I \cong -5c_v$, and thus equal concentrations of vacancies and interstitials in this material lead to a net lattice expansion.

The average increase of lattice parameter, as measured by a shift in position of x-ray reflection, has been observed in a number of irradiated materials. Primak and co-workers (83) have observed lattice expansions in diamond, silicon carbide, quartz, magnesium oxide, spinel, and sapphire, the effects in the first three being an order of magnitude more prominent than in the others. Crawford and Wittels (84) report x-ray observations of the lattice expansion in zircon ($ZrSiO_4$), beryl ($Be_3Al_2Si_6O_{18}$), chrysoberyl ($BeO.Al_2O_3$), phenacite ($2BeO.SiO_2$), and other minerals. Binder and Sturm (85) and Keating (86) have observed lattice expansion in LiF. In this substance the (n,α) reaction of the isotope Li^6, which gives an α-particle with energy of 2.06 Mev and a tritium atom with energy of 2.74 Mev, is responsible for a major portion of the damage. In zircon, Crawford and Wittels (84) report that an exposure of 2.5×10^{20} fast neutrons/cm^2 (nvt) produces a 1.0% expansion in the a axis and a 1.4% expansion in the c axis. Up to this level, at least, the expansion is related linearly to the exposure with high accuracy. The response of this substance is fairly typical of tightly bound refractory insulators.

Graphite shows anomalous lattice expansion effects under irradiation, due undoubtedly to the peculiarly mixed nature of its bonding and its resultant anisotropy. Its c-axis spacing expands, in room temperature irradiations, approximately four times as fast as the c-axis spacing of zircon, while its a axis generally shrinks a little (87). The c-axis expansion is probably due to the presence of interstitials between the weakly bound graphite planes.

As noted previously, common metals have not shown appreciable lattice expansion effects under ordinary reactor irradiation. However, irradiations and x-ray examinations of copper single crystals at extremely low temperatures (12° K) have been carried out by Simmons and Balluffi (88). The bombarding particles were 12-Mev deuterons from a cyclotron, and the specimens were sufficiently thin that the energy loss of the deuterons in the specimen was small. The Bragg reflections broadened very slightly with irradiation, while the lattice parameter increased steadily. After an exposure of 6.3×10^{16} deuterons/cm^2, the (400) reflection indicated a lattice expansion

$\Delta a_0/a_0$ of $(2.6 \pm 0.1) \times 10^{-4}$. Using Huntington's value of the strength c_I of the distortion by an interstitial, assuming $c_v = -0.2\, c_I$, and estimating the number of displaced atoms by the radiation damage theory of Chapter 2, equation 4-8 predicts $\Delta a_0/a_0 \cong 2.4 \times 10^{-3}$, which is an order of magnitude too large. The reason for the discrepancy is not understood, but it is possibly significant that the amount of damage as determined by electrical resistivity is in rough agreement with the value derived from lattice expansion. During a low warm up (10° K per hour) 55% of the fractional change disappeared between 15° K and 42° K, and a negligible amount was left after a room-temperature anneal. This is strong confirmation of the hypothesis that lattice expansion of similar metals has not been observed under reactor irradiation because the high mobility of the defects allows the expansion to anneal as fast as it is formed. The fact that lattice expansion does occur shows that interstitials are present, for vacancies in a metal could not produce an expansion.

The inhomogeneous expansion in the vicinity of each imperfection causes further x-ray effects. Huang (89) has considered the problem of x-ray diffraction of dilute alloys, and Tucker and Senio (90) have pointed out the direct applicability of Huang's analysis to the case of irradiated materials. Matsubara (115) and Cochran (116) have also published treatments of this problem. Huang's work has been modified by Eshelby (82), Sampson and Tucker (91), and Borie (92). Huang treats the problem of a monatomic lattice that departs from perfection only in containing a random distribution of distortion centers. Each center is assumed to produce displacements according to equation 4-2, that is, it acts as a pressure center in an isotropic elastic continuum. Huang (as modified by Borie) finds three effects. First, there is a reduction in intensity of the Bragg reflections by an artificial "temperature factor," that is a factor of e^{-2M}, where, for a close-packed cubic crystal

$$2M = (n/N)\, c^2\, 33.7\, \mathrm{k}^2/a_0^4 \tag{4-9}$$

Here n/N is the atomic fraction of defects, c^2 is the mean square defect strength, a_0 is the edge of the cubic unit cell, and $k = 4\pi \sin\theta/\lambda$, where θ is half the scattering angle and λ is the x-ray wavelength.

Second, he finds a slowly varying background scattering

$$Nf^2(1 - e^{-2M}) \tag{4-10}$$

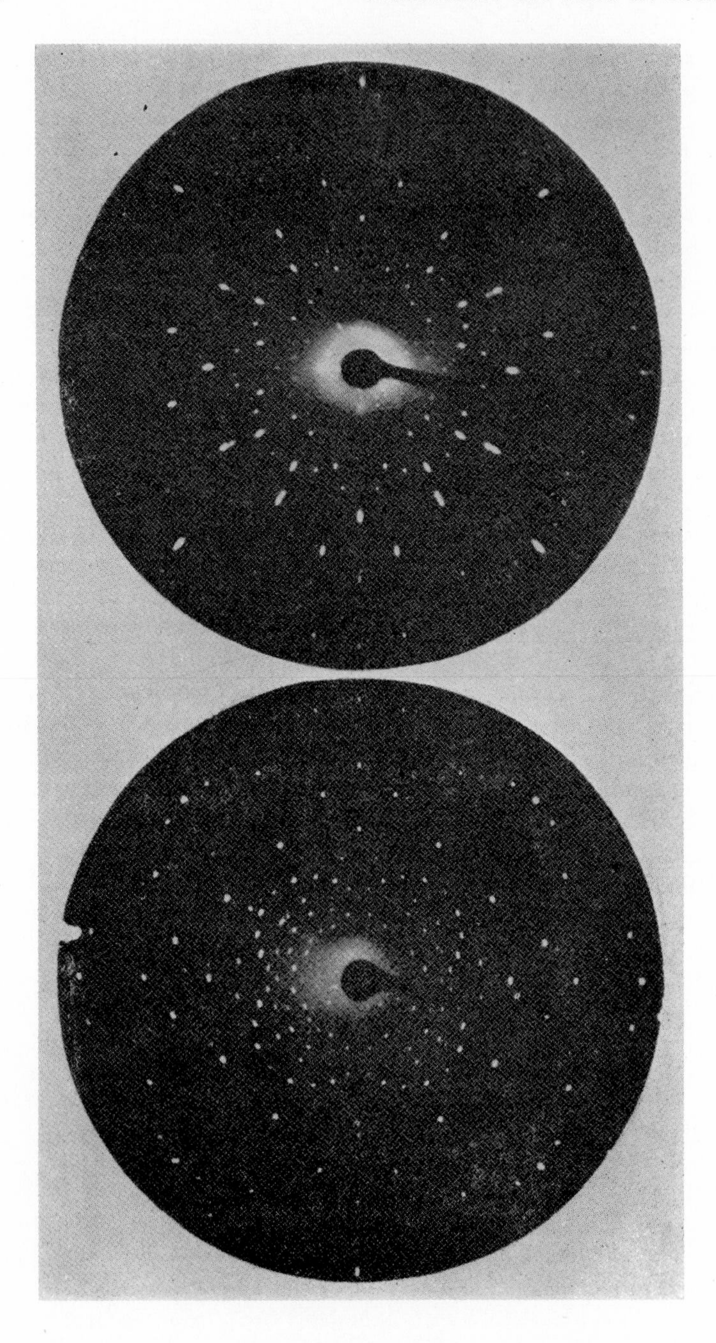

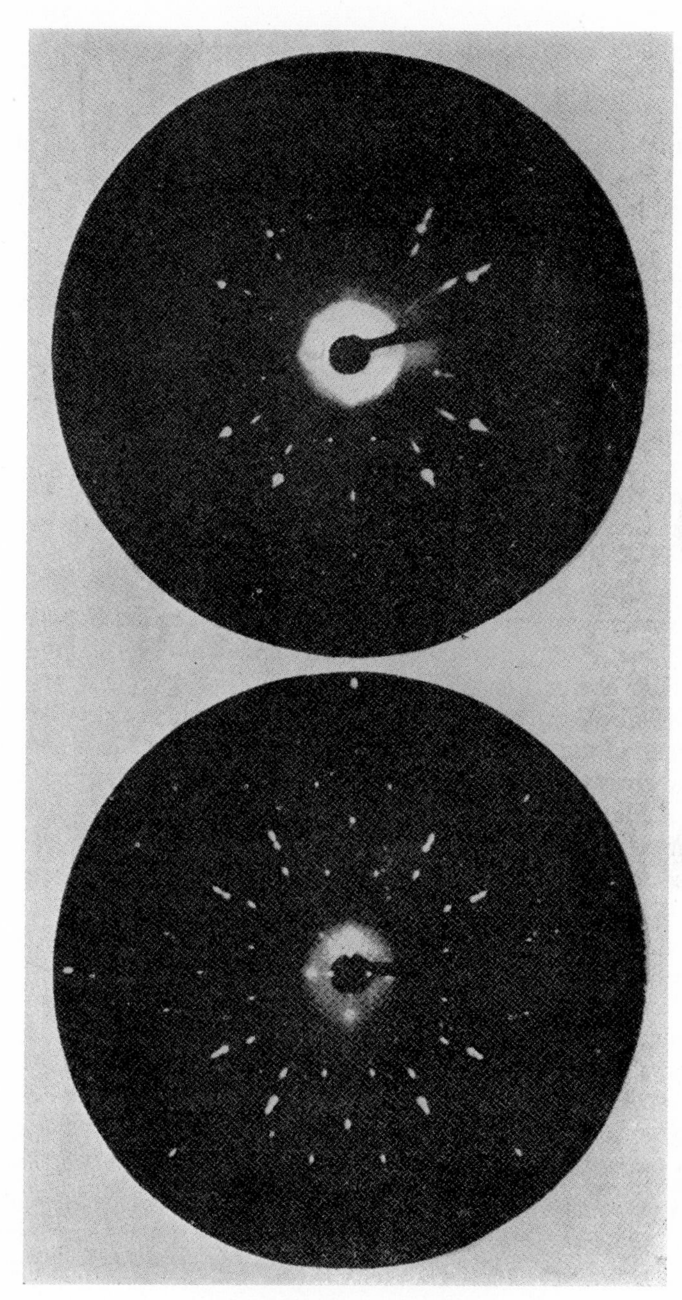

Figure 4.5 Laue transmission patterns of fast-neutron bombarded zircon single crystals (from reference 84).

where N is the number of atoms and f is the atomic structure factor.

Third, there is a characteristic diffuse scattering in the neighborhood of the Bragg directions. This "Huang effect" scattering is distributed around the reciprocal lattice points in the form of a lemniscate whose axis is parallel to the line from the origin to the reciprocal lattice point and whose center is at the reciprocal lattice point. The intensity of this scattering is proportional to c^2* and is rather small in most cases.

The Huang analysis is equally valid whether the pressure centers are on lattice sites or not, and thus there is immediate application to the radiation damage situation, in which the pressure centers are interstitials and vacancies, assumed to be in low concentration and randomly located. It must be remembered, however, that the three effects are superimposed on the previously mentioned effects from scattering centers moved on lattice sites (the interstitials and vacancies themselves) and uniform lattice expansion. The replacement and expansion effects may be considered first-order effects; the Huang distortion effects are in the nature of corrections to these.

Experimental evidence for the Huang effects in irradiated substances is not extensive, although Tucker and Senio (90) have interpreted their observations of irradiated boron carbide in this manner. It should also be mentioned that the Huang analysis predicts no broadening of the Bragg reflections; this rule is obeyed in a number of cases when the irradiations are not too heavy, but there are also some notable exceptions such as LiF (86,93), graphite, and uranium. Peak broadening must occur to some extent whenever a lattice is distorted, and the fact that it is not predicted in Huang theory is apparently due to mathematical approximations in that theory. These approximations are seemingly sound in the cases for which they were designed, namely in which the distortion centers are not too strong, and the physical meaning of this is that the distortion line broadening in such cases is much smaller than the existing line breadth in the crystal. In very heavy irradiations, or in cases where thermal spikes produce large distortion centers of the mobility of the point imperfections allows large clusters of defects to form, the distortions are too large to satisfy the Huang approximations, and observable

*As pointed out by Sampson and Tucker (91) this c^2 and the c^2 in equation 4-9 are *not* to be multiplied by $3(1 - \sigma)/(1 + \sigma)$ as suggested by Eshelby (82). Eshelby's factor should occur only in the lattice expansion terms.

line broadening occurs. It would seem plausible that LiF, graphite, and uranium all possess one or more of these special features.

Finally a brief survey will be given of the diffraction effects found in cases where the Huang or small-distortion type of analysis breaks down. The Oak Ridge observations on zircon crystals reported by Crawford and Wittels (84) included Laue transmission photographs taken after various reactor exposures. Figure 4.5 shows their results. The progressive disruption of the crystal lattice is evident. In the last picture the density of the crystal has been reduced by more than 4%. At this level of damage the higher-angle reflections have disappeared, the inner reflections have broadened, and a pronounced small-angle scattering has become visible. There are also extra reflections in the small-angle region at some stages. Crawford and Wittels interpret these extra reflections as indicating that mosaic blocks in the crystal have been disoriented by more than 3 degrees. The damage is quite stable against annealing at temperatures below 1000° C; annealing above 1600° C considerably reduces the lattice distortion and tends to restore the original diffraction pattern. The diffraction effects shown in Figure 4.5 cannot be adequately explained by isolated atomic centers of strain, such as are involved in the Huang model. Undoubtedly the defects are too numerous and tend to be associated into larger structures. The x-ray information is not sufficient, however, to decide precisely what these structures are.

Similar deterioration in the sharpness of the diffraction pattern has been observed in many other materials at high exposures. Keating's (86) observations of LiF showed pronounced line broadening, which was attributed to lattice strains. The analysis showed rms strains in the vicinity of 0.004 for exposures of about 5×10^{17} neutrons/cm^2 (nvt). The mean strain was only 0.0001, indicating that positive and negative strains occurred in about equal proportions. Also the strains were found to extend over distances of at least 120 A, suggesting again that the damage centers were large.

Graphite also shows pronounced line-broadening effects in addition to the c_0 expansion mentioned above. Figure 4.6 shows profiles of the 002 reflection of graphite after various reactor exposures at about room temperature (87). At exposures up to about 4×10^{20} neutrons/cm^2(nvt) the line shifts progressively without broadening. At higher exposures it commences to be broadened at the base and eventually becomes very diffuse. The explanation apparently involves aggregations of defects, although the details are not yet clear.

Similar effects have been observed in crystalline quartz (84,94) and boron nitride (95). In α-quartz the expansion is highly anisotropic; the change along the a-axis is about a factor of three larger than along the c-axis. One might argue, as in the case of graphite, that this effect is to be expected since the largest interstitial sites are arranged in channels parallel to the c-axis in α-quartz.* The behavior of boron nitride (95) is similar to that of graphite, as might be expected from the similarity in crystal structure. The dimensional

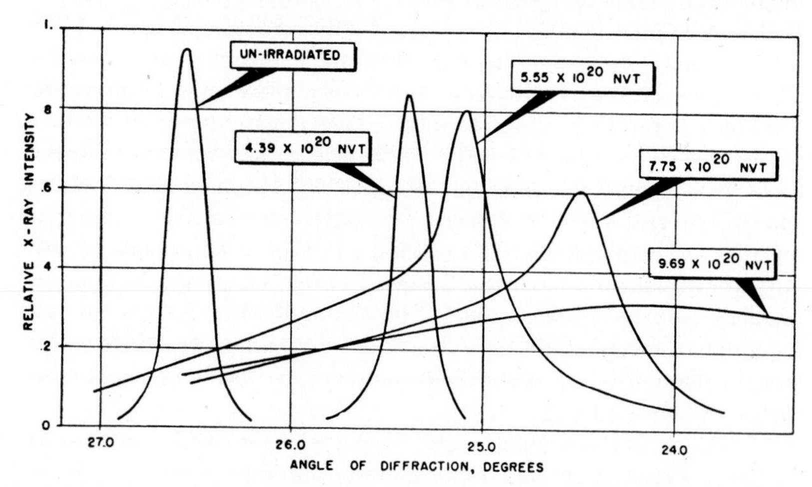

Figure 4.6 X-ray diffraction line shapes for graphite 002 reflection. Irradiation in cooled test holes (from reference 87).

change is anisotropic, with expansion in the c-axis and a much smaller contraction in the a-axis. The main features of the crystal structure remain unaltered even at the high doses because a saturation phenomenon intervenes at a dose corresponding to about 5% interstitials. The dimensional changes show that the atoms are displaced to sites between the layers of the crystal. The saturation of the effect has been attributed to a saturation of the concentration of the interstitial atoms. The saturation is presumably caused by the recombination

*It is of interest to note that while the density of crystalline quartz decreases, that of vitreous quartz increases upon neutron irradiation (96).

of interstitial and vacancies whenever they approach within a critical distance (see Chapter 5 for a detailed discussion of annealing effects).

A particularly striking example of lattice disruption is seen in the case of diamond. Primak (83) and Crawford and Wittels (84) report lattice expansion effects but the maintenance of a high degree of long-range order up to rather heavy levels of irradiation. Levy and Kammerer (97) have made x-ray studies on diamond irradiated in the Materials Testing Reactor to a total exposure of 3.8×10^{20} fast neutrons/cm^2 (nvt) at a temperature not exceeding 65° C. In contrast to the Crawford and Wittels observations, the latter experiments show a highly diffuse diffraction pattern closely resembling that of a typical liquid. Keating (98) has shown that this pattern may be interpreted by assuming about half the atoms have been displaced to interstitial sites and severe lattice distortion has resulted. The level of exposure was about right to have produced this number of displacements. On the other hand the maximum exposure in the Crawford and Wittels experiments was about the same, and yet distinctly crystalline reflections were observed there. The Crawford and Wittels irradiations were carried out in an Oak Ridge reactor (the LITR) under much lower fluxes and with correspondingly longer irradiation times. The temperatures of irradiation in the two cases seem not to have differed significantly. The tentative conclusion is that in diamond a drastic breakup of the crystalline lattice sets in rather suddenly at sufficiently high exposures.

H. Diffusion

It is generally accepted at the present time that diffusion in solids takes place via defects in the crystal, which are primarily vacancies in metals and either vacancies or interstitials in ionic salts (99). Since fast-particle irradiation results in the production of such defects, a close connection between diffusion and irradiation is to be expected. Some aspects of this connection had been discussed by Feldman and Dienes (100), and a full theoretical calculation has been carried out by Lomer (101). The main point is that by means of irradiation a nonequilibrium number of defects can be produced in a crystal, and therefore diffusion rates can be increased in a temperature region where they are normally very low. The diffusion coefficient, D, can be expressed as a function of temperature by the relation

$$D = AC_v e^{-E_m/RT} \tag{4-11}$$

where C_v = atomic fraction of vacancies, E_m = activation energy for motion of a vacancy, and A = constant. In the following it will be assumed that diffusion occurs by means of vacancies. The same general argument is applicable to interstitials or to a combination of the two defects. In equilibrium C_v is given by

$$C_v = A' e^{-E_f/RT} \tag{4-12}$$

where E_f = energy of formation of a vacancy. Under irradiation with fast particles additional vacancies are formed, and at temperatures where diffusion occurs these move about and get annihilated. Under irradiation with a flux ϕ there is thus a steady-state concentration of these vacancies C_v', which depends on ϕ, and supplements the equilibrium concentration C_v. For a diffusion experiment conducted in the presence of radiation these considerations lead to a diffusion coefficient

$$D = Ae^{-E_m/RT}[C_v + C_v'(\phi)] \tag{4-13}$$

Qualitatively, then, one can say the following:

(*a*) At high temperature C_v is larger than C_v' because most of the extra defects are annealing out and the irradiation has a very small effect on D.

(*b*) At low temperature $C_v' > C_v$, and the diffusion coefficient can be increased enormously by irradiation. At low temperatures the temperature dependence will be characterized by E_m alone since all the defects are frozen in and C_i' becomes independent of the temperature.

(*c*) In the intermediate temperature range D will be increased. The temperature dependence will not be purely exponential in $1/T$, since C_v' depends in a complicated way on the temperature because of annealing However C_v' is always less temperature dependent than C_v.

Detailed calculations by Lomer (101) for copper confirm this qualitative picture. His main results are shown in Figure 4.7 where the diffusion length expected in three months in copper is plotted against 1/T under various conditions. The assumed energy parameters are indicated in the figure and both vacancies and interstitials are taken into account, as well as annihilation at trapping sites (fraction $= 10^{10}$) at low temperature where equilibrium concentrations are not valid. Lomer also indicates the practical limits of detection of atom movement in a macroscopic diffusion experiment as well as by indirect techniques such as internal friction. It is quite clear that

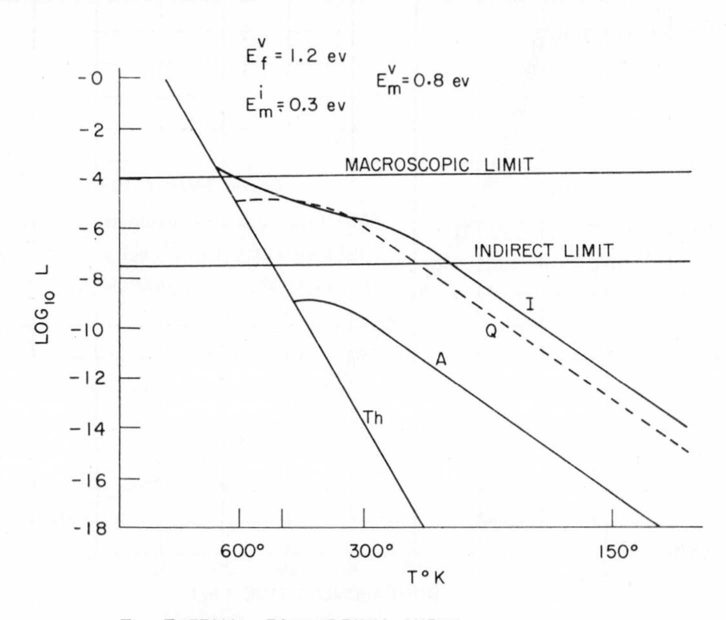

Figure 4.7 The diffusion length L in an experiment lasting three months plotted against temperature for various conditions of copper (from reference 101).

as far as macroscopic diffusion measurements are concerned the expected irradiation effects are practically undetectable, primarily because the defects anneal out too fast.

There is some experimental evidence which supports Lomer's analysis. Johnson and Martin (102) investigated the effect of 10-Mev protons on the self-diffusion of silver in the 525–852° C temperature range by conventional tracer techniques. Their data show no observable effect of proton irradiation, in agreement with the preceding theoretical considerations.

There are some indirect effects of defect motion that do not require that the defect stay in the crystal but depend only on the total number of defect jumps that have occurred. Increased rate of

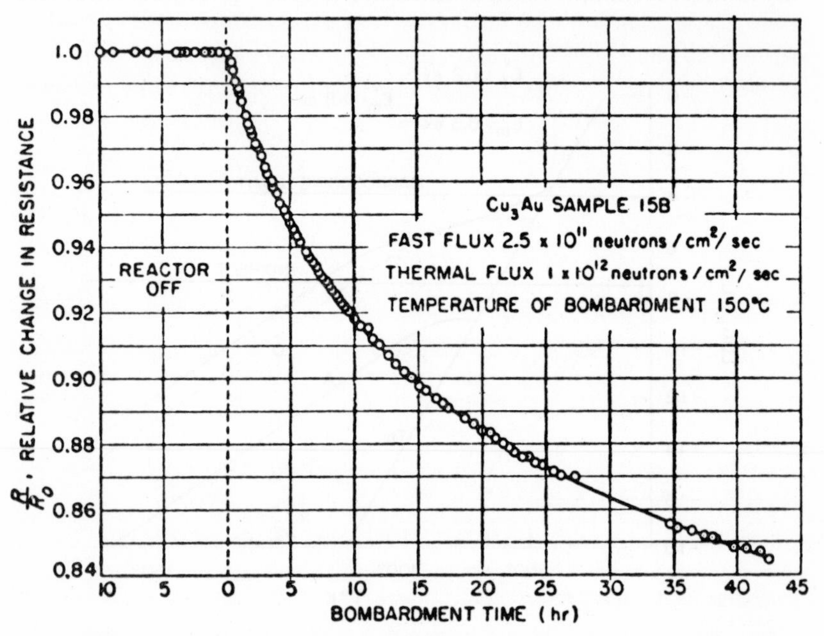

Figure 4.8 The effect of neutron irradiation on the resistance of partially ordered Cu_3Au. The original resistivity was 7.92 $\mu\Omega$-cm. The resistivity of Cu_3Au at equilibrium at 150° C is 5.50 $\mu\Omega$-cm. After 500 hours at a flux of 2.5 × 10^{11} fast neutrons/cm^2/sec and 1 × 10^{12} thermal neutrons/cm^2/sec the resistivity dropped to 5.94 $\mu\Omega$-cm (from reference 105).

ordering in an alloy is such an effect and has been studied in several systems. These studies are described in the following paragraphs as important examples of radiation-induced solid-state reactions.

Adam and Dugdale (103) and Blewitt and Coltman (104,105) were the first ones to observe ordering in an alloy, in this case Cu_3Au, brought about by neutron bombardment. If a disordered specimen of Cu_3Au is irradiated in the reactor at a somewhat elevated temperature, say 150° C, the resistivity decreases and approaches the equilibrium ordered value after a long irradiation. Slight ordering can be achieved even at 80° C (106). A typical curve is shown in Figure 4.8. Thermal ordering at these temperatures is far too slow to be observable. Similar effects have been achieved with 3-Mev electrons (107) and with gamma-rays (108). X-ray measurements proved that the long-range order has been increased as a result of the irradiation (109). The interpretation of these experiments is that the diffusion rate has been increased by the production of vacancies and interstitials during the irradiation. Those defects that are not

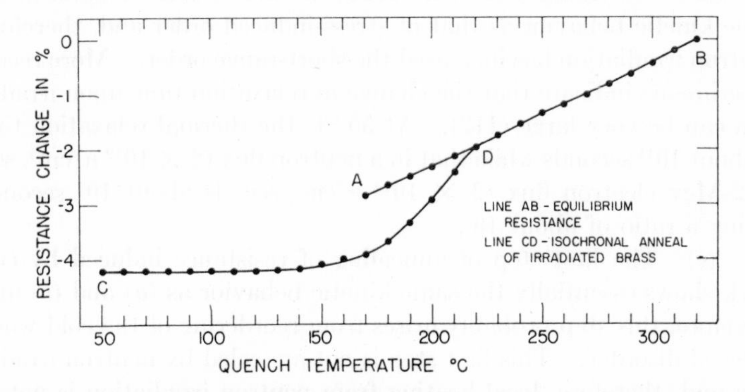

Figure 4.9 Line *AB*, equilibrium resistance quenched from indicated datum point temperature and measured at liquid nitrogen; line *CD*, isochronal anneal (measurements made in liquid nitrogen) of specimen equilibrated at 210° C and irradiated 20 days at 50° C (from reference 111).

immediately annihilated by recombination migrate through the crystal leaving a wake of partial order until they are annihilated or trapped either at dislocation or at severely damaged regions of the lattice. Blewitt and Coltman (105) estimate that, in their irradiation experiment at 200° C with a fast-neutron flux of about 10^{12} neutrons/cm^2/sec, the mean free path of defects before annihilation is of the order of 100 A.

Another set of experiments was performed by Rosenblatt, Smoluchowski and Dienes on α-brass (110). These workers found that reactor irradiation of α-brass at 50° C resulted in a decrease in electrical resistivity, and they interpreted this change as an increase in the short-range order. Damask (111) investigated these resistivity effects in some detail by studying the annealing kinetics of resistance changes produced in 30% Zn α-brass by quench, neutron irradiation at 50° C, and cold work. His studies indicate the following:

(*a*) Resistance decreases in a brass can be induced by proper heat treatment. The rate of change of resistance with annealing time follows the same kinetics as that of stress-induced changes in local order. Thus, the resistance changes arise from changes in short-range order.

(*b*) Reactor irradiation of α-brass at 50° C in an "equilibrium" resistance state produces a decrease in resistance. Some typical data are shown in Figure 4.9. An anneal of this decrease results in the same kinetic behavior as that of stress-induced order and, therefore, neutron irradiation has increased the short-range order. More recent experiments indicate that the change in relaxation time upon irradiation can be very large (112). At 50° C the thermal relaxation time is about 10^{11} seconds while that in a neutron flux (2×10^{12} n/cm²/sec) or 2-Mev electron flux (2×10^{14} e/cm²/sec) is about 10^4 seconds, giving a ratio of about 10^7.

(*c*) The first step of annealing of resistance induced by cold work shows essentially the same kinetic behavior as (*a*) and (*b*) and, therefore, this step probably arises from reordering of the cold-work-induced disorder. This first step is not annealed by neutron irradiation and, therefore, local heating from neutron irradiation is not an important mechanism in changing the state of local order. The defects themselves are ineffective in this case because they are apparently trapped by dislocations introduced by the cold work.

These two sets of experiments fully support the conclusion that local or microdiffusion has been greatly enhanced by the presence of the extra defects produced by fast-particle irradiation.

The intense spike effects produced by neutron irradiation of fissionable materials and heavy metals may also give rise to enhanced diffusion by a mechanism quite different from that discussed in this section. A treatment of this has been given in section 2.6C of Chapter 2.

References

1. F. Seitz, "On the Generation of Vacancies by Moving Dislocations," *Phil. Mag. Suppl.*, **1,** 43 (1952).
2. G. J. Dienes, "Activation Energy for the Diffusion of Coupled Pairs of Vacancies in Alkali Halide Crystals," *J. Chem. Phys.*, **16,** 620 (1948).
3. J. R. Reitz and J. L. Gammel, "Dissociation Energies of the Cd^{++} Vacancy Complex and of the Double Vacancy in Sodium Chloride," *J. Chem. Phys.*, **19,** 894 (1951).
4. J. H. Bartlett and G. J. Dienes, "Combined Pairs of Vacancies in Copper," *Phys. Rev.*, **89,** 848 (1953).
5. A. Seeger and H. Bross, "Electronentheoretische Untersuchungen über Fehlstellen in Metallen," *Z. Physik*, **145,** 161 (1956).
6. K. F. Stripp and J. G. Kirkwood, "Lattice Vibrational Spectrum of Imperfect Crystals," *J. Chem. Phys.*, **22,** 1579 (1954).
7. E. W. Montroll and R. B. Potts, "Effect of Defects on Lattice Vibrations," *Phys. Rev.*, **100,** 525 (1955); *Phys. Rev.*, **102,** 72 (1956).
8. J. D. Eshelby, "The Elastic Interaction of Point Defects," *Acta Met.*, **3,** 487 (1955).
9. C. Y. Li and A. S. Nowick, "Atomic Mobility in a Cu-Al Alloy after Quenching and Neutron Irradiation," *Phys. Rev.*, **103,** 294 (1956).
10. J. W. Kauffman and J. S. Koehler, "The Quenching-in of Lattice Vacancies in Pure Gold," *Phys. Rev.*, **88,** 149 (1952).
11. H. Letaw, Jr., "Thermal Acceptors in Germanium," *J. Phys. Chem. Solids*, **1,** 100 (1956).
12. For a general review of imperfections in crystals see: F. Seitz, "Imperfections in Nearly Perfect Crystals, a Synthesis" in *Imperfections in Nearly Perfect Crystals*, edited by Shockley, Hollomon, Maurer and Seitz, John Wiley and Sons, New York, 1952.
13. D. Bowen and G. W. Rodeback, "The Influence of Cold Work and Radiation Damage on the Debye Temperature of Copper," *Acta Met.*, **1,** 649 (1953).
14. S. Siegel, "Effect of Neutron Bombardment on Order in the Alloy Cu_3Au," *Phys. Rev.*, **75,** 1823 (1949).
15. L. G. Cook and R. L. Cushing, "The Effects of Neutron Irradiation in the NRX Reactor on the Order-Disorder Alloy Cu_3Au," *Acta Met.*, **1,** 539 (1953); **1,** 549 (1953).
16. L. R. Aronin, "Radiation Damage Effects on Order-Disorder in Nickel-Manganese Alloys," *J. Appl. Phys.*, **25,** 344 (1954).
17. R. R. Eggleston and F. E. Bowman, "Radiation Damage of Beta-Brass," *J. Appl. Phys.*, **24,** 229 (1953).
18. K. Lark-Horovitz, "Nucleon Bombarded Semiconductors," *Reading Conference on Semiconducting Materials*, Butterworth's Scientific Publications, London, 1951, pp. 47–78.
19. J. W. Cleland, J. H. Crawford, K. Lark-Horovitz, J. C. Pigg, and F. W. Young, "The Effect of Fast Neutron Bombardment on the Electrical Properties of Germanium," *Phys. Rev.*, **83,** 312 (1951).
20. H. Y. Fan and K. Lark-Horovitz, "Fast Particle Irradiation of Germanium

Semiconductors," *Report of the Bristol Conference on Defects in Crystalline Solids*, The Physical Society, London, 1955, pp. 232–245.

21. See also the review by J. W. Glen, "A Survey of Irradiation Effects in Metals," *Phil. Mag. Suppl.*, **4**, 381 (1955).
22. For a recent review on imperfections in the alkali halides see: F. Seitz, "Color Centers in Alkali Halide Crystals, II," *Rev. Mod. Phys.*, **26**, 7 (1954).
23. J. H. O. Varley, "A Mechanism for the Displacement of Ions in an Ionic Lattice," *Nature*, **174**, 886 (1954); *J. Nuclear Energy*, **1**, 130 (1954).
24. D. Mapother, "Effect of X-ray Irradiation on the Self-Diffusion Coefficient of Na in NaCl," *Phys. Rev.*, **89**, 1231 (1953).
25. C. M. Nelson, R. L. Sproull, and R. S. Caswell, "Conductivity Changes in KCl Produced by γ and Neutron Irradiation," *Phys. Rev.*, **90**, 364 (1953) (A).
26. For a review of this work see: R. Smoluchowski, "Effect of Nuclear Irradiation on Ionic Crystals," *Proceedings of the International Conference on the Peaceful Uses of Atomic Energy*, United Nations, 1956, Vol. 7, p. 676 (Paper No. 748).
27. For a review see: R. Berman, "The Thermal Conductivity of Dielectric Solids at Low Temperatures," *Phil. Mag. Suppl.*, **2**, 103 (1953).
28. R. Berman, P. G. Klemens, F. E. Simon, and T. M. Fry, "Effect of Neutron Irradiation on the Thermal Conductivity of a Quartz Crystal at Low Temperature," *Nature*, **166**, 864 (1956).
29. R. Berman, "The Thermal Conductivities of Some Dielectric Solids at Low Temperatures," *Proc. Roy. Soc.* (*London*), *A***208**, 90 (1951).
30. P. G. Klemens, "The Thermal Conductivity of Dielectric Solids at Low Temperatures," *Proc. Roy. Soc.* (*London*), *A***208**, 108 (1951).
31. R. Berman, E. L. Foster, and H. M. Rosenberg, "The Thermal Conductivity of Irradiated Dielectric Crystals at Low Temperatures," *Report of Bristol Conference on Defects in Crystalline Solids*, The Physical Society, London, 1955, pp. 321–327.
32. P. W. Levy and G. J. Dienes, "Colour Centers Induced in Al_2O_3 by Reactor and Gamma-Ray Irradiation," *Report of Bristol Conference on Defects in Crystalline Solids*, The Physical Society, London, 1955, pp. 256–260.
33. W. W. Tyler and A. C. Wilson, Jr., "Thermal Conductivity, Electrical Resistivity, and Thermoelectric Power of Graphite," *Phys. Rev.*, **89**, 870 (1953).
34. R. Berman, "The Thermal Conductivity of Some Polycrystalline Solids at Low Temperatures," *Proc. Phys. Soc.* (*London*), *A***65**, 1029 (1952).
35. W. K. Woods, L. P. Bupp, and J. F. Fletcher, "Irradiation Damage to Artificial Graphite," *Proceedings of the International Conference on the Peaceful Uses of Atomic Energy*, United Nations, 1956, Vol. 7, p. 455 (Paper No. 746).
36. E. J. Prosen and F. R. Rossini, "Some Experimental Data on the Heats of Combustion of Benzoic Acid and Carbon (Graphite)," *J. Res. Natl. Bur. Standards*, 33, 439 (1944), R. P. 1619.
37. W. Primak, L. H. Fuchs, and P. P. Day, "Radiation Damage in Diamond and Silicon Carbide," *Phys. Rev.*, **103**, 1184 (1956).
38. G. R. Hennig and J. E. Hove, "Interpretation of Radiation Damage to

Graphite," *Proceedings of the International Conference on the Peaceful Uses of Atomic Energy*, United Nations, 1956, Vol. 7, p. 666 (Paper number 751).

39. A. W. Overhauser, "Stored Energy Measurements in Irradiated Copper, *Phys. Rev.*, **94,** 1551 (1954).
40. K. Kobayashi, "Annealing of Irradiation Effects in Sodium Chloride Irradiated with High Energy Protons," *Phys. Rev.*, **102,** 348 (1956).
41. T. H. Blewitt, R. R. Coltman, T. S. Noggle, and D. K. Holmes, "Very Low Temperature Irradiation of Metals; Energy Release at 35°K," *Bull. Am. Phys. Soc.*, II **1,** 130 (1956).
42. For a review of the work in the U.S.S.R. see: V. I. Klimenkov and Y. N. Aleksenko, *Proceedings of the Moscow Conference on the Peaceful Uses of Atomic Energy* (July 1–5, 1955); for a review of the French work see: G. Mayer, P. Perio, J. Gigon, and M. Tournarie, "Modifications Produced in Non-Metallic Materials by Radiation, and the Thermal Healing of these Effects," *Proceedings of the International Conference on the Peaceful Uses of Atomic Energy*, United Nations, 1956, Vol. 7, p. 674 (Paper number 362).
43. G. J. Dienes, "A Theoretical Estimate of the Effect of Radiation on the Elastic Constants of Simple Metals," *Phys. Rev.*, **86,** 228 (1952).
44. F. R. N. Nabarro, "Effect of Radiation on Elastic Constants," *Phys. Rev.*, **87,** 665 (1952).
45. G. J. Dienes, "Effect of Radiation on Elastic Constants," *Phys. Rev.*, **87,** 666 (1952).
46. J. Friedel, "Anomaly in the Rigidity Modulus of Copper Alloys for Small Concentrations," *Phil. Mag.*, **44,** 444 (1953).
47. D. O. Thompson and D. K. Holmes, "Effects of Neutron Irradiation upon the Young's Modulus and Internal Friction of Copper Single Crystals," *J. Appl. Phys.*, **27,** 713 (1956); see also H. S. Sellers, D. A. Powell, E. C. Crittenden, Jr., and E. A. Milne, "Effects of Electron Irradiation on the Shear Modulus and Internal Friction of Copper," *Bull. Am. Phys. Soc.*, II **1,** 379 (1956).
48. D. O. Thompson, D. K. Holmes, and T. H. Blewitt, "Neutron Irradiation Effects Upon Young's Modulus and Internal Friction of Copper," *J. Appl. Phys.*, **26,** 1188 (1955).
49. H. Dieckamp and A. Sosin, "Effect of Electron Irradiation on Young's Modulus," *J. Appl. Phys.*, **27,** 1416 (1956).
50. R. Truell, L. J. Teutonico, and P. W. Levy, "The Detection of Directional Neutron Damage in Silicon by Means of Ultrasonic Double Refraction Measurements," *Phys. Rev.*, **105,** 1723 (1957).
51. F. B. Johnson and R. S. Pease, "The Pile Irradiation of Quartz Crystal Oscillators," *Phil. Mag.*, **45,** 651 (1954).
52. G. Mayer, *Proceedings of the International Conference on the Peaceful Uses of Atomic Energy*, United Nations, 1956, Vol. 7, p. 686–689 (Paper No. 362).
53. For a recent review see: F. Seitz, "Color Centers in Alkali Halide Crystals, II," *Rev. Mod. Phys.*, **26,** 7 (1954).
54. R. A. Dugdale, Unpublished work from Harwell, England, AERE-N/PC-15 (1950).

55. P. Pringsheim and R. C. Voreck, "Farbenzentren in Diamanten," *Z. Physik*, **133,** 2 (1952).
56. P. Pringsheim, "Reversible Bleaching of a Band in the Absorption Spectrum of Diamond," *Phys. Rev.*, **91,** 551 (1953).
57. R. W. Ditchburn, E. W. J. Mitchell, E. G. S. Paige, J. F. Custers, H. B. Dyer, and C. D. Clark, "The Optical Effects of Radiation Damage in Diamond and Quartz," *Report of Bristol Conference on Defects in Crystalline Solids*, The Physical Society, London, 1955, pp. 92–107.
58. A. J. Cohen, "Regularity of the F-Center Maxima in Fused Silica and Quartz," *J. Chem. Phys.*, **22,** 520 (1954).
59. G. W. Arnold, "Color Centers in Synthetic Quartz," *J. Chem. Phys.*, **22,** 1259 (1954).
60. A. J. Cohen, "Impurity Induced Color Centers in Fused Silica," *J. Chem. Phys.*, **23,** 765 (1955).
61. A. J. Cohen, "A Neutron-Specific Color Center in Fused Silica and an Impurity Band of Identical Wave Length," *Phys. Rev.*, **105,** 1151 (1957).
62. G. Mayer and J. Gueron, "Cinetique de la Decoloration de Verres Colors par Irradiation dans la Pile de Chatillon," *J. chim. phys.*, **49,** 204 (1952).
63. E. W. J. Mitchell and E. G. S. Paige, "On the Formation of Color Centers in Quartz," *Proc. Phys. Soc.* (*London*), *B***67,** 262 (1954).
64. M. Levy and J. H. O. Varley, "Radiation Induced Color Centers in Fused Quartz," *Proc. Phys. Soc.* (*London*), *B***68,** 223 (1955).
65. P. W. Levy, "Reactor and Gamma-Ray Induced Coloring in Crystalline Quartz and Corning Fused Silica," *J. Chem. Phys.*, **23,** 764 (1955).
66. J. H. Crawford, Jr. and M. C. Wittels, "Radiation Effects in Crystals," *Proceedings of the International Conference on the Peaceful Uses of Atomic Energy*, United Nations, 1956, Vol. 7, p. 654 (Paper No. 753).
67. T. H. Davies, "A Survey of Recent Irradiation Studies with Glass," *Fourth International Congress on Glass*, Paris, 1956.
68. J. M. Stevels and A. Kats, "The Systematics of Imperfections in Silicon-oxygen Networks," *Philips Research Repts.*, **11,** 103 (1956); A. Kats and J. M. Stevels, "The Effect of U.V. and X-Ray Radiation on Silicate Glasses, Fused Silica, and Quartz Crystals," *Philips Research Repts.*, **11,** 115 (1956).
69. E. W. J. Mitchell and E. G. S. Paige, "The Optical Effect of Radiation Induced Atomic Damage in Quartz," *Phil. Mag.*, **1,** 1085 (1956).
70. M. C. M. O'Brien, "The Structure of the Color Centers in Smoky Quartz," *Proc. Roy. Soc.* (*London*), *A***231,** 404 (1955).
71. A. J. Cohen, "Anisotropic Color Centers in α-Quartz, Part I. Smoky Quartz," *J. Chem. Phys.*, **25,** 908 (1956).
72. E. W. J. Mitchell and E. G. S. Paige, "The Anisotropic Absorption of the Visible Bands in Irradiated α-Quartz," *Phil. Mag.*, **46,** 1353 (1955).
73. J. H. E. Griffiths, J. Owen and I. M. Ward, "Magnetic Resonance in Irradiated Diamond and Quartz," *Report of Bristol Conference on Defects in Crystalline Solids*, The Physical Society, London, 1955, pp. 81–88.
74. J. D. McClelland and J. J. Donoghue, "The Effect of Neutron Bombardment Upon the Magnetic Susceptibility of Several Pure Oxides," *J. Appl. Phys.*, **24,** 963 (1953).
75. M. C. M. O'Brien and M. H. L. Pryce, "Paramagnetic Resonance in Irra-

diated Diamond and Quartz: Interpretation," *Report of Bristol Conference on Defects in Crystalline Solids*, The Physical Society, London, 1955, pp. 88–91.
76. R. A. Weeks, "Paramagnetic Resonance of Lattice Defects in Irradiated Quartz," *J. Appl. Phys.*, **27,** 1376 (1956).
77. A. Pabst, "The Metamict State," *Am. Mineralogist,* **37,** 137 (1952).
78. G. L. Hall, *J. Phys. Chem. Solids* (in press).
79. H. B. Huntington, "Elastic Strains Around an Interstitial Atom," *Acta Met.*, **2,** 554 (1954).
80. H. B. Huntington and F. Seitz, "Mechanism for Self-Diffusion in Metallic Copper," *Phys. Rev.*, **61,** 315 (1942).
81. G. J. Dienes, "A Theoretical Estimate of the Effect of Radiation on the Elastic Constants of Simple Metals," *Phys. Rev.*, **86,** 228 (1952).
82. J. D. Eshelby, "Distortion of a Crystal by Point Imperfections," *J. Appl. Phys.*, **25,** 255 (1954).
83. W. Primak, L. H. Fuchs, and P. Day, "Radiation Damage in Insulators," *Phys. Rev.*, **92,** 1064 (1953).
84. J. H. Crawford, Jr. and M. C. Wittels, "A Review of Investigations of Radiation Effects in Covalent and Ionic Crystals," *Proceedings of the International Conference on the Peaceful Uses of Atomic Energy*, United Nations, 1956, Vol. 7, p. 654 (Paper No. 753).
85. D. Binder and W. J. Sturm, "Equivalence of X-Ray Lattice Parameter and Density Changes in Neutron-Irradiated Li F," *Phys. Rev.*, **96,** 1519 (1954).
86. D. Keating, "X-Ray Measurements of Pile-Irradiated LiF," *Phys. Rev.*, **97,** 832 (1955).
87. W. K. Woods, L. P. Bupp, and J. F. Fletcher, "Radiation Damage to Artificial Graphite," *Proceedings of the International Conference on the Peaceful Uses of Atomic Energy*, United Nations, 1956, Vol. 7, p. 455 (Paper No. 746).
88. R. Simmons and R. Balluffi, "X-Ray Study of Deuteron Irradiated Copper at 12°K," *Bull. Am. Phys. Soc.*, II, **2,** 151 (1957) (A).
89. K. Huang, "X-Ray Reflections from Dilute Solid Solutions," *Proc. Roy. Soc. (London)*, A**190,** 102 (1947).
90. C. W. Tucker and P. Senio, "X-Ray Scattering Effects Due to Localized Static Lattice Defects," *Phys. Rev.*, **99,** 1777 (1955).
91. J. B. Sampson and C. W. Tucker, Jr., "Intensity Distribution of the X-Ray Diffraction Pattern of a Finite Crystal Containing Point Defects," *Phys. Rev.* (in press).
92. B. Borie, "X-Ray Diffraction Effects of Atomic Size in Alloys," *Acta Cryst.*, **10,** 89 (1957).
93. M. Lambert and A. Guinier, "Étude par les diagrammes de diffusion des rayons x du fluorure de lithium irradie," In *Action des rayonnements de grande energie sur les solides* (editor, Y. Cauchois) Gauthier-Villars, Paris, 1956.
94. F. B. Johnson and R. S. Pease, "The pile irradiation of quartz crystal oscillators," *Phil. Mag.*, **45,** 651 (1954).
95. R. S. Pease, "Irradiation Effects in Boron Nitride," *Acta Cryst.*, **7,** 633 (1954).
96. W. Primak, L. M. Fuchs and P. Day, "Effect of Nuclear Reactor Exposure on Some Properties of Vitreous Silica and Quartz," *J. Am. Ceram. Soc.*, **38,** 135 (1955).

97. P. W. Levy and O. F. Kammerer, "Radiation-Induced Amorphism in Diamond," *Phys. Rev.*, **100,** 1787 (1955).
98. D. T. Keating (to be published).
99. For recent reviews of this topic see: F. Seitz, *Phase Transformation in Solids*, John Wiley and Sons, New York, 1951, pp. 77–145; A. D. Le Claire, *Progress in Metal Physics*, Pergamon Press, London, 1953, pp. 265–332.
100. M. H. Feldman and G. J. Dienes, "Silver Self-Diffusion in a Radiation Field," *U. S. Atomic Energy Comm.*, Document NAA-SR-Memo-22 (1951).
101. W. M. Lomer, "Diffusion Coefficients of Copper under Fast Neutron Irradiation," *A.E.R.E.*, Report 1540 (1954). For earlier work see: F. R. N. Nabarro, "Deformation of Crystals by the Motion of Single Ions," in *Strength of Solids*, The Physical Society, London, 1948, pp. 75–90.
102. R. D. Johnson and A. B. Martin, "The Effect of Cyclotron Bombardment on Self-Diffusion in Silver," *J. Appl. Phys.*, **23,** 1245 (1952).
103. J. Adam and R. A. Dugdale, "Some Experimental Work Carried out in Physics with the Larger Harwell Pile," *Nature*, **168,** 581 (1951).
104. T. H. Blewitt and R. R. Coltman, "The Effect of Neutron Irradiation on Metallic Diffusion," *Phys. Rev.*, **85,** 384 (1952).
105. T. H. Blewitt and R. R. Coltman, "Radiation Ordering in Cu_3Au," *Acta Met.*, **2,** 549 (1954).
106. H. L. Glick, F. C. Brooks, W. F. Witzig, and W. E. Johnson, "The Resistivity of Cu_3Au during Neutron Irradiation," *Phys. Rev.*, **87,** 1074 (1952).
107. J. Adam, A. Green, and R. A. Dugdale, "An Effect of Electron Bombardment on Order in Cu_3Au Alloy," *Phil. Mag.*, **43,** 1216 (1952).
108. R. A. Dugdale, "Recent Experiments at Harwell on Irradiation Effects in Crystalline Solids," *Report of the Bristol Conference on Defects in Crystalline Solids*, Physical Society, London, 1955, p. 246; "Some Properties of Vacancies and Interstitials in Cu_3Au," *Phil. Mag.*, **1,** 537 (1956).
109. R. R. Coltman and T. H. Blewitt, "The Effect of Neutron Irradiation on Metallic Diffusion," *Phys. Rev.*, **86,** 641 (1952) (A).
110. D. B. Rosenblatt, R. Smoluchowski, and G. J. Dienes, "Radiation Induced Changes in the Electrical Resistivity of α-Brass," *J. Appl. Phys.*, **26,** 1044 (1955).
111. A. C. Damask, "Some Resistivity Effects of Short Range Order in α-Brass," *J. Appl. Phys.*, **27,** 610 (1956).
112. A. C. Damask, private communication.
113. H. Kanzaki, "Point Defects in Face-Centered Cubic Lattice. I. Distortion around Defects," *J. Phys. Chem. Solids*, **2,** 24 (1957).
114. H. Kanzaki, "Point Defects in Face-Centered Cubic Lattice. II. X-Ray Scattering Effects," *J. Phys. Chem. Solids* (in press).
115. T. J. Matsubara, "Theory of Diffuse Scattering of X-Rays by Local Lattice Distortions," *J. Phys. Soc. Japan*, **7,** 270 (1952).
116. W. Cochran, "Scattering of X-Rays by Defect Structures," *Acta Cryst.*, **9,** 259 (1956).
117. W. L. Kosiba, G. J. Dienes, and D. H. Gurinsky, "Some Effects Produced in Graphite by Neutron Irradiation in the BNL Reactor," *Proceedings of the Conference on Carbon*, University of Buffalo, Buffalo, New York, 1956.

CHAPTER 5

Annealing of Defects

5.1 Introduction

The defects produced by irradiation of a solid are capable of moving about if the temperature is sufficiently high. In this way the damage is altered and eventually annealed out. From low-temperature irradiations it is known that some defects are mobile at surprisingly low temperatures (30° K in common metals) and thus partial annealing even during irradiation is the rule rather than the exception. Furthermore, study of the various annealing processes tests the theories of radiation effects and illuminates the basic properties of defects. Thus controlled studies of annealing are an important part of the field of radiation damage. In this chapter these matters will be discussed and current ideas will be reviewed. Emphasis will be given to experiments that involve simple systems and well controlled conditions so that some theoretical interpretation is possible. The attempt will not be made to give an exhaustive survey of empirical results.

At the outset it should be said that the annealing behavior of irradiated substances is complicated and not yet well understood in even favorable cases. A number of hypotheses have been put forward, but no single interpretation has proved to be entirely satisfactory.

In the first section of this chapter theoretical and experimental information on the mobility of point defects will be reviewed. In the second section theories of the kinetics of annealing processes will be outlined and a variety of possible models will be considered. The third section deals with fundamental experiments and their interpretations in the light of these models. In a final section a practical application in the annealing of the graphite moderator of a reactor will be considered.

5.2 Mobility of Defects

According to the view developed in this book primordial radiation damage consists largely of vacancies and interstitials with a variety of separations. To understand annealing the first question that must be asked is, how mobile are these defects? A few attempts have been made to answer such questions for simple substances by direct calculation.

A. Metals

Huntington and Seitz (1,2,3) have considered vacancies and interstitials in copper, calculating both heats of formation and activation energies of motion. Their calculations were made with the assumption that the *s* and *p* electrons behave as if free, while the other

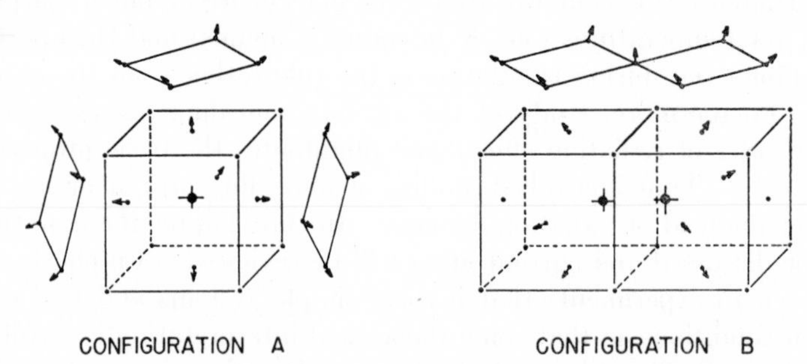

Figure 5.1 Suggested equilibrium configurations of the interstitial in copper (after Huntington, reference 3).

electrons form an ion core that repels other cores according to a Born-Mayer potential. It is found that at equilibrium the vacancy occupies a normal lattice site and has an energy of formation, E_f, of 1.0 to 1.2 ev.* The interstitial, on the other hand, has two conceivable equilibrium configurations, and the calculations are not sufficiently accurate to show which has the lower energy. These are shown in Figure 5.1 as configurations *A* and *B*. Whichever one is stable, the other represents a saddle point in the transition between two successive stable interstitial positions. If an interstitial undergoes diffusion in this type of crystal it does so by successive inter-

*Huntington (2) actually gave 1.8 ev. Brooks (4) and Fumi (5) have pointed out that his result should be modified to the value quoted here.

changes with lattice atoms. Thus a tagged atom that starts as an interstitial will be transferred to a normal lattice site in its first diffusive act, and the configuration, not the specific atom, wanders about. This conclusion is true whether configuration A or B is the more stable. Seitz has designated this form of diffusion "interstitialcy" movement. Huntington's calculations predict a formation energy of 5.1 to 6.1 ev for the interstitial in copper. Although the reliability of these numbers is not high, in view of the approximations made in their derivation, it is unmistakable that thermal fluctuations can form the vacancy far more easily than the interstitial. On the other hand, the same calculations showed that movement is much easier for the interstitial, once it has been formed, than for the vacancy. Huntington estimates the activation energy of movement, E_m, for the interstitial in copper to be between 0.07 and 0.27 ev, and for the vacancy to be in the vicinity of 0.9 or 1.0 ev.

On the basis of these calculations it can be concluded that self-diffusion in copper should proceed by the motion of vacancies. The activation energy for self diffusion, E_d, must be the sum of the formation and motion energies of the defect

$$E_d = E_f + E_m \tag{5-1}$$

This equation allows a cross check with values of E_d determined by diffusion experiments. The presently accepted value (6) of E_d in copper is 2.05 ev, which is seen to be in reasonably good accord with Huntington's values and the assumption of a vacancy mechanism.

Experimental information on activation energies for motion of defects can be gleaned from many sources if needed assumptions are liberally made. Direct and convincing experimental values for these quantities are much less abundant, however. Perhaps the best example is seen in carefully controlled quenching experiments on gold carried out by Koehler and co-workers (7–10). In these experiments fine gold wires are rapidly quenched to room temperature from temperatures in the range 700–900° C. The treatment produces an increase in electrical resistivity which can be annealed out in the vicinity of 60° C. The rapidity of quenching and other considerations lead to the conclusion that the resistivity increase has been caused by isolated vacancies. These vacancies are retained during quenching at the equilibrium concentration appropriate to the upper temperature. By observing the dependence of quenched resistivity on temperature before quenching, one measures the equilibrium concentration of vacancies as a function of temperature. This is found to follow an Arrhenius expression with a formation energy 1.02 ± 0.06 ev. The rate of annealing of this resistivity in the vicinity of 60° C indicates the mobility of the vacancies. The annealing obeys first-order kinetics and shows an activation energy for motion $E_m = 0.66 \pm 0.06$ ev. The sum of E_f and E_m is 1.68 ± 0.12 ev, which agrees very well with the best available activation energy for self-diffusion in gold, measured by radioactive tracers, of 1.71 ± 0.01 ev (11).

Table 5.1. Selected energies of formation (E_f) and motion (E_m) of defects, and energy of self diffusion (E_d) in copper, gold and platinum. Energies in ev

Metal	Defect	E_f	E_m	E_d	References
Copper	Interstitial	5.1–6.1	0.07–0.27		3
Copper	Vacancy	1.0–1.2	0.9–1.0		1,2;4;5
Copper	Di-vacancy	1.5	0.3–0.4		16
Copper				2.05	6
Gold	Vacancy	0.6			5
Gold	Vacancy (presumably)	1.02	0.66		7–10
Gold	Vacancy (presumably)	0.7	0.5		55
Gold				1.71	11
Platinum	Vacancy (presumably)	1.2	1.1		55

Fumi (5) has calculated the formation energies of vacancies in monovalent metals, using approximations similar to those employed by Huntington. The results are admittedly rather unreliable, but Fumi's best estimate for E_f for gold is 0.6 ev. This is somewhat different from the value 1.02 obtained by Koehler. It should finally be mentioned that quenching experiments on gold and platinum have also been reported by Lazarev and Ovcharenko (55), which are in disagreement with the results of Koehler, *et al.* Lazarev and Ovcharenko find, for gold, $E_f = 0.7$ ev, $E_m = 0.5$ ev. These values of E_f and E_m do not add up to the observed activation energy for self-diffusion. In the absence of more complete information on the experimental details than is presently available, they may be regarded as somewhat less reliable than those of Koehler *et al.*

Copper and gold are sufficiently similar in most properties that the characteristic energies under discussion would not be expected to differ very greatly. This argument, together with the experiments of Koehler, lends support to the values calculated by Huntington for copper. Thus in both copper and gold the formation energy for a vacancy will tentatively be assumed to be in the vicinity of 1.0 ev and the energy of movement of a vacancy to be roughly 0.7 ev. The uncertainty in these numbers should not be minimized, however, and it is quite possible that future work will change the picture substantially. The foregoing results are brought together in Table 5.1. Summaries and discussions of present evidence on the mobility of defects in metals have been given by Brooks (4), Broom (12), Fumi (5), Seeger (13), Seitz and Koehler (14), and van Bueren (15).

Little theoretical work exists concerning the mobilities of point defects in metals other than copper and gold. In general one would expect mobilities of a given kind of defect in different metals to be roughly correlated with the melting point. Thus, defects in silver should be about as easily mobile as in copper and gold, those in the alkali metals should have lower activation energies of motion, and those in refractory metals should have somewhat higher energies.

Vacancies and interstitials are expected to interact with one another, although the details of the interaction forces are known in only the sketchiest way. It is easily seen that vacancies have a tendency to congregate, for the formation energy of a vacancy can be roughly understood as the surface energy of a tiny cavity [Brooks (4)], and two vacancies have less surface area when they join to form a di-vacancy. Similarly, larger number of vacancies should also be capable of forming stable aggregates. Bartlett and Dienes (16) have considered the di-vacancy in copper, and calculate from a simplified model that its binding energy should be 0.6 ev, or a little less. They have also examined the mobility of this entity and find that it possesses substantially lower activation energy for motion than a single vacancy, their estimated value being about half that of a single vacancy. From the above considerations this means E_m is roughly 0.3 to 0.4 ev. The elementary jump of a di-vacancy in a face-centered-cubic metal consists in the interchange of one of the vacancies with any one of the four atoms that is a nearest neighbor to both vacancies. It is entirely reasonable that the presence of the second vacancy turns out to make this interchange easier, for it relieves some of the crowding as the atom passes through its saddle point.

The interaction of two point defects at distances large compared to an interatomic spacing depends upon subtle effects. In simplest approximation one defect produces the strain field of a center of pressure in an isotropic elastic continuum (see section 4.2G of Chapter 4). This strain field is dilation free, however, and hence it does not alter the work needed to create a second center of pressure in the medium. Thus in this approximation there is no interaction. If the medium is considered to have cubic symmetry rather than isotropy, an elastic interaction does appear, as Eshelby (17) has demonstrated. The energy of this interaction varies as the inverse cube of the separation of the defects, multiplied by a function depending on the orientation of the pair that is alternately positive and negative, with a zero average. A second elastic model proposed by Eshelby represents the point defect as a sphere of isotropic elastic material of atomic dimensions embedded in an isotropic elastic medium of different moduli. This model gives rise to an interaction depending on the inverse sixth power of the separation, repulsive for two interstitials, attractive for two vacancies, and probably repulsive for a vacancy and interstitial. The actual magnitudes of these interactions are left unsettled by existing calculations. At close separations, nonlinear elastic effects, the atomic nature of the lattice, and the electric charge in and around the defect would be expected to modify these predictions. In addition the spectrum of lattice vibrations is altered by the defects in a way that depends on the separation of the defects, and at low and intermediate temperatures this may alter the free energy of the crystal significantly [Stripp and Kirkwood (18), Montroll and Potts (19,20)]. In simplest approximation, pairs of vacancies are rendered attractive by this effect, as are pairs of interstitials.* On the other hand an interstitial and a vacancy would repel each other. It is impossible at present to combine these diverse pieces of information into a reliable picture of the net interaction of a pair of point defects despite the importance of the question. Experimental

*However, Letaw (30) concludes from annealing experiments with germanium that pairs of vacancies in germanium repel each other at large separations. The theoretical justification for this conclusion has not been supplied.

information is likewise very difficult to interpret with any assurance, and further theoretical developments would be highly useful.

One further kind of defect whose existence has been suggested and which may prove important in radiation effects is the "crowdion." This is an interstitial that has settled in a close-packed line of atoms and crowded these outward for several atom spacings along the line. It can be thought of as a linear region of compression or a sort of one-dimensional edge dislocation. Paneth (49) has suggested that self-diffusion in alkali metals takes place by the motion of crowdions, and has made exploratory calculations of their properties in sodium. Paneth suggests that the extra atom forming the crowdion in body-centered-cubic metals will lie at a $^1/_4$, $^1/_4$, $^1/_4$ position in the unit cell, that is, between nearest neighbors, rather than at a face center, and will spread the atoms along a cube diagonal for a distance of about eight interatomic spacings. His calculations indicate that the energy of formation of a crowdion in sodium is less than 0.3 ev and that the energy of motion is less than 0.1 ev. The most interesting characteristic of a crowdion would be that its easy motion is restricted to one dimension. The alkali metals, because of their open structure and low elasticity, would be the most likely to harbor crowdions, if these defects exist at all, and the prevailing opinion has been that crowdions would not be stable in close-packed metals. However, peculiarities of annealing after irradiation have led recently to suggestions that crowdions do occur in close-packed metals (50,51). No theoretical work has yet been published on the stability of the crowdion in such materials.

It must also be noted that measurements of the pressure dependence of activation energy for self-diffusion in alkali metals are entirely in accord with the vacancy mechanism [Nachtrieb, *et al.* (59)]. This is a good argument that the crowdion has a higher energy of formation than the vacancy, contrary to Paneth's results. However, this does not show whether interstitials formed during irradiation would take up the crowdion configuration or not.

B. *Ionic Crystals*

In ionic crystals, both self-diffusion and conduction of electricity (above room temperature) proceed by the motion of lattice vacancies. These processes have had some theoretical and considerable experimental study, which has produced results of use in understanding radiation effects. Because of the additional grip on the problem afforded by ionic conduction, a little more information on the mobility of point defects is available in the case of ionic crystals than in the case of metals. In general the variation in mobility from one ion to another depends primarily on the sizes of the ions, smaller ions being more mobile as interstitials. Also, vacancies in the lattice of the smaller ions in a salt are somewhat more mobile than vacancies in the lattice of larger ions. Mott and Littleton (21) calculated the activation energy for motion of a sodium vacancy and a chlorine vacancy in rock salt, and found 0.51 ev for the former, 0.56 ev for the latter. Dienes (22) calculated the activation energy for the motion of a neutral vacancy pair in KCl and found 0.38 ev.

Table 5.2. Activation energies for motion of lattice vacancies, E_m, in alkali halides

Substance	Vacancy	E_m(ev)	References
NaCl	Na^+	0.85	23,24
NaBr	Na^+	0.80	25
NaBr	Br^-	1.18	25
KCl	K^+	0.68	24
LiF	Li^+	0.65	26
LiCl	Li^+	0.41	26
LiBr	Li^+	0.39	26
LiI	Li^+	0.38	26

The electrical conductivity of the alkali halides is known to be essentially ionic. At low concentrations of the defect responsible for conduction, the conductivity is proportional to the concentration of defects multiplied by the mobility of defects, the latter being proportional to $T^{-1} \exp(-E_m/kT)$. In pure crystals, the concentration of defects is also temperature dependent, but in crystals doped with a divalent metal impurity such as Cd^{++} a cation vacancy automatically occurs with each divalent ion in order to maintain electrical neutrality, and with the proper doping a constant concentration of cation vacancies can be maintained. The temperature dependence of electrical conductivity in such a crystal then immediately determines E_m. Table 5.2 gives results obtained in this way (supplemented by diffusion measurements in the case of Br^- and K^+).

The experimental value for Na^+ vacancies in NaCl is seen to be somewhat higher than the calculated value of Mott and Littleton, but the ion-size rules are seen to be well obeyed, with the exception of K^+ in KCl, for which E_m seems to be low.

Some data exist on defect mobilities in other ionic substances, particularly silver halides. The reader is referred to Mott and Gurney (27), Seitz (28), and the Bristol conference report (29) for further details.

C. *Semiconductors*

Extensive conclusions concerning the energies of formation and motion of certain defects in germanium have been reached recently by Letaw (30). These are deduced from experiments on self-diffusion and on the alteration of semiconducting properties by quenching and annealing. Letaw presents strong evidence for believing that the acceptor levels which can be introduced into germanium by quenching (thermal acceptors) come from lattice vacancies, and that these defects anneal by the formation of di-vacancies, as a first step, and the gathering of these into larger clusters and the movement to surfaces as a second step. From this, the following energies are deduced:

(1)	Self energy of a vacancy:	2.0 ev
(2)	Self energy of a di-vacancy:	1.1 ev
(3)	Activation energy of motion of a vacancy:	0.96 ev
(4)	Activation energy of motion of a di-vacancy:	2.2 ev
(5)	Activation energy for coalescence of vacancies into di-vacancy:	1.7 ev
(6)	Activation energy for coalescence of di-vacancies into a cluster of four:	2.8 ev

To clarify these results further, it may be stated that (1) and (2) imply a binding energy of the di-vacancy against dissociation into two vacancies, of 2.9 ev; (3) and (5) imply a long-range repulsion between two vacancies giving a barrier against coalescence of about 0.7 ev; (4) and (6) imply a barrier between two di-vacancies of about 0.6 ev. These results should be accepted with some reservations, but form a useful starting point for attempting to understand annealing in germanium, and perhaps to some extent, in other diamond-lattice elements. Unfortunately, the energy and mobility of an interstitial are not provided.

5.3 Theories of Annealing

The process of annealing point defects involves their diffusion in the lattice until they encounter traps, where they are immobilized, or sinks where they are absorbed. Vacancies and interstitials can annihilate each other by combining, or they can be absorbed on surfaces, on grain boundaries, or at jogs in dislocations. Substitutional impurities can trap vacancies and interstitials by virture of their local stress fields. There is also a process whereby an interstitial replaces a substitutional impurity atom, becoming a lattice atom and forcing the impurity to an interstitial position. This tends to occur whenever the impurity is smaller than the normal atom, so that its energy as an interstitial is relatively lower. As a converse to this, an interstitial impurity can unite with a vacancy, becoming substitutional in the process. Finally, there are also the possibilities that vacancies can unite with vacancies and interstitials with interstitials. The former event is more likely, but the latter is believed to occur in some cases, particularly in the annealing of graphite.

In all of these processes there is a close analogy to chemical reactions, although the reaction rate is frequently limited by diffusion, which is less often a consideration in aqueous-phase and gas-phase chemical reactions.* In computing the rates of such processes care is needed in taking proper account of the various steps. Although it is quite impossible to give a thorough treatment of all processes in a short space, consideration will be given in this section to the major processes. The attempt will be made, by the use of simple models, to give the reader a feeling for the characteristics and kinetics of the reactions.

A. Diffusion

The distribution of a particular defect in a crystal can be described by its concentration c at each point $\mathbf{r}$ and time t. The net current density, $\mathbf{j}$, of these defects at any point is given in terms of the gradient of c by Fick's law

$$\mathbf{j} = -D\nabla c \tag{5-2}$$

where D is the diffusion coefficient for the particular defect. In a

*There is, however, a growing literature on diffusion-limited reactions. See in particular Smoluchowski (31,32), Collins and Kimball (33), Noyes (34), Reiss, Fuller, and Morin (35), Reiss (36), and Waite (69).

homogeneous medium free of sources and sinks, this leads to the diffusion equation

$$D\nabla^2 c = \partial c/\partial t \tag{5-3}$$

Equation 5-3, together with initial conditions and boundary conditions, suffices to determine c.

The diffusion coefficient D is proportional to the frequency with which a defect jumps from one site to an adjoining site, ν_J

$$D = \gamma a^2 \nu_J \tag{5-4}$$

Here a is the lattice constant, and γ is a simple numerical factor that depends on the geometry of the lattice and the sites neighboring the defect (37). For interstitial diffusion in a body-centered cubic lattice, for instance, $\gamma = {}^1/_{24}$. For vacancy diffusion in a body-centered or face-centered cubic lattice $\gamma = 1$. The jump frequency ν_J is given by an Arrhenius expression

$$\nu_J = \nu_0 e^{-E_m/kT} \tag{5-5}$$

where E_m is the previously discussed activation energy for motion of the defect in question and ν_0 is an effective frequency. ν_0 can be thought of as approximately the frequency with which the jumping action oscillates in its equilibrium position, and is therefore usually in the vicinity of 10^{13} sec^{-1}. It may be somewhat different from this, and a full definition requires consideration of the many-body aspects of the problem (38). The temperature dependence of D is very pronounced and comes mainly from the exponential in equation 5-5. In the approximation that quantum corrections to rate theory are negligible and all atoms are oscillating at small amplitude, this is the only place in which temperature enters (39).

The simplest annealing problem is that in which defects of one species diffuse to fixed, unfillable sinks. Such sinks can be represented in diffusion theory by surrounding them with imaginary closed surfaces and requiring that the defect concentration be zero on these surfaces at all times. This is a classical problem in diffusion theory, and the general properties of the solution are well known (40). A sufficient account will be given here to display the features important for annealing. Suppose a region R is bounded by various absorbing surfaces S (see Figure 5.2), on which c is required to be zero. For an arbitrarily shaped region R, a set of functions $\varphi_i(\mathbf{r})$ can always be found, such that

$$\nabla^2\varphi_i(\mathbf{r}) + \lambda_i\varphi_i(\mathbf{r}) = 0 \text{ everywhere in } R$$

and

$$\varphi_i = 0 \text{ on the boundaries } S.$$

Here λ_i is a constant and is determined by the size and shape of the region. It will be supposed that the numbers λ_i are labelled in ascending order, $\lambda_0 < \lambda_1 < \lambda_2 < \ldots\ldots$ The infinite set of eigenfunc-

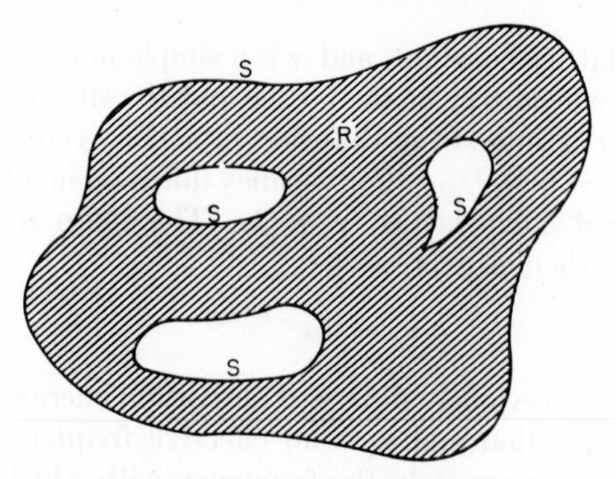

Figure 5.2 A region, R (shaded), in which diffusion takes place. Bounding surfaces, S, are perfect sinks.

tions $\varphi_i(\mathbf{r})$ can be shown to form a complete set and to be orthogonal; they may also be assumed to have been normalized. Thus

$$\int_R \varphi_i(\mathbf{r})\,\varphi_j(\mathbf{r})\,dv = \delta_{ij} \tag{5-6}$$

where the integration is over the region R.

A general solution of the diffusion equation in R with the stated boundary conditions can now be expressed in terms of the eigenfunctions $\varphi_i(\mathbf{r})$. It is

$$c(\mathbf{r}, t) = \sum_{i=0}^{\infty} a_i\,\varphi_i(\mathbf{r})\,e^{-\lambda_i Dt} \tag{5-7}$$

Here the coefficients a_i are determined by the initial concentration distribution, $c(\mathbf{r}, 0)$. With the orthonormality condition of equation 5.6 one finds

$$a_i = \int_R \varphi_i(\mathbf{r})\, c(\mathbf{r}, 0)\, dv \tag{5-8}$$

The concentration at each point, $\mathbf{r}$, and also the total amount of diffusing substance left in R, is seen to decay as a sum of damped exponentials of time, and the diffusion coefficient D sets the scale. Other things being equal, the decay time is always inversely proportional to D. This is a complicated time dependence, not reducible in general to any simple description in terms of orders of reaction. However, after a long enough time the solution does simplify: Since the higher-order terms damp more rapidly they can eventually be ignored, and the concentration thereafter is proportional to a simple exponential. Thus, at large t

$$c(\mathbf{r}, t) \cong a_0\, \varphi_0(\mathbf{r})\, e^{-\lambda_0 D t} \tag{5-9}$$

In many experimental situations this form is valid during the entire course of the observations. This is the time dependence that characterizes a first-order chemical reaction, that is, one in which n, the number of unreacted molecules (or defects) present, changes according to

$$dn/dt = -Kn \tag{5-10}$$

where K is a rate constant, independent of n. This equation gives $n \sim e^{-Kt}$, and comparison with equation 5–9 shows that the effective first-order rate constant in the asymptotic form of the diffusion-limited reaction is

$$K = \lambda_0 D \tag{5-11}$$

The time required to reach the asymptotic form of equation 5-9 depends on the higher eigenvalues $\lambda_1, \lambda_2, \ldots$ and also the initial concentration distribution, $c(\mathbf{r}, 0)$. If the initial concentration is uniform, the asymptotic form is reached sooner than if it is highly localized, and if the initial concentration happens to coincide with $\varphi_0(\mathbf{r})$ the asymptotic form is valid from the beginning. A useful rough measure of the time to reach the asymptotic distribution is $(\lambda_1 D)^{-1}$, and since λ_1 is ordinarily something like $2\lambda_0$, $(\lambda_0 D)^{-1}$, which equals K^{-1}, will also serve to measure this time.

If some surfaces are present that reflect all the diffusing defects instead of absorbing them, the foregoing methods apply with the modification that, on the reflecting surface

$$\partial c/\partial n = 0 \tag{5-12}$$

rather than $c = 0$. By $\partial c/\partial n$ is meant the component of the gradient of c normal to the surface. The eigenfunctions φ_i must then be chosen to have $\partial \varphi_i/\partial n$ zero on these surfaces.

An intermediate situation can also occur. It may be that on some surfaces partial reflection of impinging defects occurs. If a fraction r of the defects jumping from sites nearest to the surface are reflected back while the remainder penetrate the surface and become absorbed, it is necessary to require that

$$(1/c)\partial c/\partial n = (1 - r)/a^* \tag{5-13}$$

everywhere on the surface. a^* is the normal component of the vector jump displacement of the defects that cross the surface. Equation 5-13 reduces to equation 5-12 when the reflectivity r is unity, and goes to the very large value $1/a^*$ when $r = 0$ (perfect absorption). This is not quite the same as the requirement that $c = 0$ on the surface but is actually more accurate, being the same as the requirement from transport theory that c vanish a little behind the surface.* The application of the preceding methods then requires that each eigenfunction φ_i also satisfy equation 5-13. No other change is required, even when r and a^* vary from one point to another on the bounding surfaces.

Simple geometrical shapes permit ready treatment by these methods, and a few useful results will be collected here. Consider a crystal containing no sinks except its external surface, which will be regarded as perfectly absorbing. If the crystal is compact and of linear dimension L, λ_0 will always be of the order $1/L^2$, giving by equation 5-11 the asymptotic decay constant

$$K \cong D/L^2 \tag{5-14}$$

In fact, for a sphere of radius R, one finds

$$K = \pi^2 D/R^2 \tag{5-15}$$

and for a rectangular parallelopiped of dimensions A by B by C

$$K = \pi^2(1/A^2 + 1/B^2 + 1/C^2)D \tag{5-16}$$

From this follows the important corollary that if one dimension is

*See the discussion of boundary conditions in diffusion in section 2.4 of Morse and Feshbach (41).

much smaller than the others, the small dimension dominates in determining K.

If the crystal contains internal sinks the surface may be unimportant. Consider the case in which fixed spherical sinks, clusters of vacancies for instance, each having radius r_0, are distributed at random in an infinite crystal. If the crystal is divided into imaginary cells such that one sink lies in each cell and near its center, the concentration of defects will have nearly a zero gradient on the surface of each cell. Idealizing further, each cell can be considered spherical with the spherical sink precisely at its center. Let r_1 be the radius of the average sphere, and suppose $r_1 \gg r_0$. One can now treat the much simpler diffusion situation in one sphere and apply the boundary condition of perfect reflection at the outer surface (r_1) and perfect absorption at the concentric inner surface (r_0). Solving this problem, one finds

$$K \cong (3r_0/r_1^3)D = 4\pi r_0 N_0 D \text{ (concentric spheres)} \qquad (5\text{-}17)$$

where N_0 is the number of traps per unit volume.

Finally, as has been noted, dislocations, are sinks for point defects, and a random distribution of dislocations in a large crystal will now be considered. Suppose each dislocation is represented by an absorbing circular cylinder of radius r_0 and infinite length, and there are N_0 dislocation lines per unit area in the crystal. Partitioning the crystal in a manner analogous to that used in the case of spherical sinks, one is left with the problem of diffusion between concentric circular cylinders, the outer cylinder being a perfect reflector and having radius r_1, where $\pi r_1^2 = 1/N_0$. The decay constant works out to be, assuming again $r_1 \gg r_0$

$$K \cong 2\pi N_0 D/\ln (r_1/r_0) \text{ (concentric cylinders)} \qquad (5\text{-}18)$$

Diffusion to a dislocation at intermediate temperatures may be strongly influenced by the stress field of the dislocation. Under these conditions the foregoing considerations are inadequate. Cottrell and Bilby (70) consider this problem and show that if the imperfections are uniformly distributed about an edge dislocation at $t = 0$, and have a drift velocity proportional only to the gradient of the stress-induced potential energy, the number of imperfections collected by the dislocation at time t is proportional to $t^{2/3}$. This result is not comparable simply with equation 5-18 because the equation allows for only one dislocation in an infinite region.

B. *Recombination of Vacancies and Interstitials*

Interstitial atoms can unite with vacancies to annihilate both defects. Let it be assumed, following the discussion of the preceding section, that interstitials are much more mobile than vacancies. Each vacancy is thus a fixed center in which diffusing interstitials can be captured. The vacancy differs from the inexhaustible traps just discussed, however, for it can receive only one interstitial. An understanding of the process can be gained from the following simple considerations.

Suppose a vacancy is surrounded by z interstitial sites that have the property that an interstitial on any one of these sites has a jump frequency ν_J' for jumping toward the vacancy, and a jump toward the vacancy means certain annihilation. It would be expected that $z \cong 10$, but its exact value will be left unspecified. Situations can be imagined in which short-range attractive forces exist and any interstitial coming within a distance many times larger than a lattice spacing will be captured. In such cases $z \gg 10$. Let there be n_v vacancies per unit volume and n_I interstitials per unit volume at any time t. Let the volume per lattice site be v and the probability that any one of the z sites around a vacancy contains an interstitial be p_I. Then consideration of the average rate of annihilation of vacancies leads to the equation

$$-dn_v/dt = \nu_J' z p_I n_v \tag{5-19}$$

The simplest approximation with which the matter may be further developed is to assume that the interstitials are randomly distributed in the beginning and that diffusion continually redistributes them as they are absorbed. Thus the sites bordering an unreacted vacancy will first be assumed to contain precisely the over-all average concentration of interstitials; that is, it will be assumed that

$$p_I = v n_I \tag{5-20}$$

It is to be emphasized that the starting approximation of equation 5-20 and the modifications to be discussed in the next four paragraphs could only be valid if the initial distribution of interstitials was not highly correlated with the distribution of vacancies. If a displaced atom has high energy it comes to rest at a site far from its point of origin and thus uncorrelated with it. This is approximately the case in fast-neutron bombardment; also, in very heavy irradiations so many displacements are created that damage regions from various primary collisions overlap, and again correlation disappears. On the other hand, if electron bombardment is employed and the exposure is not too high, each interstitial will commence life at a site near one vacancy and far from the other vacancies. This case requires special discussion and will be taken up later.

Use of the approximation of equation 5-20 with equation 5-19 leads to simple kinetics for the combination reaction. If the initial concentrations of vacancies and interstitials were n_v^0 and n_I^0, respectively, at any time

$$n_v^0 - n_v = n_I^0 - n_I \tag{5-21}$$

and one finds

$$-dn_v/dt = \nu_J' z v(n_i^0 - n_v^0 + n_v)n_v \tag{5-22}$$

If $n_I^0 \gg n_v^0$, this gives first-order kinetics, but if $n_I^0 = n_v^0$, the usual situation with radiation induced defects, equation 5-22 gives second-order kinetics for recombination. The jump frequency ν_J' is given by an Arrhenius expression similar to equation 5-5, except that the activation energy, E_m', may be somewhat different from that for motion at a distance from other defects.

In actuality the sites around an unreacted vacancy are rather special, and it is never quite true that they remain occupied with interstitials in a purely random way, even when that is the starting distribution. If the vacancy sites were inexhaustible sinks, the foregoing discussion of diffusion into a point sink could be utilized, and it would be clear that the interstitial concentration near the vacancy would be depressed, as soon as motion commences, compared with that at a distance. The exhaustible character of the vacancy as a sink complicates the calculation. It is still true that the interstitial concentration is depressed near the vacancy, but it is depressed by a more moderate factor, and this factor rises toward unity as time passes and the vacancy achieves a higher probability of being filled. A full quantitative discussion becomes intricate, and, because of the speculative nature of the parameters on which it hinges, will not be presented here. A depression factor, f, which depends on n_v and increases toward 1 as n_v approaches zero is needed on the right-hand side of equation 5-22. The importance of the depression factor is increased if $\nu_J' > \nu_J$, and is diminished if $\nu_J' < \nu_J$. That is to say, if there is an abnormally high energy barrier against jumping into the vacancy from the surrounding sites ($E_m' > E_m$), most of the interstitials approaching the vacancy are reflected away again, and there is little correlation between their positions and those of the vacancies. As a consequence $f \cong 1$ for all n_v, and the assumption of second-order kinetics becomes justified. In the more general case second-order reaction kinetics is only an approximation, possibly a poor one.

In case both defects are mobile at the same time the qualitative behavior is as before. Quantitatively, the discussion must be altered to consider the density of one type of defect at various distances about a defect of the other type, rather than about a fixed site, and the jump frequency ν_J' must be replaced by the sum of the jump frequencies of each type of defect, say $\nu_{JI}' + \nu_{Jv}'$.

The problem of the coagulation of vacancies into di-vacancies or of interstitials into trapped pairs of interstitials, if these are stable, can also be treated by the foregoing methods.

It has been mentioned that electron bombardment near threshold produces closely spaced interstitial-vacancy pairs, and that this starting situation requires special treatment. A discussion of the problem has been given by Fletcher and Brown (42) in connection with the experiments on germanium of Brown, Fletcher, and Wright (43). Fletcher and Brown choose to divide the annealing process into three stages. The first stage involves the recombination of pairs with nearest neighbor separation (r_0) and is a simple first-order process. In the second stage pairs with slightly greater separation recombine. This can be treated on the basis of diffusion theory, or more accurately and much more laboriously, as a problem in random walks on a lattice. In this stage the mobile defect either recombines with its neighboring sink or diffuses away never to return. If n_0 defects start out at a distance r_i from the center of a perfect sink of radius r_0 in an infinite isotropic medium, and move independently according to the diffusion equation, the number n remaining after a time t can be shown to be

$$n = n_0 \left[1 - \frac{r_0}{r_i} + \frac{r_0}{r_i} \operatorname{erf} \left(\frac{r_i - r_0}{2\sqrt{Dt}} \right) \right] \tag{5-23}$$

where erf (x) is the error function

$$\text{erf}\,(x) = \frac{2}{\sqrt{\pi}} \int_0^x e^{-x^2}\, dx$$

From this solution it is seen that the fraction of the defects starting at r_i that wander away to participate in the third stage is $(1 - r_0)/r_i$. Fletcher and Brown also present lattice random walk calculations for some particular cases. These show that the diffusion approximation gives a reasonably good fit to the random walk calculations if the parameters r_i and r_0 are modified slightly. In the third stage those defects that have wandered away from their original partners diffuse about until they recombine with more distant defects. This stage is assumed to follow simple second-order kinetics, which in view of the foregoing remarks, is also an approximation.

Suppose now that n, the number of defects of a particular kind per unit volume present at time t, obeys a differential equation of the type

$$-dn/dt = K\,f(n) \tag{5-24}$$

where K is a rate constant and $f(n)$ may be any of a wide variety of functions. If $f(n) = n^\gamma$, where γ is a constant, the reaction is said to be of order γ. From the preceding considerations it is reasonable to suppose that $f(n)$ is at least a monotonically decreasing function of n, and to assume that K has the form $K_0e^{-E/kT}$, where K_0 is a constant and E is an activation energy. In many experiments an irradiated sample is gradually warmed and the number of defects (or a physical property assumed to be proportional to this number) is observed during the course of the warming. Because of the exponential dependence of K on temperature, dn/dt is very small during the low-temperature stages, then grows rather suddenly, and within a small temperature range in the vicinity of a characteristic annealing temperature T_a virtually all of the defects of this species disappear. The characteristic temperature is such as to make dn/dt appreciably large, that is $K(T_a)$ is in the vicinity of unity. Since K_0 is usually rather large, T_a is usually much less than E/k. With assumptions about the magnitude of K_0 and the form of $f(n)$, observation of T_a allows a fairly precise determination of the activation energy E, and as has been shown this is a most important characteristic of the defects.

To see how this determination can be made and to examine the nature of simple annealing more closely, a special case will now be treated. Suppose the temperature is brought up from absolute zero at a constant rate, so that $T = \alpha t$, where t is the time since the start of the experiment and α is a constant. It is convenient to express the activation energy E in terms of an equivalent temperature T_0, where

$$kT_0 = E \tag{5-25}$$

The warming rate can best be specified in terms of the time τ required for the temperature to rise to T_0

$$\tau = T_0/\alpha = E/k\alpha \tag{5-26}$$

Changing the independent variable from time to temperature and introducing the parameters τ and T_0, the governing equation 5-24 can be written

$$dn/f(n) = -K_0\tau e^{-T_0/T}\, dT/T_0 \tag{5-27}$$

The solution of this can be expressed with the aid of the exponential integral (44),

$$Ei(-x) = \int_{-\infty}^{-x} \frac{e^x}{x}\, dx \tag{5-28}$$

Letting n_0 be the value of n at $t = 0$, one finds

$$\int_{n_0}^{n} \frac{dn}{f(n)} = -K_0\tau \left[\frac{T}{T_0} e^{-T_0/T} + Ei\left(-\frac{T_0}{T}\right)\right] \tag{5-29}$$

For reaction of order γ the integral on the left can be taken and a solution $n(T)$ can be found.

K_0 is an effective frequency, the frequency of defect vibration ν_0 multiplied by factors taking account of the number of jumps needed for removal of the defect. $K_0\tau$ is then the number of such "effective vibrations" of a defect in a complete warmup period from 0 to temperature T_0, and can be assumed to be very much larger than 1, say from 10^7 to 10^{17} in likely cases. It then turns out that $T/T_0 \ll 1$ during the greatest part of annealing, and the approximation (44)

$$Ei(-x) \cong e^{-x}(1/x^2 - 1/x) \tag{5-30}$$

valid for $x \gg 1$, can be used to simplify equation 5-29. Assuming now, for definiteness, that the reaction is one of first order, $f(n) = n$, one finds from equations 5-29 and 5-30

$$\ln (n/n_0) \cong -K_0\tau\, (T/T_0)^2\, e^{-T_0/T} \tag{5-31}$$

This is an important result showing the explicit course of the annealing and its dependence on the parameters T_0, K_0 and τ. The

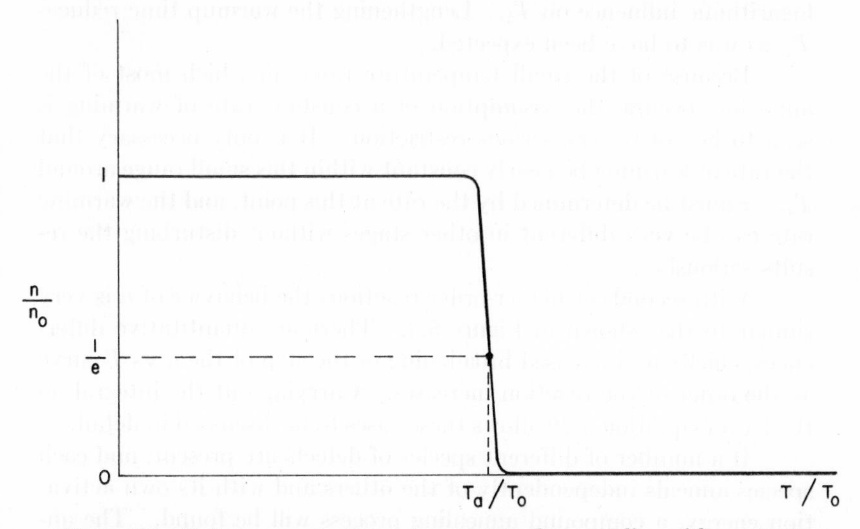

Figure 5.3 Defect concentration *vs* temperature for annealing with constant rate of warming. First-order kinetics assumed. $T_0 = E/k$, where E is the activation energy of the reaction. T_a is given by equation 5-33.

resulting curve of n/n_0 vs T/T_0 is shown in Figure 5.3. The abrupt drop in n/n_0 from 1 to 0 is seen in the figure. There is an inflection point in the curve and this is also the point at which $n/n_0 = e^{-1}$. The temperature at the inflection will be labelled T_a. T_a satisfies the equation (valid independently of the assumption that $K_0\tau$ is large)

$$1 = K_0\tau(T_a/T_0)^2 e^{-T_0/T_a} \tag{5-32}$$

This has the approximate solutions

$$T_a/T_0 \cong 1/[\ln (K_0\tau) - 2 \ln \ln (K_0\tau)] \tag{5-33}$$

$$\cong 1/[\ln (K_0\tau)] \tag{5-33a}$$

Equation 5-33 is accurate to within 2 or 3 per cent, the simpler equation 5-33a is good to about 15 per cent in typical cases. The width of the step in the n vs T curve is something like 0.05 T_a. If $K_0\tau = 10^7$, a low value, $T_a/T_0 = 0.087$; if $K_0\tau = 10^{12}$, $T_a/T_0 = 0.046$; and if $K_0\tau = 10^{17}$, a high value, $T_a/T_0 = 0.030$. The variation of T_a with $K_0\tau$ is very slow, but because of the large range that $K_0\tau$ may cover, is not to be ignored. The warmup time τ is seen to have a logarithmic influence on T_a. Lengthening the warmup time reduces T_a, as was to have been expected.

Because of the small temperature range in which most of the annealing occurs, the assumption of a constant rate of warming is seen to be not a very serious restriction. It is only necessary that the rate of warming be nearly constant within this small range around T_a. τ must be determined by the rate at this point, and the warming rate can be very different in other stages without disturbing the results seriously.

With second- or higher-order reactions the behavior of n is very similar to that shown in Figure 5.3. There are quantitative differences, chiefly an increased broadening of the step of the n vs T curve as the order of the reaction increases. Carrying out the integral on the left of equation 5-29 allows these cases to be discussed in detail.

If a number of different species of defects are present, and each species anneals independently of the others and with its own activation energy, a compound annealing process will be found. The annealing curve will be a superposition of curves of the type of Figure 5.3, each weighted according to the number of defects of the species initially present and the physical effectiveness of one defect. It is to be understood that when one kind of defect, e.g., interstitials, has a variety of sites in which it is partially trapped, with a variety of activation energies for removal, these may be counted as a variety of species. With a small number of species, well separated in activation energies, a series of steps will be resolved during slow warming. If many species are present the result will be a gradual change in physical properties over a large temperature range and it will be difficult to draw quantitative conclusions. Vand (45) and Primak (46) have given thoughtful discussions of these matters, and the mathematical and experimental difficulties will be appreciated upon consulting their papers. Unfortunately many irradiated substances show just this kind of broad-range annealing. Furthermore, the value of K and the exact nature of the function $f(n)$ for each species is usually unknown or uncertain.

In the case of consecutive reactions, where species A anneals to form species B, which anneals to species C, etc., still more complicated considerations are necessary. These will not be taken up here.

If it can be assumed that a reaction follows an equation of the type of equation 5-24 with K given by an Arrhenius expression, it is possible to find the activation energy in at least three distinct ways without knowing anything about the form of $f(n)$. Parkins, Dienes, and Brown (56) have given a method for doing this by observing the inflection point T_a in the warming curve, at two different rates of warming. A second method is to observe n as a function of time at constant temperature. The time to decay to a given value of n during an anneal at temperature T_1 is measured. Let this time be t_1. The time t_2 for an identical specimen to decay to the same value of n during an anneal at temperature T_2 is also measured. Because Kt can be adopted as the independent variable in equation 5-24 it can be seen that

$$K(T_1)/K(T_2) = t_2/t_1 \tag{5-34}$$

This, with the assumption $K(T) = K_0 e^{-E/kT}$ allows the determination of E. It is to be noted that it is not actually necessary to measure n, but only a physical property dependent on n in a temperature-independent way.

In the third method annealing is carried out for a time at constant temperature, and then the temperature is suddenly altered and held constant again at a new value. Let the two temperatures be T_1 and T_2, and the annealing rates just before and just after the temperature changes be $(dn/dt)_1$ and $(dn/dt)_2$, respectively. Because the change is sudden, n is the same just before and just after, and so

$$(dn/dt)_1 = -K(T_1)\,f(n)$$
$$(dn/dt)_2 = -K(T_2)\,f(n)$$

Taking the ratio of these equations, $f(n)$ cancels, and the ratio of the rate constants at two temperatures is again determined.

$$K(T_1)/K(T_2) = (dn/dt)_1/(dn/dt)_2 \tag{5-35}$$

From the discussion presented in these sections it should be clear that the function $f(n)$ governing the annealing of point defects, even with a single activation energy for diffusion, may take a variety of forms, and factors such as the initial distribution of defects, the distribution and character of traps, and the barrier against recombination, or lack of it, influence $f(n)$ decidedly. Diffusion-limited reactions with inexhaustible sinks have a time dependence which is a sum of exponentials; asymptotically this becomes a first-order reaction, but at short and intermediate times it simulates one of variable order. Kinchin and Pease (57, section 3-1-1) show calculations on two-dimensional diffusion, such as would occur in layered structures, in which the isothermal annealing over a wide range is approximated by a reaction of sixth order. It has been suggested by Overhauser (47) that the activation energy for movement of radiation-induced defects may depend appreciably on the concentration of defects; this introduces a further factor exp $(\alpha n/kT)$ on the right of equation 5-24, and, as has been shown by Dienes (58), a reaction of low order with this modification simulates a reaction of different (and higher) order. It has become quite usual in reporting isothermal annealing data to determine an order of reaction that fits the results. However, the authors feel that extreme caution should be used in drawing conclusions about the mechanism of an annealing process from the apparent order of the reaction.

5.4 Fundamental Experiments

In this section a selected set of annealing experiments will be discussed. The experiments have been chosen on the basis of their fundamental significance and in order to show representative annealing effects in simple irradiated substances. No attempt will be made to exhaust the voluminous literature that has accumulated in this field. The case of pure metals is treated first.

A. Annealing in Metals

As has been noted, the earliest annealing stages occur at surprisingly low temperatures, and in only a small number of cases have irradiations been done at temperatures where no annealing occurs. Blewitt, Coltman, Holmes, and Noggle (51) have irradiated a number of metals at 20° K in the Oak Ridge graphite reactor. Observations have been made of the electrical resistivity during irradiation and upon subsequent annealing. Figure 5.4 shows some of the results.

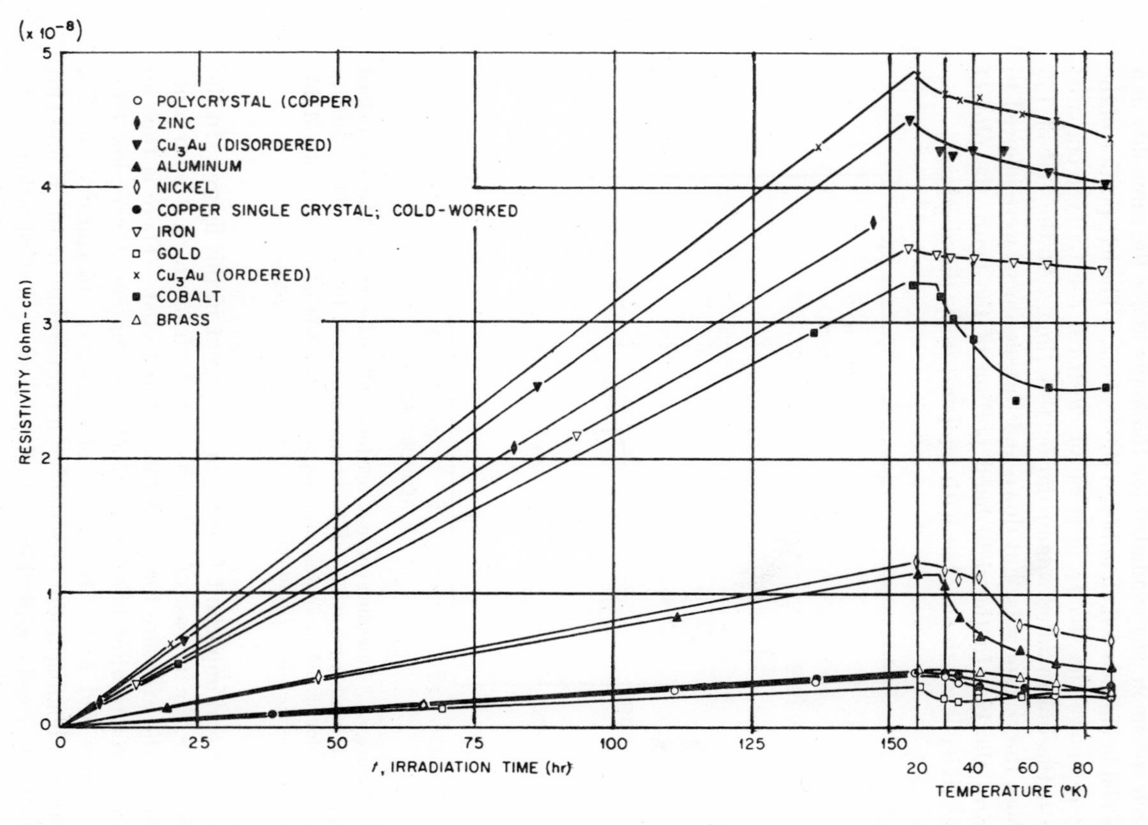

Figure 5.4 Effect of neutron bombardment on resistivity of several metals. Left part shows incremental resistivity *vs* irradiation time at about 20° K. Right part shows incremental resistivity *vs* temperature as specimens are warmed after irradiation (from reference 51).

Each specimen was irradiated for 155 hours under the same flux in a special helium-cooled chamber in the reactor. The left portion of the figure shows the steady increase of electrical resistivity (compared with the unirradiated value) during this time. At the end of 155 hours the reactor was shut down and the specimens were allowed to warm slowly. In the right-hand portion of the figure the plot of resistivity is continued, but with temperature as the abscissa.

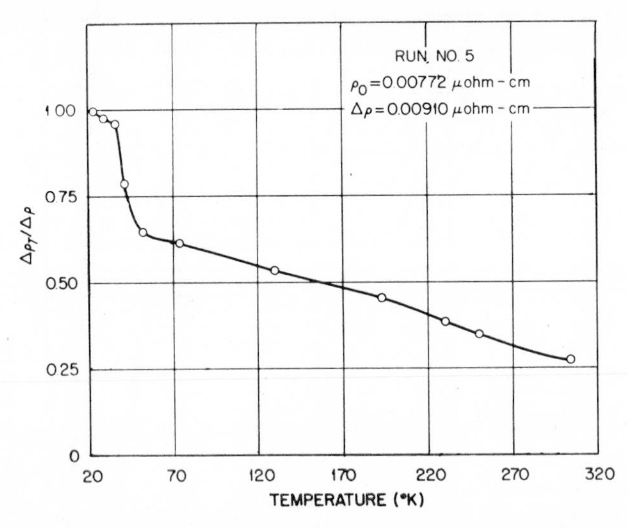

Figure 5.5 Annealing curve of reactor-irradiated copper. The zone-refined copper was bombarded at 17.5° K to an exposure of 8×10^{17} nvt. The resistivity at each point on the curve was measured at 14° K following a 3-min. pulse at this indicated temperature (from reference 51).

Several important features are apparent in this figure. In the first place, the increase of resistivity is, to high accuracy, a linear function of the exposure for all of the metals tested. There is thus no radiation annealing effect with reactor irradiation at very low temperatures and within this range of exposure. In contrast to this, deuteron bombardment of copper at a temperature of 10° K and also at 78° K causes radiation annealing, that is, a diminution in the rate of resistivity change as damage accumulates (54). The second important result displayed in Figure 5.4 is that annealing of the resistivity change sets in between 20° K and 30° K for all of these metals. The initial drop is rather sharp, but the bulk of the damage remains at 80° K and is being annealed quite gradually, in contrast to the behavior expected of a simple process with a single activation energy (see Figure 5.3). The different metals also show widely differing total resistivity increments at a given exposure. There is no obvious system to this, but quite conceivably the resistivity of a Frenkel defect differs considerably in different metals.

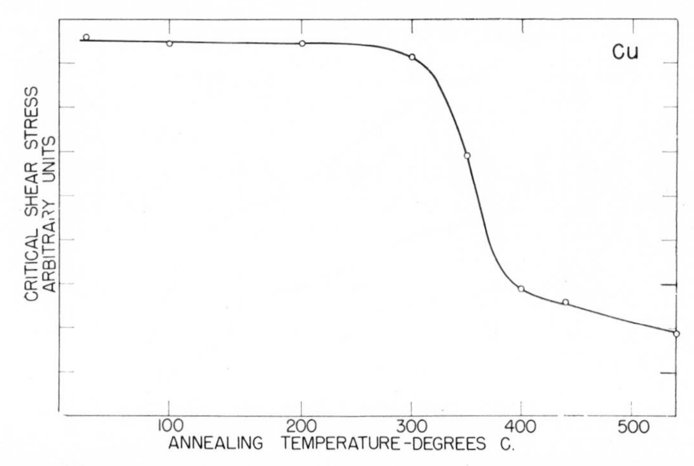

Figure 5.6 Annealing of Cu wires hardened by 30-day neutron irradiation at 80° K. Each sample was annealed 10 minutes at the indicated temperature (from reference 52).

More careful measurements on the annealing of copper have also been made, by Blewitt *et al.*, and an example is shown in Figure 5.5. In this work a zone-refined specimen of copper was bombarded in the reactor at 17.5° K to an exposure of 8×10^{17} nvt. Subsequently the specimen was annealed in 3-minute pulses at successively higher temperatures, as indicated by the points on the curve. The resistivity after each pulse, however, was measured at 14° K and is thus essentially the residual resistivity. It is seen that about 35% of the resistivity increase anneals in a sharp step in the neighborhood of 35° K. If this is ascribed to a single process with a frequency factor of about 10^{12} sec^{-1}, equation 5-33 shows that the activation energy of the process is about 0.1 ev. It is also clear from Figure 5.5 that in the range above 50° K the annealing is complex, and at best it would be necessary to assume a large variety of activation energies.

Annealing of copper to higher temperatures shows that recovery continues to perhaps 900° K [Blewitt, *et al.* (51), McReynolds, *et al.* (52), Eggleston (53)], with about three fourths of the resistivity increase annealing by room temperature and the remainder coming out slowly over a large temperature range. The plastic properties of copper are particularly affected by high-temperature annealing. The

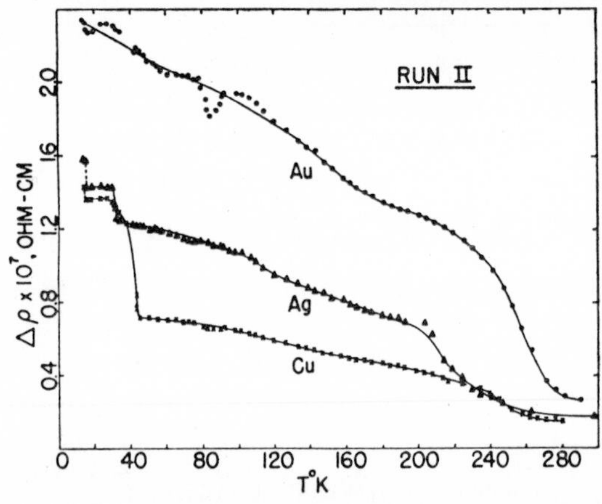

Figure 5.7 Thermal recovery of bombardment-induced resistivity during warmup from 10° K (from reference 54).

critical shear stress, which is markedly increased by reactor irradiation, shows very little annealing until about 575° K, and is largely recovered by 700° K (the resistivity also drops again in this stage). Figure 5.6 (p. 155) shows the results of McReynolds, *et al.* (52) on critical shear stress of copper wires irradiated in the Brookhaven reactor at 80° K to an exposure of 10^{19} nvt. Each point on the curve represents a separate sample which was annealed for 10 minutes at the indicated temperature. Stress-strain curves were then measured at liquid-nitrogen temperature. Isothermal anneals of various durations were also made, and the region 575–625° K yielded an activation energy of 1.9 ev. The simultaneous annealing of electrical resistivity in this range gave an activation energy of 2.0 ev. Eggleston (53) bombarded 0.003-inch copper wires at about 120° K with 35-Mev alpha particles. After exposures of 8×10^{17} particles/cm^2, isothermal annealing was performed and residual resistivity was observed. Recovery over a broad range of temperatures was observed, in general agreement with the reactor results. Eggleston distinguished two rather well separated ranges of recovery, the lower being from 210° K to 255° K, with an activation energy of about 0.7 ev, the upper from 525° K to 600° K, with an activation energy of 2.1 ev. This is in reasonably good agreement with the results of McReynolds, *et al.*, and indicates that charged-heavy-particle bombardment and reactor irradiations induce defects with closely similar annealing properties. Eggleston also reported that the isothermal annealing curves in the 210–255° K range can be fitted by third-order kinetics, while those in the 525–600° K range seem to obey fourth-order kinetics. In view of the remarks made in the preceding section on apparent orders of reaction, this result can not be considered to have clear-cut significance.

The deuteron bombardment experiments of Copper, Koehler, and Marx (54) on copper, silver, and gold at 10° K have already been mentioned in section 3.3 of Chapter 3. These workers also observed the annealing of electrical resistivity in their specimens as the temperature was allowed to rise after bombardment. Figure 5.7 shows the results. All of the specimens had received 8×10^{16} deuterons/cm^2 before the start of the warm-up. The sudden drop at the very beginning in the case of copper and silver (shown by dotted lines) was caused by a brief heating pulse from the release of condensed deuterium at the start of the annealing. It is believed that this released only an insubstantial part of the defects, and thus the dotted portions of the curves should be ignored. The very low temperature annealing stage for copper and silver is clearly evident. For copper this occurs between 35° K and 45° K with 40% of the initial $\Delta\rho$ recovering, and for silver it occurs in the range 27° K to 33° K, with a recovery of about 13% of the initial $\Delta\rho$. Gold does not show this annealing stage, and in view of the similarity of these three metals this is somewhat surprising. It may be that the stage exists but occurs at too low a temperature or is too small to be resolved. It should also be noted that this first annealing stage was seen in gold in the reactor irradiation experiments (Figure 5.4). The reason for the difference is not understood.

From 50° K to 200° K a gradual recovery is seen in all three metals. Between 200° K and 280° K there is another drop, suggestive of a simple process but less well defined than the low-temperature stage. At 280° K approximately 10% of the initial $\Delta\rho$ remains in all three cases.

Further light should be shed on these annealing processes by observing the release of stored energy that accompanies them. Blewitt and co-workers (51) have measured the stored-energy release associated with the low-temperature annealing of copper and aluminum. The irradiations were made in the reactor at about 20° K, for a period of 160 hours (4×10^{17} nvt.). Afterwards the reactor was shut down and the samples, under conditions of good thermal insulation from their surroundings, were allowed to warm slowly under the heating from the γ-rays in the reactor. This heating is very steady and is quite uniformly distributed through the sample. After the sample had been warmed to 60° K it was cooled and then warmed again to 60° K without further neutron irradiation. In the second warming it could be assumed that no stored energy was being released, and thus the temperature rise required a longer time. The difference between the gamma-ray heat inputs in the first and second warmings is then the stored-energy release. (See also the discussion in section 4.2C of Chapter 4.) A check on the assumed rate of gamma heating was afforded by observing the time-temperature curve in the second warming. From this the heat capacities could be calculated, and were found to agree very closely with accepted values.

For both copper and aluminum it was found that the energy liberated in warming through the temperature range 30 to 50° K did not exceed, and was possibly close to, the experimental error of 0.1 cal/mole. This is a surprisingly low value. If the theoretical results of Blatt (see Table 3.4) for the electrical resistivity of a Frenkel defect in copper are accepted, the observed increment of resistivity in the copper specimen indicated that it contained about 10^{19} Frenkel defects per mole at the start of the annealing. If $^1/_3$ of these annealed out in the 30–50° K range, as indicated in Figure 5.5, an energy release of 0.1 cal/mole means a release of $^3/_4$ ev per defect annealed. On the other hand, the calculations of Huntington discussed earlier (see Table 5.1) indicate that a Frenkel pair should release 6 to 7 ev upon recombination of the interstitial with the vacancy, and 5 to 6 ev upon absorption of the interstitial at a surface or a dislocation. The observed stored-energy release is thus nearly an order of magnitude lower than that predicted from a simple model of the annealing.

Overhauser has made careful measurements of the annealing of resistivity increases (47) and of the release of stored energy (48) in polycrystalline copper specimens bombarded with 12-Mev deuterons at liquid-nitrogen temperature. The increase of resistivity with exposure up to 10^{17} deuterons/cm^2 was nonlinear and dependent on bombarding flux, showing that pronounced annealing was occurring

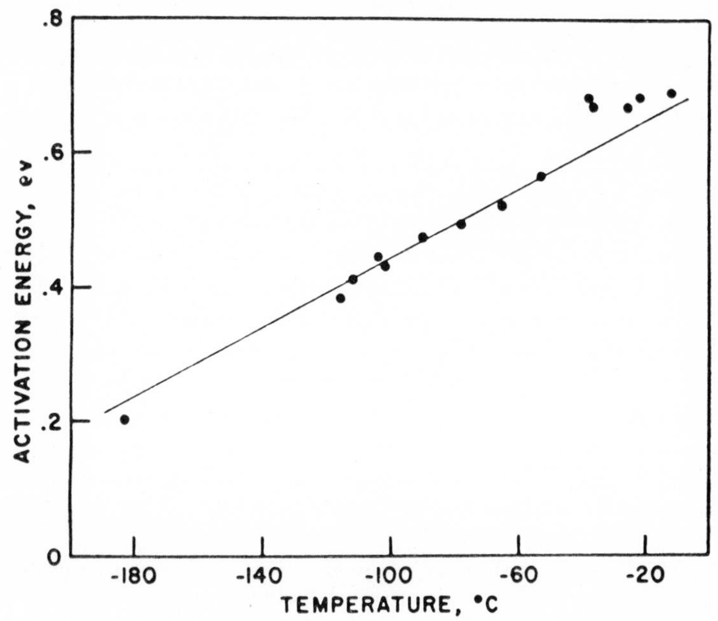

Figure 5.8 Activation energies for recovery processes operating at various temperatures in deuteron irradiated copper. The straight line is drawn through absolute zero (from reference 47).

during bombardment. Overhauser measured an activation energy for recovery at each of a series of temperatures from 90 to 255° K by the method of suddenly changing the temperature, in the vicinity of the temperature of interest, and observing the change in rate of annealing (this method is described in section 5.3B of this chapter, see equation 5-35). The annealing was found to possess a broad spectrum of activation energies, as indicated in Figure 5.8. Each dot in this figure represents an activation energy for the recovery process found to be operating in the vicinity of the indicated temperature.

Activation energies ranging almost continuously from 0.20 to 0.68 ev were found, with a predominance of the 0.68 ev process at the higher temperatures. Isothermal anneals for a larger range of time were performed at 255° K, where Figure 5.8 seems to indicate a single annealing process to be operating. The decay of excess resistivity, $\Delta\rho$, was found to obey quite accurately the equation

$$d\Delta\rho/dt = -K(\Delta\rho)^{\gamma}$$

with $\gamma = 2.5$. Overhauser interprets this by assuming that interstitials and vacancies are recombining in this stage according to second-order kinetics (see equation 5-22), but with an activation energy

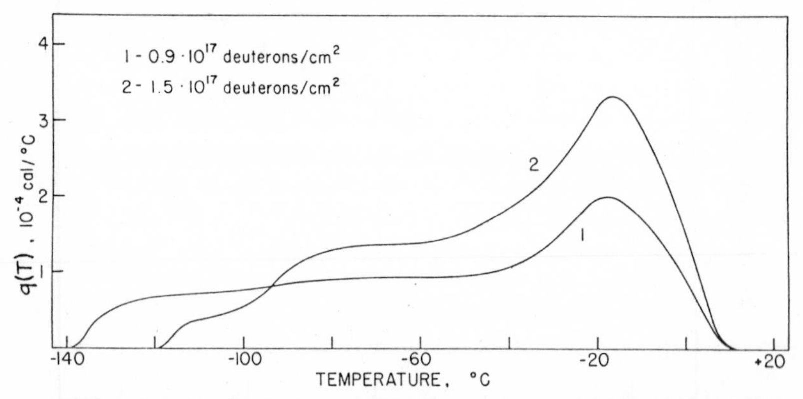

Figure 5.9 Rate of stored-energy release at various temperatures for deuteron-irradiated copper. Both samples weighed 0.219 grams (from reference 48).

dependent on the concentration of defects because of the elastic strain around each defect. He presents a calculation that shows that an effective reaction order of approximately 2.5 can result from this situation. However, in view of the remarks made in section 5.3 of this chapter about apparent orders of diffusion-controlled reactions, the significance of this numerical agreement must be viewed with reserve.

The stored-energy release experiments were made on copper foils 0.005-inch thick, also bombarded at the temperature of liquid nitrogen. By a careful technique of comparing the temperature of the irradiated foil with that of an identical unirradiated foil while both were being warmed, the stored energy released per degree of temperature rise at temperature T could be found. This quantity, denoted $q(T)$, has been discussed in Chapter 4, section 4.2C. Figure 5.9 shows the resulting $q(T)$ plotted against T for two samples that had had different exposures. The two samples were of the same weight, 0.219 grams. Both specimens were irradiated for the same length of time, so the sample with heavier exposure was subjected to greater heating effects during irradiation, which accounts for the pecularity in curve number 2 at the low-temperature end. Above $-80°$ C the curves are comparable, and the stored-energy release rates are found to be in the same proportion as the exposures.

It is seen that stored energy is released continually through the entire course of the warm up, with a pronounced peak in the vicinity of $-20°$ C. By integrating the curves in Figure 5.9 and normalizing to an exposure of 10^{17} deuterons/cm^2 it is found that 3.3 cal/mole are released between $-80°$ C and $+10°$ C. This energy release is associated with a resistivity decrease of 0.031 μohm-cm, and this amounts to 106 cal/mole/μohm-cm. In the experiments of Blewitt, *et al.*, a resistivity change of about 0.002 μohm-cm occurred on annealing from 20 to 60° K and was accompanied by not more than 0.1 cal/mole of stored-energy release, which amounts to an upper limit of 50 cal/mole/μohm-cm. The two results are not identical, but this is not at all surprising since Blewitt's irradiations were done with neutrons, at much lower temperature, and at a much lower level of damage. If each pair of defects annealed released 5 ev and contributed resistivity at the rate of 2.7 μohm-cm/per cent (see Table 3.4), the stored energy to resistivity ratio would be 425 cal/mole/μohm-cm, which is far higher than the observed values. On the other hand, the Overhauser-Gorman Figure of 12.0 μohm-cm/per cent Frenkel defects would lower this quotient to 95 cal/mole/μohm-cm, which is in good agreement with Overhauser's measured value of 106 cal/mole/μohm-cm. This agreement may be quite fortuitous since the calculated number of defects together with the 12μohm-cm resistivity figure would lead one to expect something like 50 times higher resistivity increments than are actually observed. Also the very low temperature results make it quite clear that damage formed at liquid-nitrogen temperatures is already in a partially annealed state and probably does not consist solely of independent vacancies and interstitials.

It has been pointed out that irradiation with electrons near threshold would be expected to produce ideally simple damage consisting of close Frenkel pairs, and thus annealing of such samples might also be simpler than the annealing of samples damaged in conventional ways. Such experiments have been made and do not seem to bear out this conclusion, although the full experimental results are not yet available. Meechan and Brinkman (60) have irradiated high-purity copper wires with 1.25-Mev electrons at 80° K and have followed the change of electrical resistivity as the specimens were warmed. The recovery was not unlike that seen after deuteron bombardment, going on continuously from 80 to 550° K, with only one region in which a fairly abrupt drop occurred. This region was centered around 300° K, and involved about a 50% recovery. Consideration of heating rates indicates that this is probably the same region of pronounced recovery seen by Overhauser at a slightly lower temperature and assigned the activation energy of 0.68 ev. Meechan and Brinkman find second-order recovery kinetics in this region and an activation energy of 0.60 ev. The maximum energy that a 1.25-Mev electron can impart to a copper atom is 35 ev, which is sufficiently above threshold that this damage may not actually be ideally simple.

Corbett, Denney, Fiske, and Walker (61) have irradiated copper foils at 10° K with 1.35-Mev electrons. Annealing experiments showed that recovery of electrical resistivity commenced slightly above 20° K and was 90% complete by 65° K, with a maximum recovery rate around 35° K. This is in qualitative agreement with the heavy-particle results, but considerably more of the damage anneals in these experiments. The annealing in this range has not been found to follow a single first- or second-order rate equation. The annealing of electron-induced damage thus appears to be simpler than the heavy-particle case, but much work remains to be done before it is quantitatively understood. Of particular interest would be the measurement of stored-energy release from samples bombarded at 10° K.

The above work and other experiments thus show the existence of four rather well defined stages of annealing in irradiated copper. Closely corresponding stages have been found in silver and gold, and to some extent in other metals. The stages for copper are summarized in Table 5.3. The experimental results have been discussed at considerable length, because it is highly important to understand these annealing processes and copper has been the most thoroughly studied metal. Unfortunately a complete and consistent explanation of the annealing observations is not yet available, and the best that can be done is to offer a variety of hypotheses, each of which fits some but not all of the facts.

Table 5.3. Annealing stages of irradiated copper

Stage	Temp. range (° K)	Approximate activation energy (ev)	Principal recovery
I	30–50	0.1	Electrical resistivity
II	50–240	0.2–0.6	Electrical resistivity
III	240–320	0.7	Electrical resistivity
IV	575–900	~2.0	Critical shear stress

The calculations reported in Table 5.1 strongly suggest that stage I occurs because of the motion of interstitials and stage III because of the motion of vacancies. Stage IV is unique in that it involves mostly the recovery of mechanical properties, notably the critical shear stress. The activation energy of this stage, 2.0 ev, is about the same as the activation energy for self-diffusion in copper. Very likely the recovery in this stage involves the removal of entangled dislocations and possibly dislocations pinned by combinations of point defects formed at lower temperatures. The view that vacancies are moving in stage III is also supported by the quenching experiments of Koehler, *et al.* on gold (7–10) together with the assumption that copper and gold have closely related activation energies. The simplicity of this interpretation is upset by the annealing observed in stage II, which must be ascribed either to some kind of cluster formation or to interaction of point defects with impurities. The tendencies for cluster formation have been discussed in section 5.2 of this chapter, and their possible importance in annealing can not be overlooked, although virtually no quantitative information is yet available. It must also be remembered that the defect concentration involved in most of the experiments cited is very low, being in the range 10^{-5} to a few times 10^{-4}, and thus is comparable to the concentration of impurities. The stress field around an impurity atom would be expected to interact with vacancies and interstitials. An interstitial impurity can trap a vacancy by falling into it and becoming substitutional; a substitutional impurity that is smaller than a normal atom can trap a normal interstitial by exchanging with it and becoming interstitial. Quite possibly some or all of these processes are occurring in stage II.

The stored-energy measurements of Blewitt, *et al.* are a particularly serious challenge to the vacancy-interstitial model of annealing being considered. These measurements are so recent, and the experimental difficulties involved are so great, that some reservations may be allowed concerning them. However, if they are accepted it becomes very difficult to believe that interstitials are simply being annihilated in stage I, and it is necessary to think of a mechanism by which rather large amounts of resistivity are recovered with only a small release of energy. Blewitt (51) and Lomer and Cottrell (50) have suggested, mostly on *ad hoc* grounds, that the interstitial in close-packed metals is more stable in the crowdion configuration, and that its easy movement is thus restricted to one dimension. It is then proposed that stage I annealing occurs when the crowdions can first move, and involves migration to more stable positions along their lines, these more stable positions being provided by the stress fields around impurities and dislocations. Since motion of the crowdion is restricted to a line, recombination with a vacancy will be possible only when the vacancy happens to lie on a crowdion line, and this occurrence will be rare. Thus, far less than 5 ev will be released for each crowdion trapped. In this picture stage II annealing occurs with the release of the crowdions from their traps and their migration to still more stable sites, including sites of annihilation. Since the crowdion line may lie at a variety of distances from the stress center, a variety of trapping energies would be expected, and this would explain the multiplicity of activation energies encountered in stage II. Stage III annealing would still be explained by the migration of vacancies, whether to annihilation sites or partly to coagulation centers is not certain, and stage IV would be explained by the creation and diffusion of vacancies which could free dislocations from whatever pinning centers were obstructing them.

Three objections can be raised against the crowdion model outlined in the foregoing paragraph. First, the stability of the crowdion configuration itself has had no theoretical demonstration, and remains conjectural. Second, the trapping of a crowdion near but not on a center of strain would be expected to lower the electrical resistivity somewhat, because of over-all strain reduction, but no calculations of the magnitude of this effect have been made and it seems highly plausible that the resistivity change would be very much less than that observed in stage I annealing. Third, the experiments of Simmons and Balluffi on lattice parameter changes in deuteron irradiated copper (see section 4.2G of Chapter 4) showed that 55% of the increase of lattice parameter recovered in stage I annealing. Annihilation of interstitial-vacancy pairs would account for this very well, but it is very difficult to see how the trapping of crowdions could yield anything like so much recovery of lattice expansion.

Still other interpretations of these and related annealing stages in other metals have been proposed. Brinkman, Dixon, and Meechan (62) have suggested that stage III consists of the motion of interstitials, while vacancies anneal at a higher temperature, with an activation energy of 1.19 ev in copper. This argument comes from observation on the alloy Cu_3Au, which has similar annealing behavior to copper (at any rate at temperatures above 180° K), and in which only the upper (420° K) annealing changes the state of order. Brinkman, *et al.* point out that motion of interstitials would not be expected to change the state of order, while motion of vacancies would. The comparison between copper and Cu_3Au may be criticized as overstrained in this argument, and a second objection may be found in the data on self-diffusion. Since the activation energy for self-diffusion in copper is known (6) to be near 2.04 ev, an activation energy for vacancy motion of 1.19 ev, as proposed by Brinkman, *et al.*, would require a vacancy formation energy of $2.04 - 1.19 \cong 0.85$ ev. This seems anomalously low, since it would lead to a high vacancy concentration near the melting point, and it is inconsistent with the relation between formation and motion energies of vacancies established by Koehler and co-workers in the closely related case of gold (7–10).

A somewhat different suggestion has been put forward by Li and Nowick (63), who argue that the defect in motion in stage III annealing of copper is the di-vacancy, with the single vacancy remaining fixed until higher temperatures are reached. The mechanism by which large numbers of vacancies can find themselves paired after low-temperature irradiations is not elucidated in this proposal.

Seeger (64) has proposed that stage I consists of the annealing of small regions in which something like a supercooled-liquid configuration exists. Presumably these regions are the result of thermal or displacement spikes. Seeger also visualizes stage II as the motion of various groups of vacancies, stage III as the motion of interstitials, and the early parts of stage IV as the motion of single vacancies. This scheme fits in with Seeger's explanations of the annealing of cold-worked and of quenched specimens. The high energy required for interstitial motion in this model is quite at variance with considerations already advanced here. Most importantly, the assumption that the lowest-temperature annealing stage depends on the existence of amorphous regions of damage is contradicted by the experiments of Corbett, *et al.*, in which it is shown that electron irradiation leads to even more pronounced stage I annealing than heavy-particle irradiation. It does not seem possible to argue that 1.35-Mev electrons can produce whole regions of amorphous structure.

The annealing of irradiated simple metals is thus seen to be incompletely understood at the present time. A variety of models have been proposed, but no one is wholly satisfactory. It is apparent that the annealing involves many different processes, and that our knowledge of the quantitative features of these processes is inadequate. It is also likely that point defects are associating in more complex aggregates during certain stages of annealing and that the chief defect of present models is their inadequate account of these events. It is clear that small amounts of impurities are very important in annealing, and the inconsistencies between many reported observations probably stem from this fact.

B. Annealing in Nonmetals

The work of Smoluchowski and co-workers with alkali halides irradiated by very high-energy protons has already been mentioned in section 4.2 of Chapter 4. An extension of these investigations by Kobayashi (65,66) has recently provided considerable information on the annealing of defects in irradiated NaCl. These findings will be summarized here as typical of annealing behavior in simple ionic crystals.

Kobayashi bombarded thin single crystals of NaCl with 350-Mev protons in a synchrocyclotron. The crystals had been carefully annealed prior to irradiation and were irradiated at room temperature. After irradiation stored-energy release was measured during slow warming. Also, optical absorption spectra and hydrostatic density were measured at room temperature after various anneals. The anneals consisted of warming slowly to a desired temperature and then quenching back to room temperature. The rate of stored-energy release showed peaks in three distinct regions, room tempera-

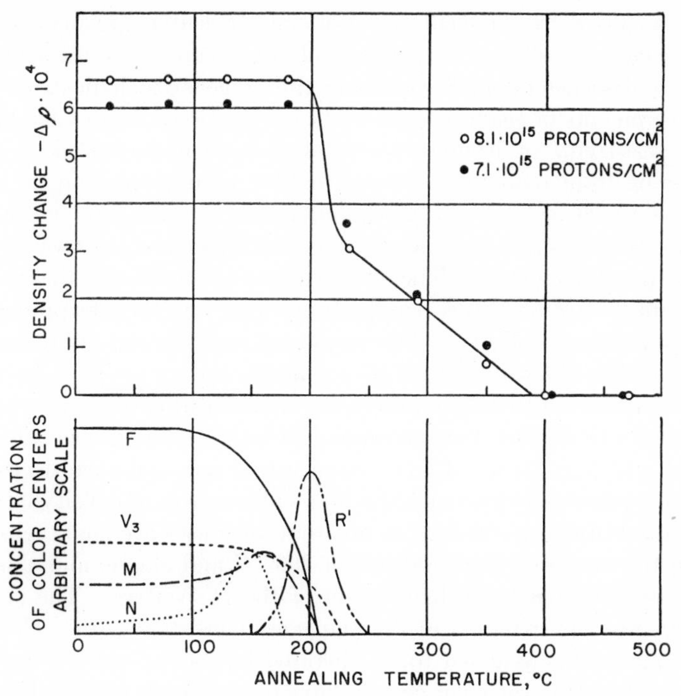

Figure 5.10 Annealing of density decrease and color center concentration in irradiated NaCl. Crystals were heated to successively higher annealing temperatures at 2° C per minute and quenched back to room temperature for each measurement (from reference 66).

ture to 150° C, 150 to 250° C, and 250 to 400° C. After an irradiation of 9.3×10^{15} protons/cm^2 the total heat release in each of the three regions was 0.72, 1.18, and 0.28 calories/gm, respectively. The absorption spectra of the irradiated crystals showed F, V_3, M, N, and R' bands, which annealed along with the density changes. Figure 5.10 shows these results. The F center is assumed to be an electron trapped at a chlorine vacancy; the V_3 is a hole trapped at a pair of positive-ion vacancies; the *M* is an electron at a triple vacancy consisting of two chlorines and one sodium; the *N* and *R′* are more complicated aggregates of lattice vacancies. It is seen from Figure 5.10 that in the annealing up to 150° C the density remains constant, while the concentration of *F* and V_3 centers declines a little and the *M* and *N* centers become more numerous. Kobayashi suggests that this is caused by the coalescence of smaller centers (*F* and V_3) into larger centers, without the removal of any vacancies from the lattice. The coalescence of small centers in this stage is also indicated by the measurements of electrical resistivity (see section 4.2A of Chapter 4). The resistivity of irradiated crystals increased very rapidly upon warming from room temperature to 120° C, and this can be interpreted as caused by an overabundance of negative-ion vacancies, which trap positive-ion vacancies as the latter become mobile, and form neutral clusters. The positive-ion vacancies are the normal carriers of current in this temperature range, and their trapping thus increases the resistivity. The surplus of negative-ion vacancies has been explained by invoking Varley's mechanism.

In the 150 to 250° C range the concentration of simple centers continues to decline, now accompanied by a declining concentration of *M* and *N* centers. The *R′* band first grows and then decreases, the decrease coinciding with the first sudden drop of density change. The drop of density change means that vacancies are being removed from the lattice at temperatures of 200° C and above, and this can be correlated with the dissociation of the *R′* centers. The stored-energy and density data in this range are consistent with each other if about 5 ev is assumed to be liberated for each *F* center annealed out. At 250° C the color centers have disappeared, while half of the original density decrease remains. This can be interpreted as meaning that half the original number of vacancies still remain, but in larger and more stable aggregates that do not give coloration. In the range 250 to 400° C these too dissociate and annihilate, giving up the last bit of stored energy, which is about 1 ev per vacancy pair released, in rough accord with theoretical expectations.

As examples of annealing of materials in which covalent binding predominates, the work of Primak and Szymanski on vitreous silica (67) and Primak, Fuchs, and Day on diamond and silicon carbide (68) can be cited. In the first of these studies the density of reactor-irradiated vitreous silica was measured during annealing. Density increases ranged up to 2.8%, and were found to anneal very gradually over a range of temperatures from 300 to 1000° C. In the second study dilatation and stored energy were observed during annealing following reactor irradiation. Dilatation as great as 3.7 per cent and stored energies as high as 400 cal/gm were seen. The annealing again was very gradual, taking place over the range 100 to 950° C. With diamond, stored-energy release rates were particularly high in the neighborhood of 200 and 350° C, and in many of the samples exceeded the specific heat, giving "catastrophic" stored-energy release (see section 4.2 C of Chapter 4). Primak, *et al.* have analyzed these gradual annealing patterns by assuming that many simple processes are operating simultaneously, each with its own activation energy. By methods developed by Vand (45) and Primak (46) they find a spectrum of activation energies for the component processes. The silica results imply, after assuming a common frequency factor of 10^9 sec^{-1}, that activation energies range from 1.2 to 3.5 ev, with a prominent maximum in the spectrum near 2.0 ev. The stored-energy and dilatation measurements on diamond and silicon carbide were consistent with each other and showed activation energy spectra in both materials extending from 1.2 to about 4 ev. In diamond there was a peak in the spectrum at 1.6 ev; in silicon carbide there were broad peaks at 1.6 and 3.4 ev. Unfortunately no analysis in terms of atomic mechanisms has yet been made. Broad annealing spectra extending over a large range with annealing continuing to high temperatures, seem particularly characteristic of covalently bonded substances.

Investigations on irradiated graphite have been discussed in various connections in previous chapters. This substance is, of course, by no means simple. It has been studied, however, in more detail than any other material. In particular, annealing of the damage has been investigated in terms of many physical properties (e.g., stored energy, dimensional changes, electronic properties, paramagnetic resonance) over a wide temperature range. The data will not be discussed here and the reader is referred to the review article by Hennig (75). Hennig and Hove (76) have attempted a comprehensive interpretation of the data for irradiated graphite, and the main features of their model are described in the following paragraphs.

During neutron bombardment near $-200°$ C nearly all the atoms that are displaced remain displaced. The vacancies trap two electrons and are diamagnetic, while the free interstitials are assumed to trap one electron. Some of the displaced atoms, perhaps one-third, are present as close vacancy-interstitial pairs. These can anneal out below room temperature by direct recombination. Some dispersion of clustered interstitials also takes place at low temperature. The next stage, which is prominent in the 100–200° C range, involves the migration of interstitials and their combination into C_2 molecules or larger clusters, although some recombination of close vacancy-interstitial pairs is also occurring. The combination reaction is not completed before a third process commences, namely reintegration of complexes, mainly C_2, with vacancies. This step apparently involves mostly the motion of the interstitial complexes. Above about 600° C all but about 20% of the vacancies and interstitials have recombined. The remaining interstitials are trapped at mosaic boundaries or dislocations, and an equal number of vacancies remain. The vacancies probably become mobile around 1200° C, in line with the self-diffusion measurements of Kanter (77) and the prediction of Dienes (78). The annealing mechanism discussed here is probably not directly applicable to heavily irradiated samples that contain more complex damage centers.

The above interpretation is the best that can be suggested at the present time, although it appears to have some difficulties (79). Interstitial carbon atoms act as electron donors in valence semiconductors and, therefore, it is somewhat unlikely that they will trap electrons. The identification of the paramagnetic resonance centers as carbon ions was inferential and could not be proved. The model implies three electrons trapped per Frenkel defect, while direct diamagnetic susceptibility measurements indicate not more than two trapped electrons per pair. This would suggest that the interstitial carbon loses an electron. If this is assumed, however, then it is difficult to account for the activation energy for recombination since the interstitials and vacancies would be oppositely charged.

It is clear, as has been mentioned before, that annealing processes are complex and intricate. A great deal of information is obtainable from such experiments, but a unique and satisfactory interpretation is not yet at hand for any irradiated solid.

5.5 Annealing of the Graphite in the Brookhaven Reactor

It has been mentioned in an earlier chapter that graphite can acquire large quantities of stored energy under neutron irradiation, and that it expands appreciably in the process. A further effect of radiation damage is to reduce drastically the thermal conductivity, reductions by a factor of 50 or more having been observed. These facts are a cause of concern in the use of graphite for the moderator in a reactor: The expansion causes fuel channels to get out of alignment and important dimensions to change, while the storage of energy and reduction of conductivity offer some hazard of a catastrophic

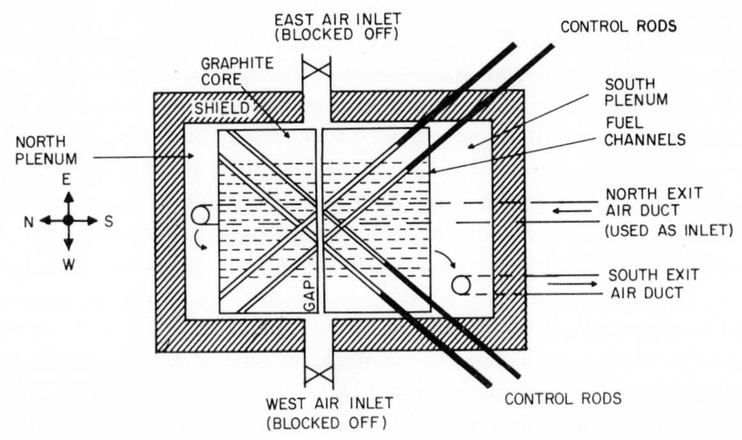

Figure 5.11 Top view of BNL Reactor. Special arrangements for pile annealing are indicated. Direction of air flow during annealing is shown by arrows.

energy release in which the graphite suddenly heats itself up to a dangerous level. These matters are of particular concern in reactors operated at low and moderate temperatures, because the rate of accumulation of damage is greater at lower temperatures.

The tendency of radiation effects to anneal themselves at higher temperatures can be used to reduce the damage in a graphite moderator by running the reactor for a short period at abnormally high temperatures. This rather drastic operation of "pile annealing" has been carried out a number of times in the reactor at the Brookhaven National Laboratory. Because it illustrates in a very practical and important way some typical annealing phenomena, a brief account of these operations will be given in this section. The interested reader is referred to reports by Fox and Powell (71), and Kosiba, Dienes, and Gurinsky (72,73) for further details.

The Brookhaven Reactor is air cooled and graphite moderated and reflected. Figure 5.11 shows the general features. The reactor consists of a graphite structure approximately in the shape of a cube 25 ft on a side. All of this except for a layer about $3^1/_2$-ft thick on the outside, which serves as a reflector, is loaded with uranium. The fuel rods lie in horizontal, north-south channels in the graphite. This basic cube is divided into two equal parts by a cut in a vertical east-west plane through its center, which leaves a 3-inch gap between the two halves. This gap is for the admission of cooling air, which is drawn in from outside, passes into the gap, divides and passes down the fuel channels through spaces around the fuel rods, and is gathered in plenum chambers at the north and south faces for exhaust. The control rods enter diagonally from the southeast and southwest corners. The normal course of the air flow and the manner in which it was diverted during the early annealing experiments are shown in Figure 5.11. The reactor ordinarily operates at a power level of 25 Mw and a central flux (total) of $\sim 5 \times 10^{12}$ neutrons/cm^2 /sec. Normally the graphite temperature is about 50° C at the central gap and increases along the directions of air flow to a maximum of about 250° C at the extremities of the central fuel channels. For a detailed description of the reactor, see Fox (74).

The reactor was put into operation in August, 1950, and by October, 1953, the graphite in the reactor had accumulated an average radiation dose of $\sim 2 \times 10^{20}$ neutrons/cm^2 (nvt). The radiation damage was expected to be most severe in the central part of the reactor near the air gap, because here the flux was highest and the operating temperature lowest. Periodic checks on the state of the graphite had been made by observing the change in dimensions of the core and by removing samples of graphite for observation outside the reactor. These samples were subjected to x-ray examination and tests of stored energy and gross physical dimensions. By October, 1953, it was known that:

(*a*) The physical growth measured on small samples of graphite, when extrapolated to apply to the entire graphite structure, agreed very well with the measured gross growth.

(*b*) The *c*-axis growth was greater than the physical growth in each specimen by a factor of about 10, and, depending on the origin of the sample, ranged from very small amounts up to about 3%.

(*c*) Heating of the more heavily damaged samples to about 300° C produced a 20–30% reduction in both the physical growth and the *c*-axis growth.

(*d*) Placing the more heavily damaged samples in a furnace at 200° C caused stored energy to be released at a moderate rate, sufficient to produce transient temperature rises to about 280° C. Placing unannealed samples in a furnace at 400° C produced about the same stored-energy release, but the spontaneous temperature rise

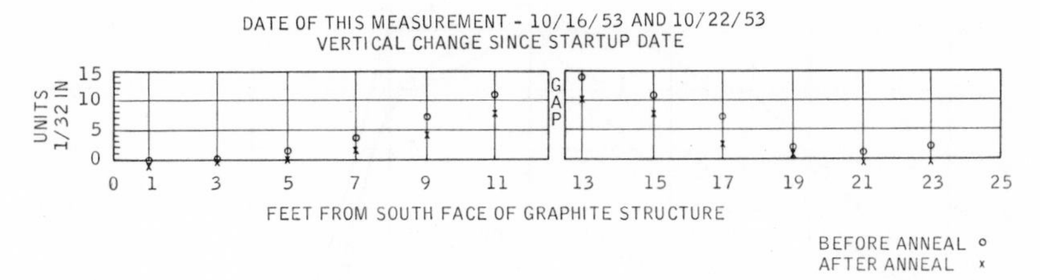

Figure 5.12 Vertical growth along channel (No. A-6-15) near top of reactor. Circles, data from October 16, 1953; crosses, data from October 22, 1953 (after first anneal) (from reference 71).

during release did not exceed 400° C. This stored energy amounted to 40 or 50 calories/gm. A typical curve showing this out-of-pile annealing has been given in section 4.2C of Chapter 4.

Furthermore, direct observations (made by optical surveying techniques) showed that the graphite core of the reactor had expanded vertically and horizontally, the greatest expansion being near the gap. In May, 1953, it was found that the maximum accumulated growth of the graphite cube, at the gap, was $^{9}/_{32}$ in. vertically and $^{18}/_{32}$ in. horizontally. The vertical growth refers to the bottom $22^{1}/_{2}$ ft of the 25-ft stack; the horizontal growth refers to the central 20 ft of the 25-ft total width. The difference between the horizontal and vertical growth was explained on the basis that the great weight of the graphite and the upper shielding hindered vertical displacements, while horizontal displacements were virtually unconstrained and gaps could appear between individual blocks. Growth near the outside faces was negligible, but the central air gap had narrowed by as much as $^1/_2$ in. out of an original width of $3^1/_8$ inches. Figure 5.12 shows the vertical displacements along a horizontal north-south channel in the reflector (No. A-6-15) at a height of $22^1/_2$ ft above the base.

The first annealing operation was carefully planned, and was conducted by altering the air flow into the reactor so as to allow a relatively high temperature near the gap. As shown in Figure 5.11 the normal inlet air channels were blocked off. The outlet duct from the north plenum chamber was used as an inlet, and the air was drawn out through the duct from the south plenum. The air flow

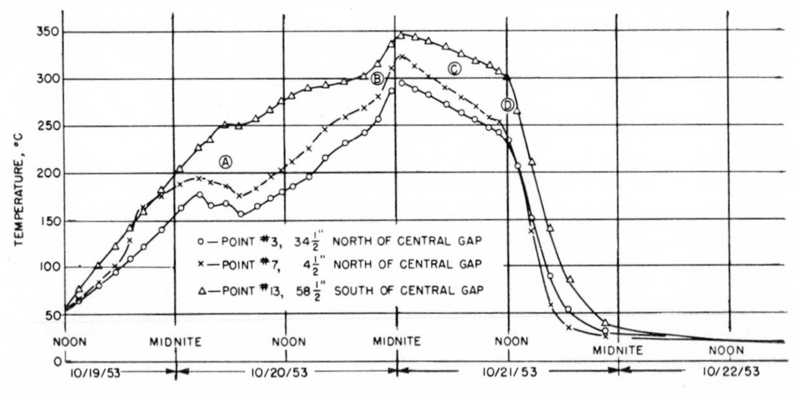

Figure 5.13 Temperature *vs* time at three points in a nearly central fuel channel (No. A-2-1) during the 1953 annealing operation (from reference 71).

through the pile was thus from north to south, and the south became the high-temperature end. Since the control rods also entered at the south end the neutron flux was depressed in this region, and the fission heat source was confined primarily to the north half of the pile. In this way it was possible to get the region near the gap to a temperature of 350° C without overheating the south end.

The operation was started at 9:40 A.M. on October 19, 1953, after a four-day shutdown. It was monitored by 130 thermocouples placed throughout the graphite structure. With the air flow throttled to about 10 per cent of normal, the reactor was started up very slowly. In 5 hours the power reached 2 Mw, and was then maintained at approximately that level for 34 hours. During this time minor adjustments of the control rods were made in order to secure a more uniform temperature distribution. During the last three hours the power was raised to 3 Mw. After this the reactor was shut down, and simultaneously the fans were shut off. There followed a 12-hour "soaking" period. It was hoped to secure, by heat conduction in this stage, a higher temperature in the reflector regions, but very little of this objective was achieved. The cooling fans were turned on at the end of this period and the graphite brought down to room temperature in about 10 hours. Measurements of distortion in the graphite structure were then repeated.

Figure 5.13 shows the history of the graphite temperature at a point near the center of the reactor and at two other points during this treatment. The down trend at *A* was caused by a control-rod

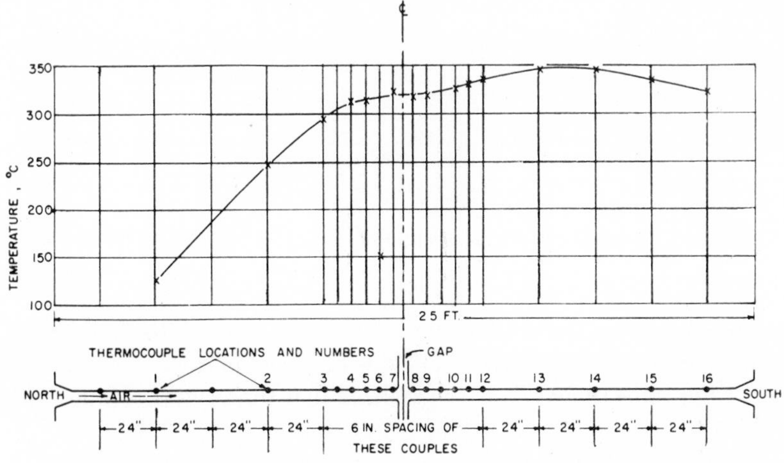

Figure 5.14 Temperature distribution along a nearly central fuel channel (No. A-2-1) at the highest temperature condition of the 1953 annealing operation (from reference 71).

readjustment, not by the release of stored energy. These points lie in a channel 18 inches from the center line of the reactor. Figure 5.14 shows the temperature distribution along the same channel at the highest temperature condition of the experiment.

The distortion remaining in a typical channel after the annealing is also shown in Figure 5.12. This and similar measurements at other locations show that between 20 and 30% of the distortion was relieved in this anneal, in good agreement with the predictions based on small samples annealed outside the pile. The width of the air gap was also partially recovered, and small samples removed from the pile at the end of the experiment showed that the low-temperature part of the stored energy had been successfully released. No sudden or unexpected releases of stored energy had occurred, and the operation was considered to have achieved its objective.

Since 1953 a continuing series of annealing operations have been carried out on the reactor. After the first anneal graphite growth continued at approximately the former rate; one year later, on October 10, 1954, a second anneal was conducted, and two years later, on November 24, 1955, a third. These were done in essentially the

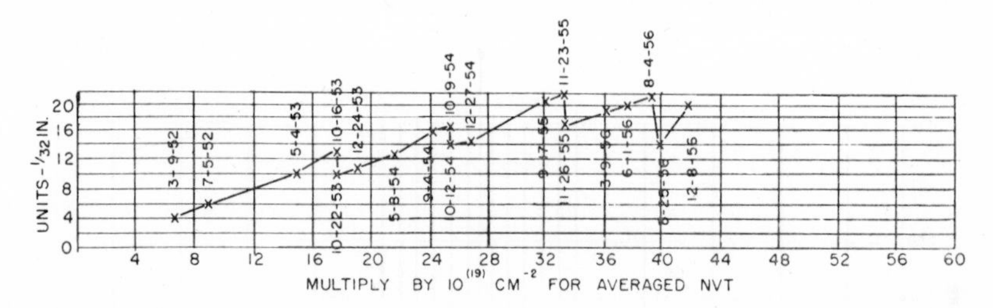

Figure 5.15 Vertical growth near center of channel A-6-15 during the life of the BNL Reactor (from reference 71).

same manner as the original anneal in 1953, and approximately the same percentage growth recovery was obtained in each.

For some time it had been realized that the exact procedure with which the reactor was shut down and started up at 10-day intervals for maintenance purposes was influencing the growth of the graphite. A change of shutdown procedures in the early part of 1955 is suspected of causing somewhat increased growth by diminishing the annealing that occurs at shutdown. By extending this idea, it was decided to anneal the reactor during regular shutdown periods by a modified procedure, much simpler and less troublesome than the original annealing method. During 1956, three special anneals were carried out in this way. These were conducted on March 31, August 24, and December 7. The reactor was simply operated for a period of several hours at reduced power with essentially zero air flow so as to heat the central parts of the core to above 300° C.

The entire course of the graphite growth during the life of the reactor is complex, but a representative idea is given by Figure 5.15, which is a graph of vertical growth *vs* time at a point near the center of channel A-6-15, the same channel depicted in Figure 5.12. Each of the three major anneals appears as a drop in the curve, and a final drop is seen for the anneal of August, 1956. Growth plots for other locations are qualitatively similar, though different in some details. The fact that the core is not a solid piece but a pile of many thousands of small graphite blocks held together only by gravity, undoubtedly has something to do with the variations. The general trend of the curve in Figure 5.15 shows that the annealing to date has reduced over-all growth by a large factor, perhaps 50%, and that the growth may even be approaching a saturation under the present regimen, although this conclusion is speculative.

A few instances of sudden energy release in localized regions of the graphite under annealing conditions have been observed. These have shown no tendency to propagate, and it is believed that stored energy represents no hazard under the conditions of operation of this reactor. Graphite growth may or may not impose an ultimate limit on the life of the reactor, but present annealing techniques have materially reduced the threat.

References

1. H. B. Huntington and F. Seitz, "Mechanism for Self-Diffusion in Metallic Copper," *Phys. Rev.*, **61**, 315 (1942).
2. H. B. Huntington, "Self-Consistent Treatment of the Vacancy Mechanism for Metallic Diffusion." *Phys. Rev.*, **61**, 325 (1942).
3. H. B. Huntington, "Mobility of Interstitial Atoms in a Face Centered Cubic Metal," *Phys. Rev.*, **91**, 1092 (1953).
4. H. Brooks, "Lattice Vacancies and Interstitials in Metals," in *Impurities and Imperfections*, American Society for Metals, Cleveland, 1955.
5. F. G. Fumi, "Vacancies in Monovalent Metals," *Phil. Mag.*, **46**, 1007 (1955).
6. A. Kuper, H. Letaw, Jr., L. Slifkin, E. Sonder, and T. Tomizuka, "Self-Diffusion in Copper," *Phys. Rev.*, **96**, 1224 (1954).
7. J. W. Kauffman and J. S. Koehler, "The Quenching in of Lattice Vacancies in Pure Au," *Phys. Rev.*, **88**, 149 (1952) (L).
8. J. W. Kauffman and J. S. Koehler, "The Quenching in of Lattice Vacancies in Pure Au," *Phys. Rev.*, **97**, 555 (1955) (L).
9. J. E. Bauerle, C. E. Klabunde, and J. S. Koehler, "Resistivity Increase in Water Quenched Gold," *Phys. Rev.*, **102**, 1182 (1956) (L).
10. J. E. Bauerle and J. S. Koehler, "Room Temperature Annealing of Quenched Au," "Interpretation of Quenching Experiments in Au," *Bull. Am. Phys. Soc.*, II, **2**, 145 (1957) (A).
11. B. Okkerse, "Self-Diffusion of Gold," *Phys. Rev.*, **103**, 1246 (1956).

12. T. Broom, "Lattice Defects and the Electrical Resistivity of Metals," *Phil. Mag. Supplement*, **3,** 25 (1954).
13. A. Seeger, "Theorie der Gitterfehlstellen," *Handbuch der Physik*, Springer, Berlin, 1955, Vol. VII, 1.
14. F. Seitz and J. S. Koehler, "Displacement of Atoms During Irradiation," in *Solid State Physics*, F. Seitz and D. Turnbull, Eds., Academic Press, Inc., New York, 1956, Vol. 2.
15. H. G. van Bueren, "Influence of Lattice Defects on the Electrical Properties of Cold Worked Metals," *Philips Research Repts.*, **12,** 1 (1957).
16. J. H. Bartlett and G. J. Dienes, "Combined Pairs of Vacancies in Copper," *Phys. Rev.*, **89,** 848 (1953).
17. J. D. Eshelby, "The Elastic Interaction of Point Defects," *Acta Met.*, **3,** 487 (1955).
18. K. F. Stripp and J. G. Kirkwood, "Lattice Vibrational Spectrum in Imperfect Crystals," *J. Chem. Phys.*, **22,** 1579 (1954).
19. E. W. Montroll and R. B. Potts, "Effect of Defects on Lattice Vibrations: Interaction of Defects and Analogy with Meson Pair Theory," *Phys. Rev.*, **102,** 72 (1956).
20. E. W. Montroll and R. B. Potts, "Effect of Defects on Lattice Vibrations," *Phys. Rev.*, **100,** 525 (1955).
21. N. F. Mott and M. J. Littleton, "Conduction in Polar Crystals. I. Electrolytic Conduction in Solid Salts," *Trans. Faraday Soc.*, **34,** 485 (1938).
22. G. J. Dienes, "Activation Energy for the Diffusion of Coupled Pairs of Vacancies in Alkali Halide Crystals," *J. Chem. Phys.*, **16,** 620 (1948).
23. H. W. Etzel and R. J. Maurer, "Concentration and Mobility of Vacancies in Sodium Chloride," *J. Chem. Phys.*, **18,** 1003 (1950).
24. J. F. Aschner, Thesis, University of Illinois, Urbana (1954).
25. H. W. Schamp and E. Katz, "Self Diffusion and Ionic Conductivity in Sodium Bromide," *Phys. Rev.*, **94,** 828 (1954).
26. Y. Haven, *Rec. trav. chim.*, **69,** 1471 (1950).
27. N. F. Mott and R. W. Gurney, *Electronic Processes in Ionic Crystals*, Oxford University Press, Oxford, 1948.
28. F. Seitz, "Color Centers in Alkali Halide Crystals, II," *Rev. Mod. Phys.*, **26,** 7 (1954).
29. *Report on Bristol Conference on Defects in Crystalline Solids*,The Physical Society, London, 1955.
30. H. Letaw, Jr., "Thermal Acceptors in Ge," *J. Phys. Chem. Solids*, **1,** 100 (1956).
31. M. v. Smoluchowski, "Versuch einer mathematischen Theorie der Koagulationskinetik kolloider Lösungen," *Ann. Physik*, **48,** 1103 (1915).
32. M. v. Smoluchowski, "Über Brownsche Molekularbewegung unter Einwirkung aüsserer Kräfte und deren Zussamenhang mit der verallgemeinerten Diffusion-gleichung," *Z. physik. Chem. (Leipzig)*, **92,** 129 (1917).
33. F. C. Collins and G. E. Kimball, "Diffusion Controlled Reaction Rates," *J. Colloid Sci.*, **4,** 425 (1949).
34. R. M. Noyes, "A Treatment of Chemical Kinetics with Special Applicability to Diffusion Controlled Reactions," *J. Chem. Phys.*, **22,** 1349 (1954).

35. H. Reiss, C. S. Fuller, and F. J. Morin, "Chemical Interaction Among Defects in Si and Ge," *Bell System Tech. J.*, **35,** 535 (1956).
36. H. Reiss, "Refined Theory of Ion Pairing; I. Equilibrium Aspects, II. Irreversible Aspects," *J. Chem. Phys.*, **25,** 400; 408 (1956).
37. C. Zener, "Theory of Diffusion," Chapter II of *Imperfections in Nearly Perfect Crystals*, W. Shockley, Ed., John Wiley, New York, 1952.
38. G. H. Vineyard, "Frequency Factors and Isotope Effects in Solid State Rate Processes," *J. Phys. Chem. Solids*, (to appear).
39. G. E. Vineyard and G. J. Dienes, "The Theory of Defect Concentration in Crystals," *Phys. Rev.*, **93,** 265 (1953).
40. H. S. Carslaw and J. C. Jaeger, *Conduction of Heat in Solids*, Oxford, New York, 1947.
41. P. M. Morse and H. Feshbach, *Methods of Mathematical Physics*, McGraw-Hill, Inc., New York, 1954.
42. R. C. Fletcher and W. L. Brown, "Annealing of Bombardment Damage in a Diamond-Type Lattice: Theoretical," *Phys. Rev.*, **92,** 585 (1953).
43. W. L. Brown, R. C. Fletcher, and K. A. Wright, "Annealing of Bombardment Damage in Germanium: Experimental," *Phys. Rev.*, **92,** 591 (1953).
44. E. Jahnke and F. Emde, *Tables of Functions*, Stechert and Co., New York, 1938.
45. V. Vand, "A Theory of the Irreversible Electrical Resistance Changes of Metallic Films Evaporated in Vacuum," *Proc. Phys. Soc. (London)*, **55,** 222 (1943).
46. W. Primak, "Kinetics of Processes Distributed in Activation Energy," *Phys. Rev.*, **100,** 1677 (1955).
47. A. W. Overhauser, "Isothermal Annealing Effects in Irradiated Copper," *Phys. Rev.*, **90,** 393 (1953).
48. A. W. Overhauser, "Stored Energy Measurements in Irradiated Copper," *Phys. Rev.*, **94,** 1551 (1954).
49. H. Paneth, "The Mechanism of Self Diffusion in Alkali Metals," *Phys. Rev.*, **80,** 708 (1950).
50. W. M. Lomer and A. H. Cottrell, "Annealing of Point Defects in Metals and Alloys," *Phil. Mag.*, **46,** 711 (1955).
51. T. H. Blewitt, R. R. Coltman, D. K. Holmes, and T. S. Noggle, "Mechanism of Annealing in Neutron Irradiated Metals," *Oak Ridge National Laboratory Report*, ORNL-2188 (unpublished).
52. A. W. McReynolds, W. Augustyniak, M. McKeown, and D. Rosenblatt, "Neutron Irradiation Effects in Copper and Aluminum at 80° K.," *Phys. Rev.*, **98,** 418 (1954).
53. R. R. Eggleston, "The Annealing of Copper After Radiation Damage at Low Temperatures," *Acta Met.*, **1,** 679 (1953).
54. H. G. Cooper, J. S. Koehler, and J. W. Marx, "Irradiation Effects in Cu, Ag, and Au near 10° K," *Phys. Rev.*, **97,** 599 (1955).
55. B. G. Lazarev and O. N. Ovcharenko, "The Effect of Holes in a Crystal Lattice on the Electrical Resistance of a Metal," *Doklady Akad. Nauk S.S.S.R.*, **100,** 875 (1955).

56. W. E. Parkins, G. J. Dienes, and F. W. Brown, "Pulse-Annealing for the Study of Relaxation Processes in Solids," *J. Appl. Phys.*, **22,** 1012 (1951).
57. G. H. Kinchin and R. S. Pease, "The Displacement of Atoms in Solids by Radiation," *Rept. Progr. in Physics*, **18,** 1 (1955).
58. G. J. Dienes, "Variable Activation Energy and the Motion of Lattice Defects," *Phys. Rev.*, **91,** 1283 (1953).
59. N. H. Nachtrieb, J. A. Weil, E. Catalano, and A. W. Lawson, "Self-Diffusion in Solid Sodium. II. The Effect of Pressure," *J. Chem. Phys.*, **20,** 1189 (1952).
60. C. J. Meechan and J. A. Brinkman, "Electrical Resistivity Study of Lattice Defects Introduced in Copper by 1.25 Mev Electron Irradiation at 80° K." *Phys. Rev.*, **103,** 1193 (1956).
61. J. W. Corbett, J. M. Denney, M. D. Fiske, and R. M. Walker, "Electron Irradiation of Copper Below 10° K," *Phys. Rev.*, **104,** 851 (1957) (L).
62. J. A. Brinkman, C. E. Dixon, and C. J. Meechan, "Interstitial and Vacancy Migration in Cu_3Au and Copper," *Acta Met.*, **2,** 38 (1954).
63. C. Y. Li, and A. S. Nowick, "Atomic Mobility in Cu-Al Alloy After Quenching and Neutron Irradiation," *Phys. Rev.*, **103,** 294 (1956).
64. A. Seeger, "Bestrahlungsfehlordnung und Diffusionsvorgänge in Edelmetallen," *Z. Naturforsch.*, **10a,** 251 (1955).
65. K. Kobayashi, "Annealing of Irradiation Effects in Sodium Chloride Irradiated with High-Energy Protons," *Phys. Rev.*, **102,** 348 (1956).
66. K. Kobayashi, "Density Changes of Sodium Chloride Produced by Proton Irradiation and Its Thermal Annealing," *Phys. Rev.*, (to appear).
67. W. Primak and H. Szymanski, "Radiation Damage in Vitreous Silica: Annealing of the Density Changes," *Phys. Rev.*, **101,** 1268 (1956).
68. W. Primak, L. H. Fuchs, and P. P. Day, "Radiation Damage in Diamond and Silicon Carbide," *Phys. Rev.*, **103,** 1184 (1956).
69. T. R. Waite, "Theory of Diffusion Limited Reactions; Annealing of Radiation Damage in Germanium," *Bull. Am. Phys. Soc.*, II **2,** 156 (1957) (A).
70. A. H. Cottrell and B. A. Bilby, "Dislocation Theory of Yielding and Strain Ageing of Iron," *Proc. Phys. Soc. (London)*, *A***62,** 49 (1949).
71. M. Fox and R. W. Powell, "The Annealing of the Graphite Moderator Structure in the BNL Reactor," *Brookhaven National Laboratory*, Report BNL-275 (unpublished).
72. W. L. Kosiba, G. J. Dienes, and D. H. Gurinsky, "Evaluation of BNL Pile Graphite," *Brookhaven National Laboratory*, Report BNL-255 (unpublished).
73. W. L. Kosiba, G. J. Dienes, and D. H. Gurinsky, "Some Effects Produced in Graphite by Neutron Irradiation in the BNL Reactor," *Proceedings of the Conference on Carbon*, Univ. of Buffalo, Buffalo, New York, 1956, pp. 143–8.
74. M. Fox, "The Brookhaven Reactor," *Proceedings of the International Conference on the Peaceful Uses of Atomic Energy*, United Nations, 1956, Vol. 2, (Paper No. 860).
75. G. R. Hennig, "Review of Radiation Damage to Graphite," in *Metallurgy and Fuels* (Editors, H. M. Finniston and J. P. Howe), Pergamon Press, London. 1956.

76. G. R. Hennig and J. E. Hove, "Radiation Damage to Graphite," *Proceedings of the International Conference on the Peaceful Uses of Atomic Energy*, United Nations, 1956, Vol. 7, p. 666 (Paper No. 751).
77. M. A. Kanter "Self-Diffusion in Natural Graphite Crystals," *Phys. Rev.*, **98,** 1563 (1955) (A).
78. G. J. Dienes, "Mechanism for Self-Diffusion in Graphite," *J. Appl. Phys.*, **23,** 1194 (1952).
79. In this connection see also the comments by H. Brooks in "Nuclear Radiation Effects in Solids," *Ann. Rev. Nuclear Sci.*, **6,** (1956).

CHAPTER 6

Special Topics

Irradiation effects of interest in various fields will be treated in this chapter. Many of the effects discussed here are not simply interpretable at the present time. The topics, not all of which are treated in full detail, were chosen because of impressive changes in some property or process, or because irradiation promises to be an interesting tool for further research. The particular items discussed here should be considered as illustrative examples. Particle irradiation is a rather new method in solid-state research, and it would be premature to try to assess it definitely at this time.

6.1 Mechanical Properties of Metals

Particle irradiation brings about large changes in some of the mechanical properties of metals. The increase in elastic modulus has already been discussed in Chapter 4 and has been attributed to the pinning of dislocations by radiation-induced defects. By the same argument it is expected that the critical shear stress would increase since it depends on the break-away of pinned dislocations. This is the case, and indeed this effect was observed first. Blewitt and Coltman (1) have studied the stress-strain curves of irradiated and unirradiated single crystals of copper. Some typical experimental results are shown in Figure 6.1. The critical shear stress increased from 0.241 and 2.00 kg/mm^2 for a fast-neutron exposure of about 2×10^{18} nvt (3). After appreciable plastic deformation the differences in the stress-strain curves essentially disappear as shown in Figure 6.1. The discontinuities at a shear strain of about 0.6 are due to an additional irradiation of about 2×10^{18} nvt. It is clear that after cold work the effect of irradiation is much smaller than for annealed samples. It is also clear from Figure 6.1 that there is no one-to-one correspondence between cold-work and radiation hardening. On the basis of the shape of the stress-strain curve of the irradiated specimen, Blewitt and co-workers suggest that irradiation is somewhat similar to solid-solution hardening (2,3). The slip characteristics of the

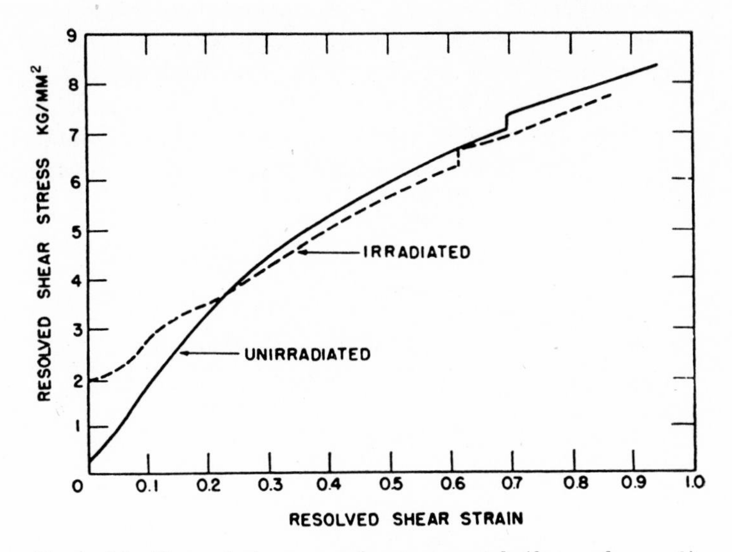

Figure 6.1 Stress-strain curves of copper crystals (from reference 1).

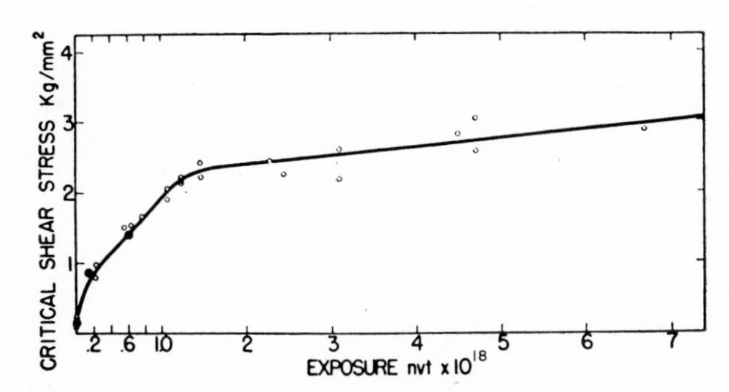

Figure 6.2 Effect of neutron irradiation on the critical shear stress of copper (from reference 3).

irradiated crystal are similar to those of α-brass, and the critical shear stress *vs* bombardment curve, given in Figure 6.2, is similar to those showing the effect of alloying (critical shear stress *vs* composition curves).

Kunz and Holden (4) obtained similar results for iron and zinc single crystals. McReynolds *et al.* (5) studied copper and aluminum after reactor bombardment at 80° K and found that the effects in Al annealed out before reaching room temperature, while temperatures of about 300° C were required before the increase in the critical shear stress of copper annealed out, in agreement with the observations of Blewitt and Coltman. The values of the critical shear stress obtained in these experiments are much larger than those obtainable by alloying. On the basis of the original number of defects introduced

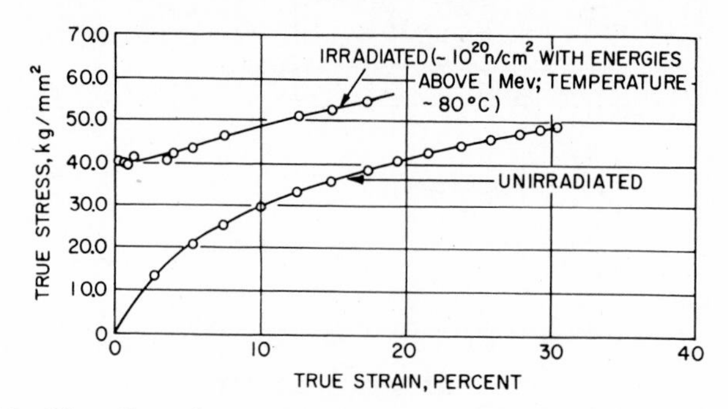

Figure 6.3 The effect of reactor exposure on the stress-strain curve of nickel (from reference 7).

by irradiation, Blewitt (6) estimated that one interstitial atom was 40 times as effective as a Zn atom in raising the critical shear stress. It is very unlikely that the defects are still present as simple point defects, and many of them must have annealed out (see Chapter 5). However, whatever the nature of the defects responsible, it is clear that they are extremely effective in raising the critical shear stress.

In some metals the whole stress-strain curve is appreciably altered by irradiation. A typical example is the curve for nickel shown in Figure 6.3, taken from the work of Bruch, McHugh, and Hockenbury (7).

Irradiation also affects the brittle-to-ductile transition temperature in those metals that exhibit a brittle behavior below a certain temperature and a ductile behavior above this temperature. Meyer (8) studied in some detail this effect in mild steel using 18.6-Mev deuterons for irradiation. Figure 6.4 illustrates the results obtained in impact tests before and after irradiation with an average total exposure of 6.7×10^{17} particles/cm^2 (29.6 μa-hr/cm^2). This irradiation increased the transition temperature from $-1°$ C to about $8°$ C. Such embrittlement appears to be characteristic of body-centered-cubic structures. Bruch, McHugh, and Hockenbury (9) found that molybdenum exhibited brittle behavior in tensile tests after an exposure of about 10^{20} nvt. The transition temperature was increased from $-30°$ C to about $70°$ C.

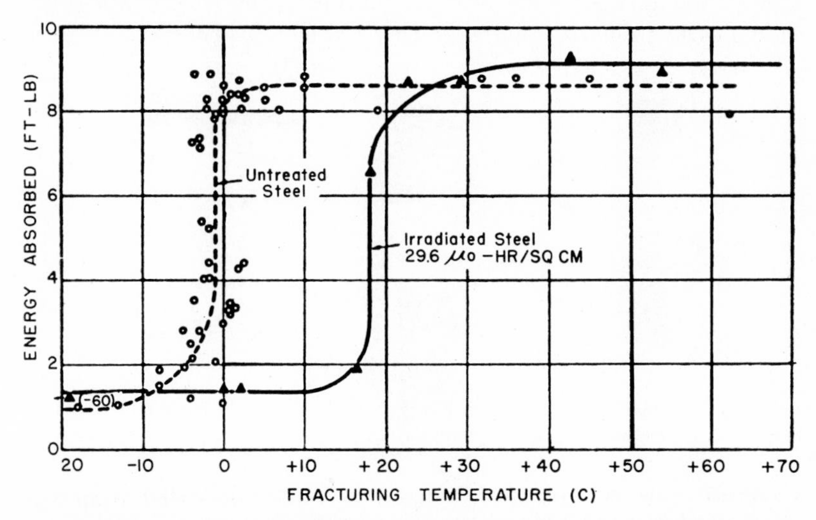

Figure 6.4 Transition curve for untreated and irradiated impact specimens (from reference 8).

6.2 Dimensional Stability (Uranium)

Changes in density brought about by particle irradiation have been discussed already in Chapter 4. In one case, that of graphite, gross dimensional distortion and its annealing have been shown to be of great practical importance (Chapter 5). In this section the large distortions of irradiated uranium will be discussed, a dimensional change which is not a change in density (which is small) and which is an order of magnitude larger than the more or less normal distortions expected in other materials. Uranium, of course, is fissionable, and a sample of the material is subjected both to fast-neutron and fission-fragment damage. Thus, severe damage is to be expected in any case. The effects to be discussed, however, appear to be connected with the highly anisotropic crystal structure of uranium rather than any particular mode of irradiation. The brief presentation given here is based to a large extent on the papers by Paine and Kittel (10) and Pugh (11).

A. The Phenomenon of Radiation Growth

Figure 6.5 shows a series of photographs of a single crystal of alpha-uranium before and after irradiation. The crystal was originally nearly a right circular cylinder 0.125 inch in diameter. A great

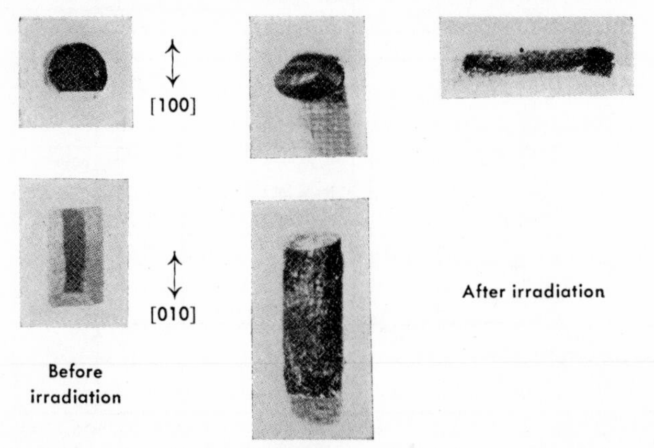

Figure 6.5 Views of a cylindrical single crystal of alpha uranium before and after irradiation (0.1% atom burnup) in a reactor (from reference 10).

deal of lengthening and shortening has occurred in the [010] and [100] directions, respectively, and the circular cross section has become elliptical. It is convenient to express the growth caused by irradiation in terms of the dimensionless quantity G_i, defined by

$$G_i = \frac{\ln (L/L_0)}{\text{Ratio of fissions to total atoms}} \tag{6-1}$$

where L_0 and L are the linear dimensions before and after irradiation, respectively. For small elongations the relation

$$G_i = \text{Per cent growth}/\text{Per cent burnup} \tag{6-2}$$

is adequate. Typical growth values are shown in Table 6.1. These numbers show that the length of a uranium rod would roughly double for about 0.2% burnup.

Table 6.1. Irradiation growth coefficients of a single crystal of alpha-uranium (Argonne National Laboratory, specimen irradiated to 0.1% burnup at approximately 100° C)

Direction pole	Irradiation growth coefficient, G_i (equation 6-1)
[100]	-420 ± 20
[010]	$+420 \pm 20$
[001]	0 ± 20

Imperfect lineage crystals have the same general behavior as single crystals, but the magnitude of the elongation is greater and the geometrical regularity of the distorted specimens is less.

Cylindrical polycrystalline specimens in which the grains are not randomly oriented also deform under irradiation. The magnitude and character of the deformation and surface distortion depend upon structural factors. Longitudinal growth rates more than double those measured in single crystals have been observed in highly oriented polycrystalline specimens irradiated at the same temperature.

Polycrystalline uranium also exhibits marked deformation as a result of thermal cycling. This effect does not occur in single crystals. There are some similarities to irradiation growth, but the above difference in single crystals shows clearly that there must be a basic difference in the mechanism, and this analogy will not be pursued any further.

B. Suggested Interpretations

A number of mechanisms have been proposed to account for the irradiation growth of alpha-uranium. It is clear that anisotropy plays an important role in leading to differential strains which have to be at least partly irreversible. Two major mechanisms in single crystals are generally considered important at the present time: (*a*) anisotropic diffusion and (*b*) plastic deformation accompanying fission spikes.

(*a*) *Diffusion mechanism.* Seigle and Opinsky (10,12) have proposed a mechanism based upon anisotropic diffusion of interstitials and vacancies. The alteration of shape arises from this diffusion by gross material transfer (13,14,15). Seigle and Opinsky propose that interstitials migrate with some preference for the [010] direction while vacancies would migrate in the [100] and [001] directions. It is assumed that the diffusion of interstitials and vacancies essentially balances in the [001] direction, leading to a net shrinkage in the [100] direction. The theory predicts that the rate of growth in the [010] direction will vary as the $^3/_4$ power of the neutron flux and the square root of the diffusion coefficient for interstitials. As in all diffusion mechanisms, a temperature dependence is, of course, predicted. An estimate (16,17) of the number of defects produced per fission shows that there is a plentiful supply of defects for the operation of this mechanism. The model is partially supported by the work of Kunz and Holden (4), who showed that the deformation rate of cold-rolled uranium foil is greatly reduced when irradiation is done at liquid-air temperatures where diffusion would be largely suppressed.

(*b*) *Plastic deformation accompanying fission spikes.* A growth mechanism can be based on the thermal expansion in the fission spike. An essential part of such a mechanism is that plastic deformation should be caused by the local expansion and that there should be a difference in behavior on heating and cooling. Pugh (11) ascribed growth to fission spikes accompanied by anisotropic plastic deformation. The anisotropic plastic properties of uranium have been deduced by Cahn from the observed slip and twin systems (18). The proposed mechanism is as follows: The uniform compressive stress around the site of fission causes local preferential plastic yielding by twinning in uranium single crystals in the longitudinal [010] direction. When the fission spike cools, the outer region is subjected to a uniform tensile stress and therefore yields plastically, this time by twinning in the [100] and [001] directions. The net result is a local increase in length in the [010] direction in the outer region. This local extension throws a stress on the surrounding matrix, which is relieved by equal amounts of slip on both the (110) planes. Since tension in the [010] direction produces no resolved shear stress on the (010) plane, slip in this plane does not occur even though it is the major slip mode. The macrodeformation of the crystal is, therefore, by (110) [110] shears, which agrees with experiment in that extension occurs in the [010] direction, contraction in the [100] direction, and no change in the [001] direction. No limit is imposed on the extent of growth.

Since slip is a reversible process, in a geometrical sense it could not be the basis of a ratchet mechanism. The above model predicts, therefore, that growth rates would diminish above 350° C and be practically zero at 600° C, because at the higher temperature slip would occur rather than twinning and slip. Below 200° C growth would diminish with decreasing temperature because of the increase in the yield strength of the crystal. Experimental observations are in agreement with these predictions.

The main difficulty with the preceding model is that fission spikes are of very short duration and are rather small. The two recoiling fission fragments will dissipate the energy of fission along a line 10^{-4} to 10^{-3} cm long. At distances greater than about 500 atoms from this line the yield stress will no longer be exceeded, while usually around 1000 atoms need to be affected to cause operation of a Frank-Read source. A part of the energy, however, is temporarily stored as interstitials and vacancies, which also cause a local expansion. Above 500° C these defects recombine very fast, but below this temperature they will keep the fission spike expanded somewhat, although the concentration of defects is probably too small to be very effective. If flow occurs, therefore, it must occur very rapidly. More detailed calculations by Seitz and Koehler (19) indicate, however, that plastic flow is likely to occur in the zone of highest stress as a result of the generation of dislocation rings of the order of five atomic distances in diameter. Thus, the twinning mechanism appears to be a plausible mechanism. It will take much detailed experimentation to decide between this and the diffusion mechanism.

6.3 Phase Transformations

Many phase transformations are highly structure sensitive and many different disturbances in the crystal may lead to nucleation and growth of another phase. Thus, phase transformations are certainly expected to be sensitive to particle irradiation. Very few detailed studies have been made, and the conditions of the effectiveness of irradiation have not been established in any general sense, although particle irradiation promises to be a powerful new tool for studying nucleation and growth processes. Some of the studies in this field are discussed in this section with emphasis on pure materials. Transformations which can be interpreted either as disordering by irradiation (ordered alloys, quartz) or enhanced ordering due to increased diffusion (Cu_3Au, CuZn) have already been discussed in Chapter 4 and are not treated any further here.

The first indication of an allotropic phase change induced by reactor irradiation came from x-ray diffraction studies of reactor-irradiated black phosphorus (20). In addition to the anticipated expansion in the *c*-axis due to the presence of interstitials, extra lines appeared in the pattern of the irradiated material corresponding to one or another of the forms of the more stable red phosphorus. Although complete correspondence with the red phosphorus pattern was not observed, this result suggested strongly a radiation-induced phase change.

For a basic and detailed study of such a radiation-induced process the system under investigation should satisfy several requirements. Fleeman and Dienes (21) chose the white to grey tin transformation for investigation for the following reasons:

(*a*) The transformation is a first-order phase change between two well known structures in a monotomic system.

(*b*) The transformation temperature, 13.2° C, is in a convenient temperature range, and the transformation rate is slow and beomes negligible below −80° C. Thus, the substance can be put in a metastable state and irradiated in that state.

(*c*) The radioactivity produced in the reactor in tin causes no appreciable experimental difficulties.

(*d*) The transformation is easily followed by dilatometry by virtue of the very large volume increase accompanying the white to grey tin phase change (27 per cent).

The effect of low-temperature (liquid nitrogen) reactor irradiation on this transformation was investigated. Exposures of about 10^{18} nvt were used. It was found that, compared to an unirradiated control sample, the transformation is drastically accelerated by prior irradiation. The irradiation apparently eliminated the normally very long induction period preceding the transformation. Unirradiated control specimens showed no transformation at all in the time intervals required to transform the irradiated samples. X-ray diffraction patterns showed that the irradiation itself did not cause any transformation. The kinetic behavior of reactor irradiated samples and of samples seeded with grey tin were found to be qualitatively similar. These results indicated that the defects introduced into white tin by reactor irradiation serve as nuclei, or at least embryos of nucleation, for the subsequent phase transformation.

The nature of the defects responsible for this transformation has not yet been established. The rather large strains expected around interstitial atoms, for example, may well serve as foci for nucleation. Thermal spikes associated with neutron knock-ons may serve the same purpose by taking a small volume of material into a temperature region where nucleation can be initiated. The main argument against this view is that the control samples do not transform within the experimental time interval at any temperature and, therefore, if the interpretation is to be in terms of thermal spikes it is essential to invoke the lattice distortion of plastic deformation around the spike. Preliminary experiments by Sosin (22) apparently support this view since he found that low-temperature electron irradiation, which does not produce thermal spikes, does not lead to nucleation. Sosin's exposures were, however, too low to be properly comparable. Further detailed experiments are necessary. Annealing studies, for example, may throw light on the mechanism. The anneal of interstitials and vacancies can be followed by resistivity measurements, and their concentration correlated with the transformation characteristics. The nuclei produced by thermal spikes would probably not anneal out except near the transformation temperature.

A rather different radiation-induced transformation has been observed by Wittels and Sherill (23) in zirconia. They found that, as a result of fast-neutron bombardment of about 10^{20} nvt at about 100° C, monoclinic ZrO_2 was transformed into the cubic phase normally stable only above 1900° C. The radiation-induced cubic phase is stable to about 800° C and begins to revert to the low-temperature modification above this temperature. The suggested interpretation for this transformation, which, it will be noted, is away from thermodynamic equilibrium, invokes both displaced atoms and thermal spikes. It is suggested that the high temperatures of a spike render small regions capable of thermal transformation and that the internal stresses about interstitials cause a collapse of the lattice to the smaller volume and closer packing of the high-temperature phase. That interstitials are indeed present is indicated by the increase in the lattice parameter of the cubic phase in a stabilized (cubic ZrO_2 plus monoclinic ZrO_2) sample. Apparently there are some further complications, as some recent data indicate that certain high-purity samples of ZrO_2 will not transform under irradiation (24).

6.4 Precipitation from Solid Solution

Precipitation from solid solution is a far more complicated phase change than the ones considered in the previous section. Precipitation, however, is a very important metallurgical process, and the influence of fast-particle irradiation has been investigated in a few cases (25).

The copper-beryllium system was investigated by Billington and Siegel (26) and in more detail by Murray and Taylor (27). These investigators studied the effect of reactor irradiation (exposures up to 3×10^{19} nvt total, temperature of exposure 0–40° C) upon the properties of a 2.2% (by weight) beryllium alloy initially in the solution-treated condition. Electrical resistivity and hardness were found to change in a way similar to that caused by aging the alloy at low temperatures, the heat treatment being carried out 75–150° C above the temperature of irradiation. Retrogression, or resolution, phenomena were also similar to retrogression following low-temperature aging. The changes during irradiation are attributed to the formation of small precipitate nuclei, presumably formed by accelerated micro-diffusion caused by the presence of the radiation-induced defects. An anomalous density increase and corresponding x-ray line shift were observed, which probably resulted from homogeneously distributed precipitate nuclei. It is to be noted that no direct evidence was obtained for the presence of precipitate particles in any of the above experiments.

More direct evidence for precipitation was obtained by Kernohan, Billington and Lewis (28) in their study of the nickel-beryllium system. A nickel-2% beryllium alloy was used whose precipitation hardening reaction is very similar to that of copper-beryllium. However, there is an important advantage to the Ni-Be system in that it is ferromagnetic and its ferromagnetic Curie temperature is a linear function of the amount of beryllium in solid solution. Another difference is that the activation energy for the precipitation process is higher in Ni-Be than in Cu-Be and, therefore, irradiation effects may set in at a higher temperature where there is sufficient mobility of the defects. The experimental results, some of which are shown in Figure 6.6, confirmed these expectations. No effects were found at room temperature. Irradiation at 300° C, however, for an integrated fast flux of 4×10^{17} nvt resulted in an increase in the Curie temperature as shown in Figure 6.6. This change in the Curie temperature is equivalent to an additional precipitation of 1.3 atomic

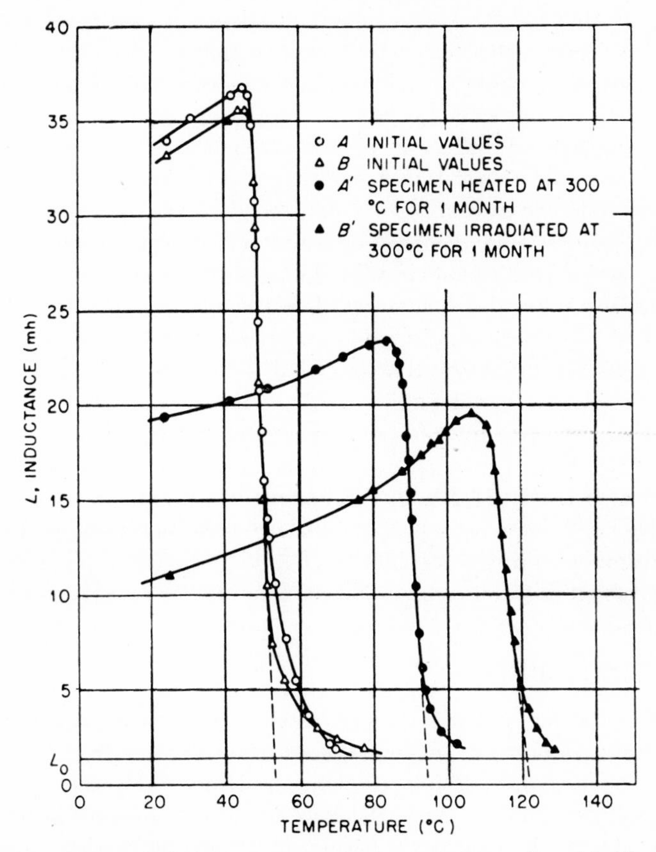

Figure 6.6 Magnetic inductance *vs* temperature curves for nickel-beryllium (from reference 28).

per cent of beryllium. In this case thermal spikes probably do not play an important role because of the temperature dependence of the process, and an interpretation in terms of enhanced diffusion due to the extra concentration of defects is more reasonable.

A combination of defect migration and the action of thermal spikes appears to occur when the copper-iron system is irradiated. Denney (29) found that the metastable coherent gamma-iron precipitate in a 2.4% iron alloy begins to transform to alpha-iron upon irradiation by electrons. Upon proton irradiation the alpha-iron precipitate reverts to the gamma structure (30). This result is similar to that for the U-Mo system discussed in Chapter 3 and may well be caused by thermal or displacement spikes. Independent work by Boltax (31) confirmed the above effects. Boltax was able to investigate the process further by preparing, by means of proper aging, samples of different precipitate particle sizes for neutron irradiation. He found that resolution of the precipitate is favored by small particle size and solid-solution depletion by large particle size. Resolution may be due to the action of thermal or displacement spikes, while additional precipitation is facilitated by increased microdiffusion via the augmented defect concentration.

The effect of neutron irradiation (below 100° C) upon the stability of austenite in stainless steel (AISI Type 347) was investigated by Reynolds, Low and Sullivan (32). They found that the transformation to ferrite by cold work was enhanced by prior irradiation. Very little difference, if any, could be observed in the absence of plastic deformation. This is in agreement with the work of Konobeevsky and co-workers (33) who found that, upon neutron irradiation of stainless steel (18% Cr, 9% Ni, 0.6% Ti, 0.1% C), no ferromagnetism appeared if care was taken to prevent plastic deformation.

6.5 Chemical Effects

Irradiation of materials with various types of nuclear radiation may have important chemical consequences. Ionizing radiation causes the formation of ions, and free radicals result upon neutralization of these ions. Both the ions and the free radicals may be chemically highly reactive. Displaced atoms, since they represent quite drastic disturbances in the solid, may have an important effect on any chemical reaction involving the solid itself, particularly surface properties and surface reactions. These topics really fall within the province of Radiation Chemistry (34). However, there are several effects peculiar to solids and of particular interest to solid-state physics. These are reviewed briefly in this section.

A. Decomposition of Salts

Certain salts decompose when exposed to ionizing radiation. Allen and Ghormley (35) have shown, for example, that irradiated barium nitrate yields nitrite ion and oxygen upon dissolution in water. During irradiation the gas is trapped in the crystal as O atoms or O_2 molecules. Further contribution in such decompositions came from Hennig, Lees, and Matheson (36) who irradiated sodium nitrate, potassium nitrate and potassium chlorate for 2–4 weeks in the Argonne heavy-water reactor. Gas evolution was found not only upon dissolution but also by melting the crystal or heating to a crystal transition point. Irradiation with low-energy x-rays led to about the same yield per unit energy absorbed as reactor irradiation. It is clear, therefore, that the decomposition results from electronic ionization and excitation rather than from the displacement of atoms by elastic collision. In the case of the nitrates the gas was shown to be largely oxygen, which is trapped during irradiation in the gaseous form in small pockets in the crystal. The gas was identified by chemical analysis and by the paramagnetism of the irradiated crystals. Oxygen and nitrite ions were formed in equivalent amounts. Upon heating below the melting point the gas pockets grow and coalesce, resulting in a decrease in crystal density. The highest gas yields were observed in potassium chlorate, which is probably due to the weakness of the Cl—O bond relative to the N—O bond.

Pringsheim (37) correlated optical properties with decomposition by investigating the absorption spectrum of irradiated $NaNO_3$. He found two absorption bands, one at 345 mμ with a characteristic structure when observed at low temperature, the other a color-center band which is continuous with a peak near 335 mμ. The 345 mμ band is identified with NO_2^- ions since the same band appears upon adding $NaNO_2$ to the melt. The color-center band is bleached by ultraviolet light even at low temperature and is partially destroyed by ionizing radiation at room temperature, while the NO_2^- ions are quite stable. Thus, the NO_2^- band is stronger in crystals exposed at elevated temperatures, while the color-center band predominates in crystals x-rayed at low temperatures. The color centers were found to be anisotropic, as shown by differential bleaching with polarized light.

Rosenwasser, Dreyfus, and Levy (38) investigated the coloring of sodium azide, most likely brought about by decomposition, under exposure to a variety of radiations. They found that gamma-rays alone produce an absorption band at 3600 A that is little affected by heating at 90° C, and poorly defined bands at 6600 and 7600 A that decay completely at room temperature. Fast-neutron irradiation at room temperature, slow-neutron irradiation at 100° C, or slow-neutron irradiation at room temperature followed by heating at 90° C, gave rise to a band at 6000 A. This band does not appear, even with prolonged heating at 90° C, in crystals exposed only to gamma-rays, but it does appear if the crystal is heated to higher temperature. The 6000 A band has not been definitely identified, and it could be associated with a number of different color centers. One plausible interpretation is that this band is the result of the aggregation of sodium into colloidal particles, this process being facilitated by the disruption of the lattice. The sodium itself, as well as free nitrogen, are formed by the radiation decomposition of the crystal.

B. Polymerization in the Solid State

An interesting manifestation of free-radical formation is the gamma-ray-induced polymerization in the solid state, a process which does not occur thermally in those crystals that have been studied. The first experiments were carried out with acrylamide, a monomer which shows little or no tendency to polymerize thermally below its melting point (39).

The samples were irradiated in vacuum and the polymer isolated by using methanol as a precipitant. Rate curves were obtained at several temperatures, as shown in Figure 6.7. Residual crystallinity of the bulk sample, as determined by the intensity of several x-ray reflections, is also shown for comparison. The temperature remained constant during these experiments to ±1° C, and no sintering was ever observed. The fact that appreciable crystallinity remains even at high conversions (Figure 6.7) demonstrates that the crystalline domain of unreacted monomer in the vicinity of polymer chains is only slightly affected by the latter.

It is evident from the rate curve at 5° C that a long induction period prevails at this temperature before the onset of polymerization. At still lower temperatures no reaction is detectable. Radicals are, however, produced since, on warming a previously irradiated sample to room temperature, violent polymerization occurs. The radicals are, therefore, frozen in at low temperatures. Their presence has been confirmed by some preliminary paramagnetic resonance measurements (courtesy of M. M. Weiss and V. W. Cohen of Brookhaven National Laboratory). A series of samples irradiated to 15, 25 and 50 megaroentgens gave approximately 0.3×10^{-4} to 10^{-4} molal radicals by comparison with α,α diphenyl-β-picryl hydrazyl.

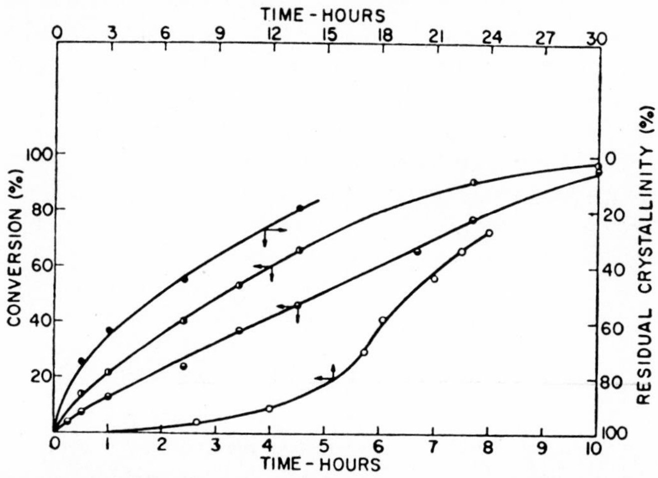

Figure 6.7 Solid state polymerization of acrylamide initiated by gamma-radiation (Co^{60}, 220,000 r/hour) at several temperatures. ● Residual crystallinity in material exposed at 35° C. ◑ Per cent conversion at 55° C. ◒ Per cent conversion at 35° C. ○ Per cent conversion at 5° C (from reference 39).

More detailed studies have been performed and reported recently on acrylamide and on a variety of crystalline monomers (40). Acrylamide, methacrylamide, methylene-*bis*-acrylamide, vinyl carbazole, vinyl stearate, acrylic acid, methacrylic acid and potassium, calcium and barium acrylates have been polymerized in the solid state by irradiation with γ-rays. The molecular weight of polyacrylamide obtained at low conversion was constant over a 270-fold variation of radiation intensity and in the temperature range 20 to 65°, but increased slightly with the energy of the radiation. The polymerization rate, however, was linear with field intensity, independent of the energy of radiation, and had an over-all activation energy of 4.7 kcal/mole.

The extension of these studies to the solid-state polymerization of acrylic acid salts was primarily performed to determine whether a monomer whose crystal lattice is stable up to a high temperature is subject to polymerization with γ-rays at room temperature. The heats of polymerization of liquid vinyl monomers range from 17.5 to 21.3 kcal/mole for styrene and vinyl acetate, respectively. The heat

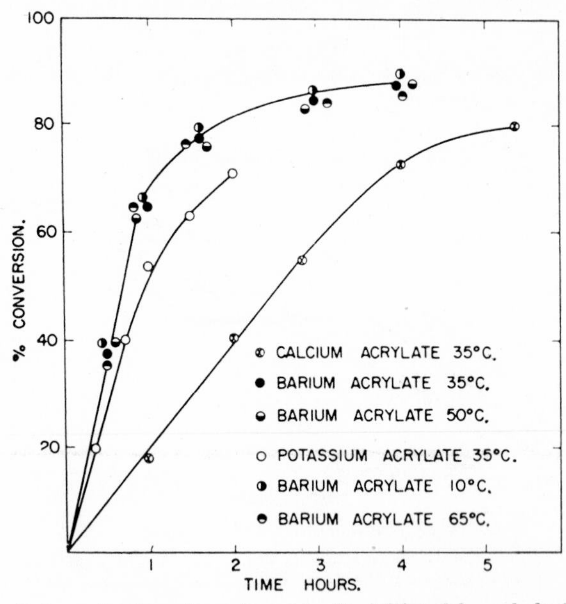

Figure 6.8 Polymerization of acrylic acid salts initiated by cobalt-60 γ-rays of 190,000 r/hour (from reference 40).

of polymerization of crystalline monomers will be less than that of the corresponding liquid monomer by the heat of fusion. Although in the case of acrylamide polymerization at room temperature, the heat of polymerization per mole is not sufficient to melt more than 3 to 5 molecules per reacted monomer, with crystalline monomers having high molar specific heats or monomers having high melting points the heat of polymerization will be insufficient to cause any melting. Assuming for potassium acrylate a specific heat of 0.3 cal/g/° C, a heat of fusion $\Delta H_m = 3$ kcal/mole, a heat of polymerization of the crystalline monomer (based on an assumed heat of polymerization of liquid monomer ~ 20 kcal/mole) of $20 - \Delta H_m =$

17 kcal/mole, and neglecting heat conduction in the crystal, 80% of the heat of polymerization is required to raise one neighboring monomer molecule from room temperature to the melting point of 360°. It is evident that one is dealing here with some thermal excitation but nothing akin to melting.

Barium, potassium and calcium acrylate were found to polymerize rapidly, as shown in Figure 6.8. Thus, monomers which melt at very high temperatures are nevertheless polymerizable at considerably lower temperatures. As with acrylamides, the polymerized crystals show no evidence of sintering, and the birefringence of poly(potassium acrylate) observed in a polarizing microscope is nearly identical to that of the unirradiated monomer. In addition, since it has been reported that fully ionized acrylic acid will not polymerize in aqueous media, due to electrostatic repulsion between the charged monomer and radical, one may conjecture that the order of acrylate ions in a crystalline lattice markedly enhances propagation along crystallographic directions. An interesting feature of the polymerization of acrylic acid salts is the absence of any temperature coefficient for barium acrylate polymerizations between 10 and 65°. If such behavior should be found to be typical of the solid-state polymerization of monomers with very high melting points, it would strongly indicate that lattice defects or spur spacings determine the kinetic chain length whenever the heat of polymerization is insufficient to disrupt the lattice order.

C. *Effects on Reaction Rates*

In this section the work on heterogeneous solid-gas and solid-liquid reactions is discussed. The imperfections in the crystal, which are created by high-energy bombardment, may be expected to alter the chemical properties of a crystal in a significant way. This aspect of irradiation research has only received cursory attention in the past. Taylor and Wethington (41) have investigated the effect of γ-ray irradiation of ZnO on its catalytic activity for the hydrogenation of C_2H_4. They found that the catalytic activity was lowered, either as a result of electronic changes or poisoning by polymerization of residual C_2H_4 on the surface. With γ-irradiation no appreciable production of displaced atoms is expected. Hurst and Wright (42) reported recently that at temperatures where the thermal oxidation of graphite is very low, the radiation-induced oxidation in a reactor is many times faster. They gave similar results for the graphite-CO_2 reaction. The details of these experiments are not yet available. Weisz and Swegler (43) have indicated that fast-

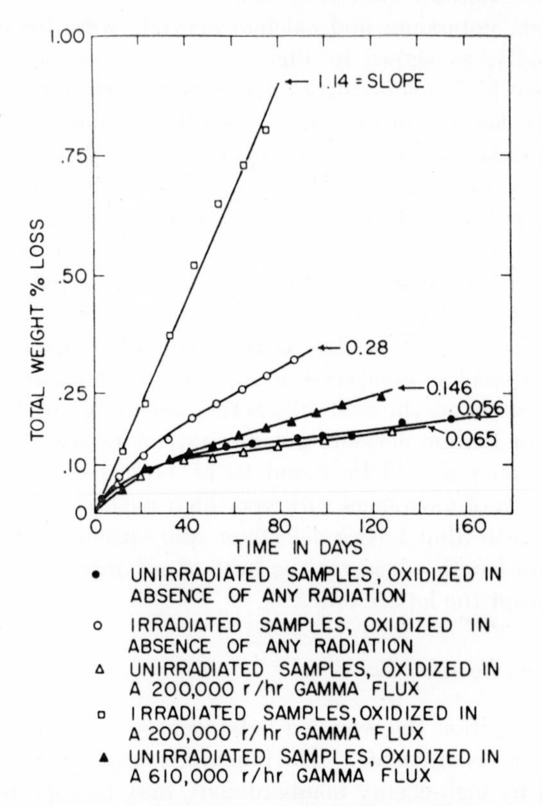

Figure 6.9 Per cent weight loss *vs* time curve for graphite at 300° C. Slopes given as % loss/100 days (from reference 46).

neutron irradiation of a pure silica gel produces an increase in catalytic activity for the double-bond isomerization of hexene. There was a lot of spread in their experimental results, but the radiation effect was statistically significant. Simnad and Smoluchowski (44,45) have shown that fast-proton irradiation alters the electrochemical properties of tungsten as well as the rate of solution of

Fe_2O_3 in hydrochloric acid. Chemical reactivity was increased in both cases.

A systematic investigation was carried out by Kosiba and Dienes (46) on the effect of displaced atoms and ionizing radiation on the oxidation of graphite in the 250–450° C temperature range as

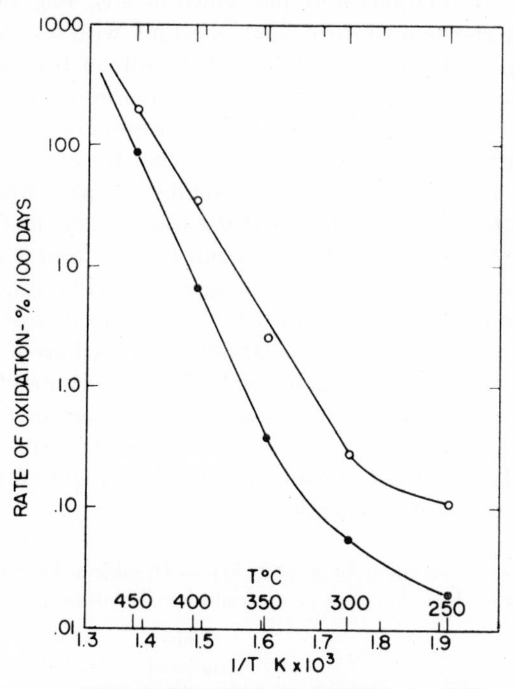

Figure 6.10 Rate of oxidation *vs* $1/T$ for graphite oxidized under various conditions (from reference 46).

an example of a heterogeneous solid-gas reaction. Graphite was chosen for this study because it is known that a fast-neutron exposure of 1×10^{20} nvt produces of the order of 2.5% displaced atoms in this material and that an appreciable faction of these displaced atoms remain in the material up to high temperatures. Such examples were available from the Brookhaven reactor. It is also known that

γ-irradiation has no permanent effect upon the properties of graphite, thus permitting one to study separately the effects of displaced atoms and of ionizing radiation on this gas-solid reaction.

The graphite samples were oxidized by passing dried and preheated oxygen over weighed samples in a furnace kept at a constant temperature. Oxidations were performed at 450, 400, 350, 300 and 250° C with the temperature kept constant with n $\pm 5°$ C. The oxygen was passed over the graphite at the rate of 1.5 liters/minute, and the exhaust gases were allowed to escape into the atmosphere, except in the case of previously reactor irradiated samples where care was exercised to exhaust the gases so that the atmosphere would not become contaminated. The graphite samples were weighed before and after each oxidation and the total weight loss was determined. The time of each oxidation run ranged from 3 to 20 days, with the total time of oxidation extending up to 170 days. A typical set of results is shown in Figure 6.9. The rates of oxidation were determined from the slopes of the straight-line portions of the various curves. This usually meant ignoring the initial portions of the curves and considering the steady-state portions as the pertinent oxidation rates. The oxidation rates at various temperatures are compiled in Table 6.2. Log rate *vs* $1/T$ plots are shown in Figure 6.10 with the corresponding activation energies.

Table 6.2. Rates of oxidation for graphite in pure O_2 subjected to various irradiations. Reaction rates in % weight loss/100 days

T° C	Unirradiated samples	Irradiated samples	Unirradiated samples + 200,000 r/hr γ-flux	Unirradiated samples + 610,000 r/hr γ-flux	Irradiated samples + 200,000 r/hr γ-flux
450	86.2	195.6			
400	6.62	34.76			
350	0.38	2.58			
300	0.056	0.28	0.065	0.146	1.14
250	0.020	0.108	0.034		

From the experimental results one may draw the following conclusions:

(*a*) Prior reactor irradiation increases greatly the oxidation rate of graphite in the 250 to 400° C range. The increase in the reaction rate is a catalytic effect in the following sense: Some of the displaced atoms anneal out upon raising the temperature to the reaction temperature, and, at the most, about 1% displaced atoms are present at these temperatures. From the results at 400° C, for example, it is clear that the higher oxidation rate persists even when 20–25% of the specimen has been oxidized. Thus, the displaced atoms are not themselves being oxidized preferentially but facilitate in some way the over-all oxidation. This effect is not brought about by an increase in surface area, since it is known from the recent work of Spalaris (47) that the surface area and the porosity (for all sizes of pore radii) of graphite decrease upon reactor irradiation at room temperature.

(*b*) Ionizing radiation (gamma-rays) present during oxidation also increases the rate of oxidation of unirradiated graphite, but by a much smaller factor. This effect is enhanced by the presence of displaced atoms in irradiated graphite, where a further increase of the rate by about a factor of three is observed at 300° C. The gamma-ray effect is probably caused by the ionization of oxygen molecules, since gamma-rays have not been observed to have any effect on the properties of graphite at these exposures.

(*c*) The activation energy for the oxidation of unirradiated graphite was found to be 48.8 kcal/mole as evaluated from the straight-line portion of the curve of Figure 6.10. This value is higher than the 37 kcal/mole measured by Gulbransen and Andrew (48) in the 425 to 575° C range and the 40 kcal/mole mentioned by Hurst and Wright (42). This may well be due to the differences among various types of graphite. By comparison with the irradiated samples it is clear, however, that neutron irradiation results in a considerably lower activation energy for the reaction, i.e., 36.1 kcal/mole. This may be interpreted as an actual lowering of the activation energy or as a superposition of two reactions, the normal thermal reaction plus the defect-induced oxidation. This point cannot be decided until the reaction is followed over a much wider temperature range. The curvature in the log (rate) *vs* $1/T$ curves at low temperature might indicate the onset of another mechanism, although errors are very large at these low rates of oxidation. In any case, the irradiation effect persists.

A somewhat similar system was investigated by Simnad,

Smoluchowski and Spilners (49), who investigated the reduction of nickel oxide with hydrogen after proton irradiation. They found that the induction period for the reaction was greatly reduced by the proton irradiation provided the hydrogen reduction itself was carried out at rather low temperatures. The data are shown in Table 6.3. It is clear that at elevated temperatures the irradiation effect essentially disappears, presumably because of the progressively more rapid annealing of the defects.

Table 6.3. Influence of proton irradiation upon the hydrogen reduction of NiO

	Induction period	
Temp. of reduction	Unirradiated	Irradiated
250	1200	275
275	100	30
300	20	14
350	10	4
400	5	5

Taylor and Kohn described very recently a series of experiments with gamma-ray irradiated gamma-alumina (50). These workers found that the H_2-D_2 exchange reaction at $-78°$ C was much faster over the gamma irradiated (irradiated at $-78°$ C) than the untreated catalyst. The radiation-induced catalytic activity was found to anneal out quite easily. In this case the responsible defects are probably electronic defects, i.e., trapped electrons or holes.

Compound formation upon irradiation on the surfaces of crystals has also been observed. Wieninger and Adler (51) reported on the growth of microcrystallites on various alkali halides under the action of α-irradiation from a polonium source. The evidence to date points to the formation of nitrates by chemical reaction with NO_2, the NO_2 having been formed during the ionization of the air by the α-particles. Similar results were found by Blöch (52) who also studied fluorite. In the latter case calcium nitrate crystallites grow on the surface. The oxidation of copper is also affected by irradiation, as reported by Young (53), who found that the reaction is accelerated in the early stages of oxide film formation by reactor irradiation.

References

1. T. H. Blewitt and R. R. Coltman, "The Effect of Pile Irradiation on the Stress-Strain Curve of Copper," *Phys. Rev.*, **82,** 769 (1951) (A).
2. R. F. Jamison and T. H. Blewitt, "Slip lines in Pile Irradiated Copper Single Crystals," *Phys. Rev.*, **86,** 641 (1952) (A).
3. R. E. Jamison and T. H. Blewitt, "Some Deformation Characteristics of Reactor Irradiated Copper Single Crystals at 78° K and 300° K," *Phys. Rev.*, **91,** 237 (1953) (A).
4. F. W. Kunz and A. N. Holden, "The Effect of Short Time Moderate Flux Neutron Irradiations on the Mechanical Properties of Some Metals," *Acta Met.*, **2,** 816 (1954).
5. A. W. McReynolds, W. Augustyniak, M. McKeown and D. B. Rosenblatt, "Neutron Irradiation Effects in Cu and Al at 80° K," *Phys. Rev.*, **98,** 418 (1955).
6. As discussed by D. S. Billington in "Radiation Damage in Reactor Materials," *Proceedings of the International Conference on the Peaceful Uses of Atomic Energy*, United Nations, 1956, Vol. 7, p. 421 (Paper No. 744).
7. As discussed by F. E. Faris, "The Effects of Irradiation on Structural Materials," *Proceedings of the International Conference on the Peaceful Uses of Atomic Energy*, United Nations, 1956, Vol. 7, p. 484 (Paper No. 747). See also Bruch, McHugh and Hockenbury, "Variations in Radiation Damage to Metals," *J. Metals*, **8,** 1362 (1956).
8. R. A. Meyer, "Influence of Deuteron Bombardment and Strain Hardening on Notch Sensitivity of Mild Steel," *J. Appl. Phys.*, **25,** 1369 (1954).
9. C. A. Bruch, W. E. McHugh and R. W. Hockenbury, "Embrittlement of Molybdenum by Neutron Radiation," *Trans. Am. Inst. Mining, Met., Petrol. Engrs.*, **203,** 281 (1955).
10. S. H. Paine and J. H. Kittel, "Irradiation Effects in Uranium and Its Alloys," *Proceedings of the International Conference on the Peaceful Uses of Atomic Energy*, United Nations, 1956, Vol. 7, p. 445 (Paper No. 745).
11. S. F. Pugh, "Damage Occurring in Uranium During Burn-up," *Proceedings of the International Conference on the Peaceful Uses of Atomic Energy*, United Nations, 1956, Vol. 7, p. 441 (Paper No. 443).
12. L. L. Seigle and A. J. Opinsky, "Mechanism of Dimensional Instability," *U. S. Atomic Energy Comm.*, Report SEP-160 (1954).
13. F. R. N. Nabarro, "Deformation of Crystals by the Motion of Single Ions," *Report of the Conference on the Strength of Solids*, Physical Society, London, 1948, p. 75.
14. C. Herring, "Surface Tension as a Motivation for Sintering," in *Physics of Powder Metallurgy*, (edited by W. E. Kingston), McGraw-Hill Book Co., New York, 1951, p. 143.
15. C. Herring, "Diffusional Viscosity of a Polycrystalline Solid," *J. Appl. Phys.*, **21,** 437 (1950).
16. F. Seitz, "On the Disordering of Solids by the Action of Fast Massive Particles," *Discussions Faraday Soc.*, *No.* **5,** 271 (1949).
17. J. Ozeroff, "Atomic Displacements Produced by Fission Fragments and Fis-

sion Neutrons in Matter," *U. S. Atomic Energy Comm.*, Report AECD 2973 (1949).
18. R. W. Cahn, "Plastic Deformation of Alpha-Uranium, Twining and Slip," *Acta Met.*, **1,** 49–70 (1953).
19. F. Seitz and J. S. Koehler, "Displacement of Atoms during Irradiation," in *Solid State Physics*, (editors: F. Seitz and D. Turnbull), Academic Press, New York, 1956, Vol. 2, pp. 307–442.
20. D. L. Chipman, B. E. Warren and G. J. Dienes, "X-Ray Measurements of Radiation Damage in Black Phosphorus," *J. Appl. Phys.*, **24,** 1251 (1953).
21. J. Fleeman and G. J. Dienes, "Effect of Reactor Irradiation on the White to Grey Tin Transformation," *J. Appl. Phys.*, **26,** 652 (1955).
22. A. Sosin, "Effect of Electron Bombardment and Quenching on the White to Grey Tin Transformation," *Bull. Am. Phys. Soc.*, II, **1,** 129 (1956).
23. M. C. Wittels and F. A. Sherill, "Irradiation Induced Phase Transformation in Zirconia," *J. Appl. Phys.*, **27,** 643 (1956).
24. Remarks by D. S. Billington in "Irradiation Effects in Reactor Materials," IMD Special Report Series, No. 3, *Nuclear Metallurgy*, AIME, New York, 1956, Vol. III, pp. 31–54.
25. For a recent review see: D. E. Thomas, "Irradiation Effects on Physical Metallurgical Processes," IMD Special Report Series, No. 3, *Nuclear Metallurgy*, AIME, New York, 1956. Vol. III, pp. 13–31.
26. D. S. Billington and S. Siegel, "Effect of Nuclear Radiation on Metal," *Metal Prog.*, **58,** 847 (1950).
27. G. T. Murray and W. E. Taylor, "Effect of Neutron Irradiation on a Supersaturated Solid Solution of Beryllium in Copper," *Acta Met.*, **2,** 52 (1954).
28. R. H. Kernohan, D. S. Billington and A. B. Lewis, "Effect of Neutron Irradiation on the Precipitation Hardening Reaction in Alloys Containing Beryllium," *J. Appl. Phys.*, **27,** 40 (1956).
29. J. M. Denney, "Radiation Damage Energy Threshold in a Face Centered Cubic Alloy," *Phys. Rev.*, **92,** 531 (1953) (A).
30. J. M. Denney, "Experimental Evidence for Melted Regions in Metal Crystals Resulting from Particle Bombardment," *Phys. Rev.*, **94,** 1417 (1954).
31. A. Boltax, submitted to *Acta Met.* See also discussion in ref. 25.
32. M. B. Reynolds, J. R. Low and L. P. Sullivan, "Study of the Radiation Stability of Austenitic Type 347 Stainless Steel," *J. Metals*, **7,** 555 (1955).
33. S. T. Konobeevsky, N. F. Pravdyuk and V. I. Kutaitsev, "The Effect of Irradiation on the Structure and Properties of Structural Materials," *Proceedings of the International Conference on the Peaceful Uses of Atomic Energy*, United Nations, 1956, Vol. 7, p. 479 (Paper No. 680).
34. For recent reviews of Radiation Chemistry see:
a) Series of papers presented at the Geneva Conference, *Proceedings of the International Conference on the Peaceful Uses of Atomic Energy*, United Nations, 1956, Vol. 7, pp. 513–610.
b) Series of reviews on Radiation Chemistry published in issues of *Ann. Rev. Phys. Chem.*
c) Parts of *Effects of Radiation on Dielectric Materials*, Washington, 1954, ONR Symposium Report ACR-2.

35. A. O. Allen and J. A. Ghormley, "Decomposition of Solid Barium Nitrate by Fast Electrons," *J. Chem. Phys.*, **15,** 208 (1947).
36. G. Hennig, R. Lees and M. S. Matheson, "The Decomposition of Nitrate Crystals by Ionizing Radiations," *J. Chem. Phys.*, **21,** 664 (1953).
37. P. Pringsheim, "Absorption Spectrum of $NaNO_3$ Exposed to Ionizing Radiation," *J. Chem. Phys.*, **23,** 369 (1955).
38. H. Rosenwasser, R. W. Dreyfus and P. W. Levy, "Radiation Induced Coloring of Sodium Azide," *J. Chem. Phys.*, **24,** 184 (1956).
39. R. B. Mesrobian, P. Ander, D. S. Ballantine and G. J. Dienes, "Gamma-Ray Polymerization of Acrylamide in the Solid State," *J. Chem. Phys.*, **22,** 565 (1954).
40. A. J. Restaino, R. B. Mesrobian, H. Morawetz, D. S. Ballantine, G. J. Dienes, and D. J. Metz, "γ-Ray Initiated Polymerization of Crystalline Monomers," *J. Am. Chem. Soc.*, **78,** 2939 (1956).
41. E. H. Taylor and J. A. Wethington, Jr., "The Effects of Ionizing Radiation on Heterogeneous Catalysts," *J. Am. Chem. Soc.*, **76,** 971 (1954).
42. R. Hurst and J. Wright, "Chemical Problems of Power Reactors," *Proceedings of the International Conference on the Peaceful Uses of Atomic Energy*, United Nations, 1956 (Paper No. 900).
43. P. B. Weisz and E. W. Swegler, "Catalytic Activity Induced by Neutron Irradiation of Inert Silica," *J. Chem. Phys.*, **23,** 1567 (1955).
44. M. Simnad and R. Smoluchowski, "Effect of Proton Irradiation upon the Electrode Potential of Tungsten," *Phys. Rev.*, **99,** 1891 (1955).
45. M. Simnad and R. Smoluchowski, "Effect of Proton Irradiation upon the Rate of Solution of Fe_2O_3 in Hydrochloric Acid," *J. Chem. Phys.*, **23,** 1961 (1955).
46. W. L. Kosiba and G. J. Dienes, "The Effect of Displaced Atoms and Ionizing Radiation on the Oxidation of Graphite," Paper presented at the International Congress on Catalysis, Philadelphia, September, 1956, to be published in *Advances in Catalysis*, Academic Press, New York, 1957.
47. C. N. Spalaris, *U. S. Atomic Energy Comm.*, Document AECD-3679 (1954) (unpublished).
48. E. A. Gulbransen and K. F. Andrew, "Reactions of Artificial Graphite," *Ind. Eng. Chem.*, **44,** 1034 (1952).
49. M. Simnad, R. Smoluchowski and A. Spilners, *Proceedings Conference on Reactivity of Solids*, Madrid, 1956. See also R. Smoluchowski, "Irradiation Effects in Materials," in *Molecular Engineering*, M.I.T., 1956.
50. E. H. Taylor and H. W. Kohn, "An Enhancement of Catalytic Activity by Gamma Radiation," *J. Am. Chem. Soc.*, **79,** 252 (1957).
51. L. Wieninger and N. Adler, "Uber die Bildung von Mikrokristallen auf Kristallflachen bei deren Bestrahlung mit Po-α-Strahlen," *Acta Phys. Austriaca*, **4,** 81 (1950).
52. R. Blöch, "Die Bildung von Obermachen Kristallen auf Alkilhalogenen, Fluorit und Kalzit bei Bestrahlung mit Polomium," *Sitzber. Osterr. Akad Wiss. Math.-naturw. Kl.*, **163,** 99 (1953).
53. F. W. Young, Jr., "On the Effect of Reactor Exposure on the Rate of Oxidation of Copper Single Crystals," *U. S. Atomic Energy Comm.*, Document ORNL 55-3-70 (1955).

Author Index*

* *Italic* numbers refer to the bibliographies of the different papers.

Subject Index